Student Handbook for the Joy of Statistics

Learning with Real World Data

Chris P. Tsokos
Rebecca D. Wooten
University of South Florida

Cover image by Jacob Ferderigos

www.kendallhunt.com
Send all inquiries to:
4050 Westmark Drive
Dubuque, IA 52004-1840

ISBN 978-1-4652-3429-2

Printed in the United States of America
10 9 8 7 6 5 4

HANDBOOK	TABLE OF CONTENT

SECTION 1 — CHAPTER SUMMARY

SECTION 2 — PLOTS, TABLES AND CHARTS

SECTION 3 WORKBOOK

SECTION 4 USING TECHNOLOGY

Including Word, Excel, the TI-83 and the World Wide Web (WWW)

SECTION 5 PROJECTS

Chapter Summaries

Chapter Summaries

Chapter 1: Terminology and Sampling Techniques

1.1 Introduction to Statistics

Statistics	
Population	
Census	
Population Size	N
Sample Data	
Sample Size	n
Descriptive Statistics	
Distribution	
Location	
Outlier	
Shape	
Spread	
Extremes:	minimum and maximum
Central Tendencies:	mode, median and mean
Deviation:	range, inner-quartile range, variance and standard deviation
Proportion	
Frequency	
Degree of Confidence	
Statistically Significant	
Inferential Statistics	
Sensitive	
Robust	
Hypothesis Testing	
Experiment	
Experimental Design	
Individual (Subject)	
Variable	
Regression	
Response (Objective) Variable	
Explanatory Variable	
Lurking Variable	
Correlation	
Causation	
Confounded Variables	

1.2 Data Types

Instrument
Parameter
Sample Survey
Statistic
Measure
Discrete Measure

Continuous Measure

1.3 Representative Samples

Valid Measure
Bias
Variability
Reliable Measure

1.4 Levels of Measure

Nominal Measure
Ordinal Measure
Ranking
Likert Scale
Interval Measure
Ratio Measure

1.5 Random Samples

Random Sample
Simple Random Sample
Systematic Sampling
Cluster Sampling
Stratified Sampling
Convenience Sampling
Multistage Sampling

1.6 Experimental Design

Observational Study
Experimental Study
Treatment
Control Group
Placebo
Placebo Effect
Block
Block Design
Randomized-Block Design
Blind: Single and Double

1.7 Additional Terms

Internal Review Board (IRB)
Independent Ethics Committee (IEC)
Ethical Review Board (ERB)
Informed Consent
Anonymous (Anonymity)
Confidential (Confidentiality)
Simulation
Random Digit Chart

Chapter 3: Descriptive Statistics

3.1 Descriptive Statistics

3.2 Measuring Central Tendencies

Mode

Median

Sample Mean $\overline{x} = \frac{\sum_{i=1}^{n} x_i}{n}$ or $\overline{x} = \frac{\sum_{i=1}^{k} x_i f_i}{n}, n = \sum_{i=1}^{k} f_i$

Expected Value $\overline{x} = \sum_{i=1}^{k} x_i p_i, \sum_{i=1}^{k} p_i = 1$

Trimmed Mean

Weighted Mean $\hat{\mu} = \frac{\sum_{i=1}^{k} x_i w_i}{W}, W = \sum_{i=1}^{k} w_i$

Margin of Error

3.3 Measuring Deviations from the Center

Deviation

Range

Standard Population Variance

Standard Population Deviation

Standard Sample Variance

Standard Sample Deviation

Coefficient of Variation

Chapter 4: Basic Probabilities

4.1 Introduction to Set Notation

Set

Universal Set

Union

Intersection

Complement

4.2 Basic Probability

Probability $P(E) = \frac{n(E)}{n(S)}$

4.3 The Sample Space

Experiment

Sample Point

Sample Space

Event

Simple Event

Compound Event

Mutually Exclusive

4.4 Computing Probabilities

Principles: $P(S) = 1$

$0 \leq P(E) \leq 1$

$E_i \cap E_j = \emptyset, i \neq j$ and $\bigcup_{i=1}^{n} E_i = S$,

then $\sum_{i=1}^{n} P(E_i) = 1$

Odds

4.5 Basic Properties of Probability

$$P(\bar{E}) = 1 - P(E)$$
$$P(\emptyset) = 0$$
$$P(A \cup B) = P(A) + P(B) - P(A \cap B)$$

4.6 Conditional Probability

Conditional Probability

$$P(A|B) = \frac{P(A \cap B)}{P(B)} = \frac{n(A \cap B)}{n(B)}$$

Dependent Probability

$$P(A \cap B) = P(A) \times P(B|A) = P(B) \times P(A|B)$$

Independent Probability

$$P(A \cap B) = P(A) \times P(B)$$

4.7 Combinatorial Techniques

Multiplication Principle
Independent Selection
Factorials (Dependent Selection)
Permutations
Combinations

Chapter 5: Discrete Probabilities

5.1 Introduction to Random Variables

Function
Random Variable
Discrete Random Variable
Continuous Random Variable

5.2 Discrete Probability Distribution

(Discrete) Probability Distribution

5.3 Expected Value, Variance and Standard Deviation

Arithmetic Mean
Expected Value (of a Discrete RV)
Population Variance (of a Discrete RV)
Residuals

5.4 The Binomial Probability Distribution

$$P(x|n,p) = \binom{n}{x} p^x q^{n-x}$$

5.5 The Mean and Variance of a Binomial Probability Distribution

$$\mu = E(X) = np$$
$$\sigma = \sqrt{npq} = \sqrt{np(1-p)}$$

5.6 The Poisson Probability Distribution

$$P(x|\lambda = \mu) = \frac{e^{-\lambda}\lambda^x}{x!}$$

for $x = 0, 1, 2, \ldots$

$$\mu = E(X) = \lambda \text{ and } \sigma = \sqrt{V(X)} = \sqrt{\lambda}$$

5.7 **The Geometric Probability Distribution**

$$P(n|p) = p(1-p)^{n-1}$$

$$\mu = E(X) = \frac{1}{p}. \text{ and } \sigma = \frac{\sqrt{1-p}}{p}$$

Chapter 6: Continuous Probabilities

6.1 **Continuous Probability Distributions**

Continuous Random Variable

6.2 **The Normal Probability Distribution**

$$f(x|\mu, \sigma^2) = \frac{1}{\sigma\sqrt{2\pi}} e^{-\frac{(x-\mu)^2}{2\sigma^2}}$$

$$-\infty < x < \infty, -\infty < \mu < \infty, 0 < \sigma^2 < \infty$$

6.3 **The Standard Normal Probability Distribution**

$$f(z|\mu_z = 0, \sigma_z^2 = 1) = \frac{1}{\sqrt{2\pi}} e^{-\frac{z^2}{2}}$$

$$-\infty < z < \infty$$

Standard Score

$$z = \frac{x-\mu}{\sigma}$$

6.4 **The Central Limit Theorem**

Sampling Distribution

Standard Error

Central Limit Theorem (means)

6.5 **Empirical & Chebyshev's Rules**

Chebyshev's Rule

$$P[|X - \mu| \leq k\sigma] > 1 - \frac{1}{k^2}$$

Empirical Rule

6.6 The Normal Approximation to the Binomial

$$\mu = np$$
$$\sigma = \sqrt{np(1-p)}$$
$$P(x) = \binom{n}{x} p^x (1-p)^{n-x} \approx \frac{1}{\sqrt{2\pi}\sqrt{np(1-p)}} e^{-\frac{1}{2}\left(\frac{x-np}{\sqrt{np(1-p)}}\right)^2}$$

In terms of expected number of successes:

$$\mu = np, \sigma = \sqrt{np(1-p)}$$

and without correction for continuity

$$z = \frac{x-\mu}{\sigma}$$

and with correction for continuity

$$z = \frac{(x \pm 0.5) - \mu}{\sigma}$$

In terms of expected proportions:

$$\mu_{\hat{p}} = p, \sigma = \sqrt{\frac{p(1-p)}{n}}.$$

and without correction for continuity

$$z = \frac{\hat{p} - p}{\sqrt{\frac{p(1-p)}{n}}}$$

and with correction for continuity

$$z = \frac{\left(\hat{p} \pm \frac{0.5}{n}\right) - p}{\sqrt{\frac{p(1-p)}{n}}}$$

6.7 Testing for Normality & Dispersion

PP Plot
QQ Plot
Standardized Plot
Percentage Plot

Chapter 7: Point and Interval Estimates (one population)

7.1 Introduction

Point Estimates

Interval Estimates

7.2 Point Estimates & Interval Estimates (Confidence Intervals: CI)

Point Estimates: Sample mean, sample variance, sample standard deviation and relative frequency

	Population Parameter	Sample Statistic (Point Estimate)
Mean	$\theta = \mu$	$\hat{\theta} = \bar{x} = \frac{\sum x}{n}$
Proportion	$\theta = p$	$\hat{\theta} = \hat{p} = \frac{x}{n}$

Degree of Confidence

Margin of Error

	Mean	Proportion
Point Estimate	$\hat{\theta} = \bar{x}$	$\hat{\theta} = \hat{p} = \frac{x}{n}$
Standard Error	$\sigma - known$ $\sigma_{\bar{x}} = \frac{\sigma}{\sqrt{n}}$ $\sigma - unknown$ $\sigma_{\bar{x}} = \frac{s}{\sqrt{n}}$	$\sigma_{\hat{p}} = \sqrt{\frac{\hat{p}(1-\hat{p})}{n}}$
Margin of Error	$\sigma - known$ $ME = z_{\alpha/2}\frac{\sigma}{\sqrt{n}}$ $\sigma - unknown$ $ME = t_{v,\alpha/2}\frac{s}{\sqrt{n}}$	$ME = z_{\alpha/2}\sqrt{\frac{\hat{p}(1-\hat{p})}{n}}$

Confidence Interval (Interval Estimates)

7.3 CI for Means: Case I

All three assumptions satisfied: Normal, σ-known and $n \geq 30$

$$\bar{x} \pm z_{\alpha/2}\frac{\sigma}{\sqrt{n}}$$

7.4 CI for Means: Case II

Two assumptions satisfied: Unknown distribution, σ-known and $n \geq 30$

$$\bar{x} \pm z_{\alpha/2}\frac{\sigma}{\sqrt{n}}$$

7.5 CI for Means: Case III

One assumption satisfied: Normal, σ-unknown and $n < 30$

$$\bar{x} \pm t_{v,\alpha/2}\frac{s}{\sqrt{n}}$$

7.6 CI for Proportions: Case IV

$$np \geq 5 \text{ and } n(1-p) \geq 5$$

$$\hat{p} \pm z_{\alpha/2}\sqrt{\frac{\hat{p}(1-\hat{p})}{n}}$$

7.7 Estimating Sample Size

Means

$$n \geq \left(\frac{z_{\alpha/2}\sigma}{\epsilon}\right)^2$$

Proportions

$$n \geq p(1-p)\left(\frac{z_{\alpha/2}}{\epsilon}\right)^2$$

$$n \geq \frac{1}{4}\left(\frac{z_{\alpha/2}}{\epsilon}\right)^2$$

Chapter 8: Hypothesis Testing (one population)

8.1 Introduction

Hypothesis Testing

8.2 Hypothesis Testing (HT)

Null Hypothesis
Alternative Hypothesis
Type I Error
Alpha Risk
Type II Error
Beta Risk

8.3 HT for Means: Case I

All three assumptions satisfied: Normal, σ-known and $n \geq 30$

$$z = \frac{\bar{x} - \mu}{\sigma/\sqrt{n}}$$

8.4 HT for Means: Case II

Two assumptions satisfied: Unknown distribution, σ-known and $n \geq 30$

$$z = \frac{\bar{x} - \mu}{\sigma/\sqrt{n}}$$

8.5 HT for Means: Case III

One assumption satisfied: Normal, σ-unknown and $n < 30$

$$t = \frac{\bar{x} - \mu}{s/\sqrt{n}}.$$

8.6 HT for Proportions: Case IV

$$np \geq 5 \text{ and } n(1-p) \geq 5$$

$$z = \frac{\hat{p} - p}{\sqrt{\frac{p(1-p)}{n}}}$$

8.7 Determining the *p-value*

For a one-tail test

$$p - value = P(Z \geq |z|)$$

For a two-tail test

$$p - value = 2 \times P(Z \geq |z|)$$

Chapter 9: Confidence Interval and Hypothesis Testing (two population)

9.1 Introduction to Two Populations

9.2 CI & HT for Difference of Means: **Case I**

Independent Sampling

All assumptions satisfied: Normal, σ's-known and $n_1, n_2 \geq 30$

CI:

$$(\bar{x}_1 - \bar{x}_2) \mp z_{\alpha/2} \sqrt{\frac{\sigma_1^2}{n_1} + \frac{\sigma_2^2}{n_2}}$$

HT:

$$z = \frac{(\bar{x}_1 - \bar{x}_2) - (\mu_1 - \mu_2)}{\sqrt{\frac{\sigma_1^2}{n_1} + \frac{\sigma_2^2}{n_2}}}$$

9.3 CI & HT for Difference of Means: **Case II**

Independent Sampling

Two assumptions satisfied: Normal, σ's-unknown, and $n_1, n_2 \geq 30$

CI:

$$(\bar{x}_1 - \bar{x}_2) \mp t_{v,\alpha/2} \sqrt{\frac{s_1^2}{n_1} + \frac{s_2^2}{n_2}}$$

HT:

$$z = \frac{(\bar{x}_1 - \bar{x}_2) - (\mu_1 - \mu_2)}{\sqrt{\frac{s_1^2}{n_1} + \frac{s_2^2}{n_2}}}$$

9.4 CI & HT for Difference of Means: **Case III**

Independent Sampling

Two assumptions satisfied: Normal, σ's-unknown, and $n \geq 30$

Case A: $\sigma_1^2 = \sigma_2^2$

CI:

$$(\bar{x}_1 - \bar{x}_2) \mp t_{v,\alpha/2} s_p \sqrt{\frac{1}{n_1} + \frac{1}{n_2}}$$

$$s_p^2 = \frac{(n_1 - 1)s_1^2 + (n_2 - 1)s_2^2}{n_1 + n_2 - 2}$$

$$v = n_1 + n_2 - 2$$

HT:

$$t = \frac{(\bar{x}_1 - \bar{x}_2) - (\mu_1 - \mu_2)}{s_p \sqrt{\frac{1}{n_1} + \frac{1}{n_2}}}$$

Case B: $\sigma_1^2 \neq \sigma_2^2$

CI:

$$(\bar{x}_1 - \bar{x}_2) \mp t_{\alpha/2} \sqrt{\frac{s_1^2}{n_1} + \frac{s_2^2}{n_2}}$$

HT:

$$t = \frac{(\bar{x}_1 - \bar{x}_2) - (\mu_1 - \mu_2)}{\sqrt{\frac{s_1^2}{n_1} + \frac{s_2^2}{n_2}}}$$

$$v = \frac{\left(\frac{s_1^2}{n_1} + \frac{s_2^2}{n_2}\right)^2}{\frac{\left(\frac{s_1^2}{n_1}\right)^2}{n_1 - 1} + \frac{\left(\frac{s_2^2}{n_2}\right)^2}{n_2 - 1}}$$

or at minimum $$v = min\{n_1 - 1, n_2 - 1\}$$

9.5 CI & HT for Mean Difference: **Case IV**

Dependent Sampling
Matched Pairs
One assumption satisfied: Normal, σ's-unknown and $n_1, n_2 < 30$
CI:

$$\bar{d} \mp t_{v,\alpha/2}\frac{s_d}{\sqrt{n}}$$

$$\bar{d} = \bar{x}_1 - \bar{x}_2 = \frac{\sum_{i=1}^{n} d_i}{n}, d_i = x_{1i} - x_{2i}$$

$$s_d^2 = \frac{1}{n-1}\sum_{i=1}^{n}(d_i - \bar{d})^2$$

HT:

$$t = \frac{\bar{d} - \mu_d}{s_d/\sqrt{n}}$$

9.6 CI & HT for Difference of Proportions: **Case V**

$$n_1 p_1 \geq 5, n_1(1-p_1) \geq 5$$

$$n_2 p_2 \geq 5, n_2(1-p_2) \geq 5$$

CI:

$$(\hat{p}_1 - \hat{p}_2) - z_{\alpha/2} s_{\hat{p}_1 - \hat{p}_2}$$

$$s^2_{\hat{p}_1 - \hat{p}_2} = \frac{\hat{p}_1 \hat{q}_1}{n_1} + \frac{\hat{p}_2 \hat{q}_2}{n_2}$$

HT:

$$z = \frac{(\hat{p}_1 - \hat{p}_2) - (p_1 - p_2)}{\sqrt{\frac{\bar{p}(1-\bar{p})}{n_1} + \frac{\bar{p}(1-\bar{p})}{n_2}}}$$

$$\bar{p} = \frac{x_1 + x_2}{n_1 + n_2}$$

Chapter 10: Chi-squared Distribution

10.1 Introduction

10.2 Chi-square Probability Distribution

Chi-square Distribution

10.3 CI: Variance and Standard Deviation

$$\chi^2 = \frac{(n-1)s^2}{\sigma^2}$$

$$\frac{(n-1)s^2}{\chi_U^2} < \sigma^2 < \frac{(n-1)s^2}{\chi_L^2}$$

10.4 HT: Variance

$$\chi^2 = \frac{(n-1)s^2}{\sigma_0^2}$$

10.5 HT: Independence

$$\chi^2 = \sum_{\forall i,j} \frac{\left(O_{ij} - E_{ij}\right)^2}{E_{ij}}$$

$$E_{ij} = \frac{r_i \times c_j}{n}$$

$$v = (r-1)(c-1)$$

Simpson's Paradox

10.6 HT: Goodness-of-Fit

$$\chi^2 = \sum_{i=1}^{m} \frac{(O_i - E_i)^2}{E_i}$$

$$E_i = np_i$$

$$v = m - 1$$

Chapter 11: Simple Linear Regression

11.1 Introduction

11.2 The Population Correlation Coefficient ρ (rho) and the sample estimate of ρ, the Sample Correlation Coefficient r.

Covariance

$$Cov(X,Y) = E\left[(X-\mu_x)(Y-\mu_y)\right] = \sigma_{xy}$$

$$\rho = \rho_{xy} = \frac{Cov(X,Y)}{\sqrt{V(X)}\sqrt{V(Y)}} = \frac{\sigma_{xy}}{\sigma_x \sigma_y}$$

$$s_{xy} = \frac{\sum_{i=1}^{n}(x_i - \overline{x})(y_i - \overline{y})}{n-1}$$

$$r = \frac{n\sum xy - \sum x \sum y}{\sqrt{n\sum x^2 - (\sum x)^2}\sqrt{n\sum y^2 - (\sum y)^2}}$$

Hypothesis Testing for ρ

$$H_0: \rho = 0$$
$$H_a: \rho \neq 0$$
$$t = \frac{r\sqrt{n-2}}{\sqrt{1-r^2}}$$
$$v = n - 2$$

11.3 The Linear Regression Model $y = \alpha + \beta x$

$$y = \alpha + \beta x$$
$$y_i = \alpha + \beta x_i + \varepsilon_i$$
$$\hat{y} = \hat{\alpha} + \hat{\beta} x = a + bx$$
$$b = \frac{n\sum xy - \sum x \sum y}{n\sum x^2 - (\sum x)^2}$$
$$a = \bar{y} - b\bar{x}$$

Interpolation
Extrapolation
Residual Analysis

11.4 Confidence Interval and Hypothesis Testing for the Marginal Change β

Marginal Change

$$m = \beta = \frac{\Delta y}{\Delta x} \text{ and } \Delta x = 1 \text{ then } \Delta y = \beta$$

HT:

$$H_0: \beta = 0$$
$$H_a: \beta \neq 0$$
$$t = \frac{b}{s_e}\sqrt{\sum (x - \bar{x})^2}$$
$$s_e^2 = \frac{\sum (y - \hat{y})^2}{n-2}$$

CI:

$$\hat{\beta} \mp t_{v,\alpha/2} s_e \sqrt{\frac{1}{\sum (x - \bar{x})^2}}$$

11.5 Confidence Interval on the True Response y

$$\hat{y} \mp t_{v,\alpha/2} s_e \sqrt{1 + \frac{1}{n} + \frac{(x^* - \bar{x})^2}{s_x^2}}$$
$$s_x^2 = \frac{1}{n-2}\sum (x - \bar{x})^2$$
$$s_e^2 = \frac{1}{n-2}\sum (y - \hat{y})^2$$
$$v = n - 2$$

Plots, Tables, and Charts

Plots, Tables and Charts

Various Plots

A question of normality:

(i) **PP Plot** mapping $F(x_i)$ versus p_i

(ii) **QQ Plot** mapping $F^{-1}(p_i)$ versus x_i

(iii) **Percent Change** mapping x_i versus $z_i = \dfrac{x_i - \mu}{\mu}$

(iv) **Standard Z-Score** mapping x_i versus $z_i = \dfrac{x_i - \mu}{\sigma}$

Testing for normality:

P-P Plot

$F(x)$ is the **cumulative probability distribution**; that is, $F(x) = P(X \le x)$ or the area under the curve to the left of the value x.

Hence, we can compare for each data point x_i the probability as defined by the **proposed probability distribution** $F(x_i) = \hat{p}_i$ and the probability as defined by the position in the data or the **cumulative relative frequency** p_i. If we partition the closed interval $[0,1]$ into n subintervals, where n is the sample size then we can define the midpoint of each subinterval as the hypothetical probability; that is, $\hat{p}_i = \dfrac{i - 0.5}{n}$. Plotting the observed probabilities (under the assumption of the defined cumulative probability distribution) and the expected probabilities (as defined by position within the data set) we obtain the **PP Plot**.

Q-Q Plot

Now turn this image inside-out; that is compare the data point x_i to the expected data point $\hat{x}_i = F^{-1}(p_i)$ where $p_i = \frac{i}{n+1}$ we obtain the **QQ Plot**.

Both the **PP Plot** and **QQ Plot** test for goodness-of-fit, the straighter the line, the better the fit. If the cumulative probability distribution is that of the normal probability distribution, then the **PP Plot** and the **QQ Plot** test for normality.

Normalization:

To **Normalize** (or **Standardize**) data, the transformations: the **standard score**, $z_i = \frac{x_i - \mu}{\sigma}$, and the **percent change**, $z_i = \frac{x_i - \mu}{\mu}$, are often used; however, these are linear transformation of the data and hence when plotted again the data will always form a straight line. Such transformations are used more to measure dispersion and not normality. Even thought the dispersion of the data is part of normally distributed data.

Step 1: Specify (given) the desired **Level (degree0 of confidence**, $(1-\alpha)\%$; commonly used values are: $1-\alpha = 0.90, 0.95, 0.99$, corresponding to the risk (probability of **Type I Error**): $\alpha = 0.10, 0.05, 0.01$.

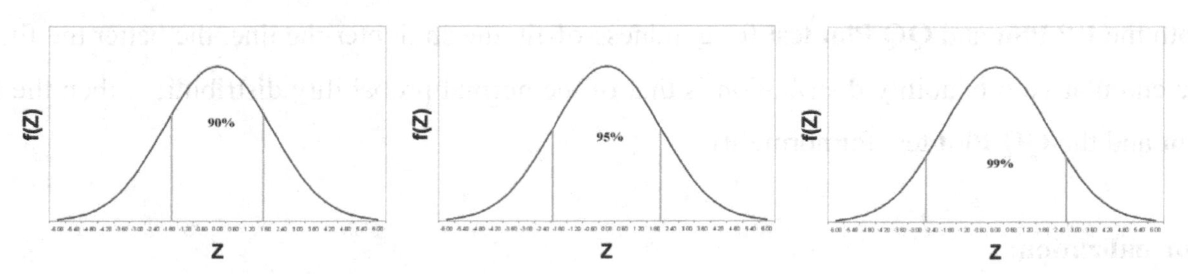

Step 2: Determine the appropriate methodology including the underlying probability distribution and formulations of the **critical statistic** Z_c, **point estimate** $\hat{\theta}$ and **margin of error** E.

$$(\hat{\theta}-\mathrm{E}, \hat{\theta}+\mathrm{E}), \text{ where } \mathrm{E} = SE_{\hat{\theta}}$$

Step 3: Perform the necessary calculations as outlined in step two including the **lower limit** x_L and **upper limit** x_U on the **interval estimate.**

$$\begin{aligned} x_L &= \hat{\theta}-\mathrm{E} \\ x_U &= \hat{\theta}+\mathrm{E} \end{aligned} \quad \Rightarrow (x_L, x_U) \quad \Rightarrow x_L < \theta < x_U$$

Step 4: Interpret the meaning and usefulness of your result in the form of a **confidence statement.**

"We are $(1-\alpha)\%$ confident that the true parameter is $\hat{\theta}$ with a E margin of error" or "We are $(1-\alpha)\%$ confident that the true parameter is between x_L and x_U."

Step 5: Verify (state) **assumptions**: is the measure quantitative/qualitative (means/proportions), are there limitations due to the sample size, is the variance known/unknown, etc.

Sampling Distribution	Statistic $\hat{\theta}$	Parameter θ	Standard Error $SE_{\hat{\theta}} = \sqrt{V(\hat{\theta})}$	Confidence Intervals $\hat{\theta} \mp Z_c SE_{\hat{\theta}}$	Assumptions
Normal $X \sim N(\mu, \sigma^2)$	$\hat{\theta} = \bar{x}$	$\theta = \mu$	$SE_{\bar{x}} = \frac{\sigma}{\sqrt{n}}$	$\bar{x} \mp z_c \frac{\sigma}{\sqrt{n}}$	$\sigma - known$
			$SE_{\bar{x}} = \frac{s}{\sqrt{n}}$	$\bar{x} \mp z_c \frac{s}{\sqrt{n}}$	$\sigma - unknown$ but $n \geq 30$
				$\bar{x} \mp t_{c,n-1} \frac{s}{\sqrt{n}}$	$\sigma - unknown$ and $n < 30$
Distribution unknown	$\hat{\theta} = \bar{x}$	$\theta = \mu$	$SE_{\bar{x}} = \frac{\sigma}{\sqrt{n}}$	$\bar{x} \mp z_c \frac{\sigma}{\sqrt{n}}$	$\sigma - known$ and $n \geq 30$
			$SE_{\bar{x}} = \frac{s}{\sqrt{n}}$	$\bar{x} \mp t_{c,n-1} \frac{s}{\sqrt{n}}$	$\sigma - unknown$ or $n < 30$
Binomial $X \sim Binomial(n, p)$	$\hat{\theta} = \hat{p} = \frac{x}{n}$	$\theta = p$	$SE_{\hat{p}} = \sqrt{\frac{\hat{p}(1-\hat{p})}{n}}$	$\hat{p} \mp z_c \sqrt{\frac{\hat{p}(1-\hat{p})}{n}}$	At least five in each category
Normal (independent) $X_1 \sim N(\mu_1, \sigma_1^2), X_2 \sim N(\mu_2, \sigma_2^2)$ n_1, n_2	Difference in Means $\hat{\theta} = \bar{x}_1 - \bar{x}_2$	$\theta = \mu_1 - \mu_2$	$SE_{\bar{x}_1 - \bar{x}_2} = \sqrt{\frac{\sigma_1^2}{n_1} + \frac{\sigma_2^2}{n_2}}$	$(\bar{x}_1 - \bar{x}_2) \mp z_c \sqrt{\frac{\sigma_1^2}{n_1} + \frac{\sigma_2^2}{n_2}}$	$\sigma' s - known$
Normal (dependent) $X_1 \sim N(\mu_1, \sigma_1^2), X_2 \sim N(\mu_2, \sigma_2^2)$ $n_1 = n_2$, matched pairs	Mean Difference $\hat{\theta} = \bar{d}$	$\theta = \mu_d$	Same idea as for means	Same idea as for means (three different possible degrees of freedom – easiest $\min(n_1 - 1, n_2 - 1)$	Same idea for means
Binomial $X_1 \sim Binomial(n_1, p_1)$ $X_2 \sim Binomial(n_2, p_2)$	$\hat{\theta} = \hat{p}_1 - \hat{p}_2$	$\theta = p_1 - p_2$	$SE_{\hat{p}_1 - \hat{p}_2} = \sqrt{\frac{\hat{p}_1(1-\hat{p}_1)}{n_1} + \frac{\hat{p}_2(1-\hat{p}_2)}{n_2}}$	$(\hat{p}_1 - \hat{p}_2) \mp z_c SE_{\hat{p}_1 - \hat{p}_2}$	At least five in each category

Step-by-Step Procedures for Hypothesis Testing: Means & Proportions

Step 1: Set up the **null hypothesis** and the **alternative hypothesis** as to reflect the question to be answered.

$$H_0 : \theta = \theta_0 \quad \text{and} \quad \begin{matrix} H_1 : \theta \neq \theta_0 \\ H_1 : \theta > \theta_0 \\ H_1 : \theta < \theta_0 \end{matrix}$$

Step 2: Specify the **level of significance**, $\alpha = 1 - c$. The risk (probability of **Type I Error**): $\alpha = 0.10, 0.05, 0.01$.

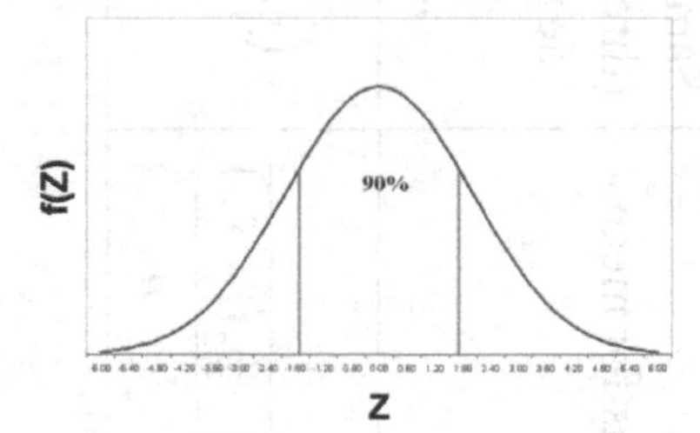

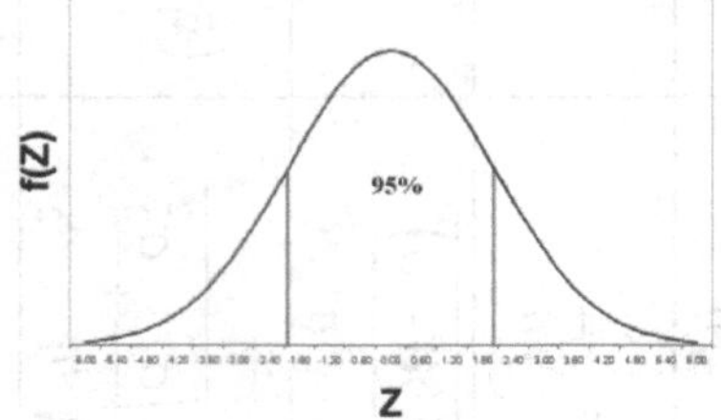

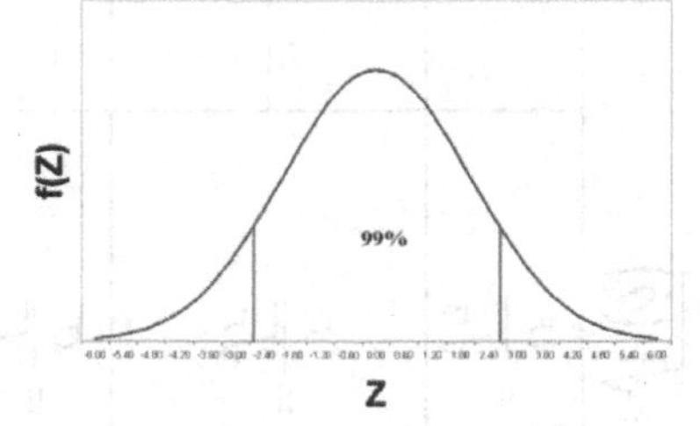

Step 3: Based on the first two steps, identify the statistical method to be used, the **test statistic** and the **critical statistic** based on the underlying probability distribution – the **normal probability distribution** or **Student's t-distribution**).

$$Z = \frac{\hat{\theta} - \theta}{SE_{\hat{\theta}}}$$

Step 4: Based on the critical statistic and test statistic found in the third step, graphically illustrate the critical regions: **acceptance region** and **rejection region(s)**.

Step 5: Perform the necessary calculations using the identified methods to determine or estimate the ***p-value***; that is, the probability of **Type I Error** according to the data.

Step 6: Make a **decision** to accept (fail to reject) or reject the null hypothesis.

Step 7: Interpret the decision as related to the question at hand in the form of a **significance statement** (which includes the level of significance and the decision.)

"At the (α)% level of significance, there is sufficient/insufficient evidence to reject the null hypothesis."

Step 8: Verify the stated **assumptions**: independent random variables – known/unknown variance – enough information to assume the sampling distribution is normal.

Sampling Distribution	Statistic	Conditions	Hypothesis $H_0: \theta = \theta_0$	Test Statistic $Z = \frac{\hat{\theta} - \theta}{SE_{\hat{\theta}}}$	Confidence Interval (Two-tail Test) $\hat{\theta} \pm ZSE_{\hat{\theta}}$
Normal In general, $n \geq 30$ However this might need to go as high as 500.	Means $\bar{x}$	σ known	$H_0: \mu = \mu_0$	$z = \frac{\bar{x} - \mu}{\frac{\sigma}{\sqrt{n}}}$	$\bar{x} \pm z_c \frac{\sigma}{\sqrt{n}}$
		σ unknown or $n < 30$		$t = \frac{\bar{x} - \mu}{\frac{s}{\sqrt{n}}}$; $df = n - 1$	$\bar{x} \pm t_c \frac{s}{\sqrt{n}}$; $df = n - 1$
	Mean Differences $\bar{d}$ for matched pairs (dependent)	σ_d known (highly unlikely)	$H_0: \mu_d = d$	$z = \frac{\bar{d} - \mu_d}{\frac{\sigma_d}{\sqrt{n}}}$	$\bar{d} \pm z_c \frac{\sigma_d}{\sqrt{n}}$
		σ_d unknown, use s_d		$t = \frac{\bar{d} - \mu_d}{\frac{s_d}{\sqrt{n}}}$; $df = n - 1$	$\bar{d} \pm t_c \frac{s_d}{\sqrt{n}}$; $df = n - 1$
	Differences of Means $\bar{x}_1 - \bar{x}_2$ (Independent) (Un-pooled) Assumption: $\sigma_1^2 \neq \sigma_2^2$	σ's known Use σ_1, σ_2	$H_0: \mu_1 - \mu_2 = d$	$z = \frac{(\bar{x}_1 - \bar{x}_2) - (\mu_1 - \mu_2)}{\sqrt{\frac{\sigma_1^2}{n_1} + \frac{\sigma_2^2}{n_2}}}$	$(\bar{x}_1 - \bar{x}_2) \pm z_c \sqrt{\frac{\sigma_1^2}{n_1} + \frac{\sigma_2^2}{n_2}}$
		σ's unknown; hence use s_1, s_2 (heterogeneous)		$t = \frac{(\bar{x}_1 - \bar{x}_2) - (\mu_1 - \mu_2)}{\sqrt{\frac{s_1^2}{n_1} + \frac{s_2^2}{n_2}}}$; $df = \min(n_1 - 1, n_2 - 1)$	$(\bar{x}_1 - \bar{x}_2) \pm t_c \sqrt{\frac{s_1^2}{n_1} + \frac{s_2^2}{n_2}}$; $df = \min(n_1 - 1, n_2 - 1)$
	Differences of Means $\bar{x}_1 - \bar{x}_2$ (Independent) (Pooled) Assumption: $\sigma_1^2 = \sigma_2^2$ (homogeneity of variance)	σ's Known Use σ_1, σ_2 (homogeneous)		$z = \frac{(\bar{x}_1 - \bar{x}_2) - (\mu_1 - \mu_2)}{s_p \sqrt{\frac{1}{n_1} + \frac{1}{n_2}}}$ $s_p = \sqrt{\frac{(n_1 - 1)\sigma_1^2 + (n_1 - 1)\sigma_2^2}{n_1 + n_2 - 2}}$ $df = n_1 + n_2 - 2$	$(\bar{x}_1 - \bar{x}_2) \pm z_c s \sqrt{\frac{1}{n_1} + \frac{1}{n_2}}$ $s = \sqrt{\frac{(n_1 - 1)\sigma_1^2 + (n_1 - 1)\sigma_2^2}{n_1 + n_2 - 2}}$

		σ's Unknown hence use s_1, s_2 (homogeneous)		$t = \frac{(\bar{x}_1 - \bar{x}_2) - (\mu_1 - \mu_2)}{s\sqrt{\frac{1}{n_1} + \frac{1}{n_2}}}$ Where $s = \sqrt{\frac{(n_1 - 1)s_1^2 + (n_1 - 1)s_2^2}{n_1 + n_2 - 2}}$; $df = n_1 + n_2 - 2$	$(\bar{x}_1 - \bar{x}_2) \pm t_c s\sqrt{\frac{1}{n_1} + \frac{1}{n_2}}$ Where $s = \sqrt{\frac{(n_1 - 1)s_1^2 + (n_1 - 1)s_2^2}{n_1 + n_2 - 2}}$; $df = \min(n_1 - 1, n_2 - 1)$

APPENDIX C1 STANDARD NORMAL

STANDARD NORMAL PROBABILITY DISTRIBUTION $P(0 \leq Z \leq z)$

	0.00	0.01	0.02	0.03	0.04	0.05	0.06	0.07	0.08	0.09
0.0	0.0000	0.0040	0.0080	0.0120	0.0160	0.0199	0.0239	0.0279	0.0319	0.0359
0.1	0.0398	0.0438	0.0478	0.0517	0.0557	0.0596	0.0636	0.0675	0.0714	0.0753
0.2	0.0793	0.0832	0.0871	0.0910	0.0948	0.0987	0.1026	0.1064	0.1103	0.1141
0.3	0.1179	0.1217	0.1255	0.1293	0.1331	0.1368	0.1406	0.1443	0.1480	0.1517
0.4	0.1554	0.1591	0.1628	0.1664	0.1700	0.1736	0.1772	0.1808	0.1844	0.1879
0.5	0.1915	0.1950	0.1985	0.2019	0.2054	0.2088	0.2123	0.2157	0.2190	0.2224
0.6	0.2257	0.2291	0.2324	0.2357	0.2389	0.2422	0.2454	0.2486	0.2517	0.2549
0.7	0.2580	0.2611	0.2642	0.2673	0.2704	0.2734	0.2764	0.2794	0.2823	0.2852
0.8	0.2881	0.2910	0.2939	0.2967	0.2995	0.3023	0.3051	0.3078	0.3106	0.3133
0.9	0.3159	0.3186	0.3212	0.3238	0.3264	0.3289	0.3315	0.3340	0.3365	0.3389
1.0	0.3413	0.3438	0.3461	0.3485	0.3508	0.3531	0.3554	0.3577	0.3599	0.3621
1.1	0.3643	0.3665	0.3686	0.3708	0.3729	0.3749	0.3770	0.3790	0.3810	0.3830
1.2	0.3849	0.3869	0.3888	0.3907	0.3925	0.3944	0.3962	0.3980	0.3997	0.4015
1.3	0.4032	0.4049	0.4066	0.4082	0.4099	0.4115	0.4131	0.4147	0.4162	0.4177
1.4	0.4192	0.4207	0.4222	0.4236	0.4251	0.4265	0.4279	0.4292	0.4306	0.4319
1.5	0.4332	0.4345	0.4357	0.4370	0.4382	0.4394	0.4406	0.4418	0.4429	0.4441
1.6	0.4452	0.4463	0.4474	0.4484	0.4495	0.4505	0.4515	0.4525	0.4535	0.4545
1.7	0.4554	0.4564	0.4573	0.4582	0.4591	0.4599	0.4608	0.4616	0.4625	0.4633
1.8	0.4641	0.4649	0.4656	0.4664	0.4671	0.4678	0.4686	0.4693	0.4699	0.4706
1.9	0.4713	0.4719	0.4726	0.4732	0.4738	0.4744	0.4750	0.4756	0.4761	0.4767
2.0	0.4772	0.4778	0.4783	0.4788	0.4793	0.4798	0.4803	0.4808	0.4812	0.4817
2.1	0.4821	0.4826	0.4830	0.4834	0.4838	0.4842	0.4846	0.4850	0.4854	0.4857
2.2	0.4861	0.4864	0.4868	0.4871	0.4875	0.4878	0.4881	0.4884	0.4887	0.4890
2.3	0.4893	0.4896	0.4898	0.4901	0.4904	0.4906	0.4909	0.4911	0.4913	0.4916
2.4	0.4918	0.4920	0.4922	0.4925	0.4927	0.4929	0.4931	0.4932	0.4934	0.4936
2.5	0.4938	0.4940	0.4941	0.4943	0.4945	0.4946	0.4948	0.4949	0.4951	0.4952
2.6	0.4953	0.4955	0.4956	0.4957	0.4959	0.4960	0.4961	0.4962	0.4963	0.4964
2.7	0.4965	0.4966	0.4967	0.4968	0.4969	0.4970	0.4971	0.4972	0.4973	0.4974
2.8	0.4974	0.4975	0.4976	0.4977	0.4977	0.4978	0.4979	0.4979	0.4980	0.4981
2.9	0.4981	0.4982	0.4982	0.4983	0.4984	0.4984	0.4985	0.4985	0.4986	0.4986
3.0	0.4987	0.4987	0.4987	0.4988	0.4988	0.4989	0.4989	0.4989	0.4990	0.4990
3.1	0.4990	0.4991	0.4991	0.4991	0.4992	0.4992	0.4992	0.4992	0.4993	0.4993
3.2	0.4993	0.4993	0.4994	0.4994	0.4994	0.4994	0.4994	0.4995	0.4995	0.4995
3.3	0.4995	0.4995	0.4995	0.4996	0.4996	0.4996	0.4996	0.4996	0.4996	0.4997
3.4	0.4997	0.4997	0.4997	0.4997	0.4997	0.4997	0.4997	0.4997	0.4997	0.4998

Appendix C2: Standard Normal Probabilities (continued)

STANDARD NORMAL PROBABILITY DISTRIBUTION $P(Z \leq z)$

	0.00	0.01	0.02	0.03	0.04	0.05	0.06	0.07	0.08	0.09
0.0	0.5000	0.5040	0.5080	0.5120	0.5160	0.5199	0.5239	0.5279	0.5319	0.5359
0.1	0.5398	0.5438	0.5478	0.5517	0.5557	0.5596	0.5636	0.5675	0.5714	0.5753
0.2	0.5793	0.5832	0.5871	0.5910	0.5948	0.5987	0.6026	0.6064	0.6103	0.6141
0.3	0.6179	0.6217	0.6255	0.6293	0.6331	0.6368	0.6406	0.6443	0.6480	0.6517
0.4	0.6554	0.6591	0.6628	0.6664	0.6700	0.6736	0.6772	0.6808	0.6844	0.6879
0.5	0.6915	0.6950	0.6985	0.7019	0.7054	0.7088	0.7123	0.7157	0.7190	0.7224
0.6	0.7257	0.7291	0.7324	0.7357	0.7389	0.7422	0.7454	0.7486	0.7517	0.7549
0.7	0.7580	0.7611	0.7642	0.7673	0.7704	0.7734	0.7764	0.7794	0.7823	0.7852
0.8	0.7881	0.7910	0.7939	0.7967	0.7995	0.8023	0.8051	0.8078	0.8106	0.8133
0.9	0.8159	0.8186	0.8212	0.8238	0.8264	0.8289	0.8315	0.8340	0.8365	0.8389
1.0	0.8413	0.8438	0.8461	0.8485	0.8508	0.8531	0.8554	0.8577	0.8599	0.8621
1.1	0.8643	0.8665	0.8686	0.8708	0.8729	0.8749	0.8770	0.8790	0.8810	0.8830
1.2	0.8849	0.8869	0.8888	0.8907	0.8925	0.8944	0.8962	0.8980	0.8997	0.9015
1.3	0.9032	0.9049	0.9066	0.9082	0.9099	0.9115	0.9131	0.9147	0.9162	0.9177
1.4	0.9192	0.9207	0.9222	0.9236	0.9251	0.9265	0.9279	0.9292	0.9306	0.9319
1.5	0.9332	0.9345	0.9357	0.9370	0.9382	0.9394	0.9406	0.9418	0.9429	0.9441
1.6	0.9452	0.9463	0.9474	0.9484	0.9495	0.9505	0.9515	0.9525	0.9535	0.9545
1.7	0.9554	0.9564	0.9573	0.9582	0.9591	0.9599	0.9608	0.9616	0.9625	0.9633
1.8	0.9641	0.9649	0.9656	0.9664	0.9671	0.9678	0.9686	0.9693	0.9699	0.9706
1.9	0.9713	0.9719	0.9726	0.9732	0.9738	0.9744	0.9750	0.9756	0.9761	0.9767
2.0	0.9772	0.9778	0.9783	0.9788	0.9793	0.9798	0.9803	0.9808	0.9812	0.9817
2.1	0.9821	0.9826	0.9830	0.9834	0.9838	0.9842	0.9846	0.9850	0.9854	0.9857
2.2	0.9861	0.9864	0.9868	0.9871	0.9875	0.9878	0.9881	0.9884	0.9887	0.9890
2.3	0.9893	0.9896	0.9898	0.9901	0.9904	0.9906	0.9909	0.9911	0.9913	0.9916
2.4	0.9918	0.9920	0.9922	0.9925	0.9927	0.9929	0.9931	0.9932	0.9934	0.9936
2.5	0.9938	0.9940	0.9941	0.9943	0.9945	0.9946	0.9948	0.9949	0.9951	0.9952
2.6	0.9953	0.9955	0.9956	0.9957	0.9959	0.9960	0.9961	0.9962	0.9963	0.9964
2.7	0.9965	0.9966	0.9967	0.9968	0.9969	0.9970	0.9971	0.9972	0.9973	0.9974
2.8	0.9974	0.9975	0.9976	0.9977	0.9977	0.9978	0.9979	0.9979	0.9980	0.9981
2.9	0.9981	0.9982	0.9982	0.9983	0.9984	0.9984	0.9985	0.9985	0.9986	0.9986
3.0	0.9987	0.9987	0.9987	0.9988	0.9988	0.9989	0.9989	0.9989	0.9990	0.9990
3.1	0.9990	0.9991	0.9991	0.9991	0.9992	0.9992	0.9992	0.9992	0.9993	0.9993
3.2	0.9993	0.9993	0.9994	0.9994	0.9994	0.9994	0.9994	0.9995	0.9995	0.9995
3.3	0.9995	0.9995	0.9995	0.9996	0.9996	0.9996	0.9996	0.9996	0.9996	0.9997
3.4	0.9997	0.9997	0.9997	0.9997	0.9997	0.9997	0.9997	0.9997	0.9997	0.9998

Appendix C3: Standard Normal Probabilities (Continued)

STANDARD NORMAL PROBABILITY DISTRIBUTION $P(Z \leq z)$

	0.00	0.01	0.02	0.03	0.04	0.05	0.06	0.07	0.08	0.09
0.0	0.5	0.504	0.508	0.512	0.516	0.5199	0.5239	0.5279	0.5319	0.5359
–0.1	0.4602	0.4641	0.4681	0.4721	0.4761	0.4801	0.484	0.488	0.492	0.496
–0.2	0.4207	0.4247	0.4286	0.4325	0.4364	0.4404	0.4443	0.4483	0.4522	0.4562
–0.3	0.3821	0.3859	0.3897	0.3936	0.3974	0.4013	0.4052	0.409	0.4129	0.4168
–0.4	0.3446	0.3483	0.352	0.3557	0.3594	0.3632	0.3669	0.3707	0.3745	0.3783
–0.5	0.3085	0.3121	0.3156	0.3192	0.3228	0.3264	0.3300	0.3336	0.3372	0.3409
–0.6	0.2743	0.2776	0.281	0.2843	0.2877	0.2912	0.2946	0.2981	0.3015	0.305
–0.7	0.242	0.2451	0.2483	0.2514	0.2546	0.2578	0.2611	0.2643	0.2676	0.2709
–0.8	0.2119	0.2148	0.2177	0.2206	0.2236	0.2266	0.2296	0.2327	0.2358	0.2389
–0.9	0.1841	0.1867	0.1894	0.1922	0.1949	0.1977	0.2005	0.2033	0.2061	0.2090
–1.0	0.1587	0.1611	0.1635	0.166	0.1685	0.1711	0.1736	0.1762	0.1788	0.1814
–1.1	0.1357	0.1379	0.1401	0.1423	0.1446	0.1469	0.1492	0.1515	0.1539	0.1562
–1.2	0.1151	0.117	0.119	0.121	0.123	0.1251	0.1271	0.1292	0.1314	0.1335
–1.3	0.0968	0.0985	0.1003	0.102	0.1038	0.1056	0.1075	0.1093	0.1112	0.1131
–1.4	0.0808	0.0823	0.0838	0.0853	0.0869	0.0885	0.0901	0.0918	0.0934	0.0951
–1.5	0.0668	0.0681	0.0694	0.0708	0.0721	0.0735	0.0749	0.0764	0.0778	0.0793
–1.6	0.0548	0.0559	0.0571	0.0582	0.0594	0.0606	0.0618	0.063	0.0643	0.0655
–1.7	0.0446	0.0455	0.0465	0.0475	0.0485	0.0495	0.0505	0.0516	0.0526	0.0537
–1.8	0.0359	0.0367	0.0375	0.0384	0.0392	0.0401	0.0409	0.0418	0.0427	0.0436
–1.9	0.0287	0.0294	0.0301	0.0307	0.0314	0.0322	0.0329	0.0336	0.0344	0.0351
–2.0	0.0228	0.0233	0.0239	0.0244	0.025	0.0256	0.0262	0.0268	0.0274	0.0281
–2.1	0.0179	0.0183	0.0188	0.0192	0.0197	0.0202	0.0207	0.0212	0.0217	0.0222
–2.2	0.0139	0.0143	0.0146	0.015	0.0154	0.0158	0.0162	0.0166	0.017	0.0174
–2.3	0.0107	0.011	0.0113	0.0116	0.0119	0.0122	0.0125	0.0129	0.0132	0.0136
–2.4	0.0082	0.0084	0.0087	0.0089	0.0091	0.0094	0.0096	0.0099	0.0102	0.0104
–2.5	0.0062	0.0064	0.0066	0.0068	0.0069	0.0071	0.0073	0.0075	0.0078	0.008
–2.6	0.0047	0.0048	0.0049	0.0051	0.0052	0.0054	0.0055	0.0057	0.0059	0.006
–2.7	0.0035	0.0036	0.0037	0.0038	0.0039	0.004	0.0041	0.0043	0.0044	0.0045
–2.8	0.0026	0.0026	0.0027	0.0028	0.0029	0.003	0.0031	0.0032	0.0033	0.0034
–2.9	0.0019	0.0019	0.002	0.0021	0.0021	0.0022	0.0023	0.0023	0.0024	0.0025
–3.0	0.0013	0.0014	0.0014	0.0015	0.0015	0.0016	0.0016	0.0017	0.0018	0.0018
–3.1	0.0010	0.0010	0.0010	0.0011	0.0011	0.0011	0.0012	0.0012	0.0013	0.0013
–3.2	0.0007	0.0007	0.0007	0.0008	0.0008	0.0008	0.0008	0.0009	0.0009	0.0009
–3.3	0.0005	0.0005	0.0005	0.0005	0.0006	0.0006	0.0006	0.0006	0.0006	0.0007
–3.4	0.0003	0.0003	0.0004	0.0004	0.0004	0.0004	0.0004	0.0004	0.0005	0.0005

APPENDIX D STUDENT T-DISTRIBUTION

(For additional rows, see the Excel file Student t-distribution under Distributions)

one-tail	0.2500	0.1250	0.1000	0.0750	0.0500	0.0250	0.0100	0.0050	0.0005
two-tail	0.5000	0.2500	0.2000	0.1500	0.1000	0.0500	0.0200	0.0100	0.0010
df\c	0.500	0.750	0.800	0.850	0.900	0.950	0.980	0.990	0.999
1	1.0000	2.4142	3.0777	4.1653	6.3138	12.7062	31.8205	63.6567	636.6192
2	0.8165	1.6036	1.8856	2.2819	2.9200	4.3027	6.9646	9.9248	31.5991
3	0.7649	1.4226	1.6377	1.9243	2.3534	3.1824	4.5407	5.8409	12.9240
4	0.7407	1.3444	1.5332	1.7782	2.1318	2.7764	3.7469	4.6041	8.6103
5	0.7267	1.3009	1.4759	1.6994	2.0150	2.5706	3.3649	4.0321	6.8688
6	0.7176	1.2733	1.4398	1.6502	1.9432	2.4469	3.1427	3.7074	5.9588
7	0.7111	1.2543	1.4149	1.6166	1.8946	2.3646	2.9980	3.4995	5.4079
8	0.7064	1.2403	1.3968	1.5922	1.8595	2.3060	2.8965	3.3554	5.0413
9	0.7027	1.2297	1.3830	1.5737	1.8331	2.2622	2.8214	3.2498	4.7809
10	0.6998	1.2213	1.3722	1.5592	1.8125	2.2281	2.7638	3.1693	4.5869
11	0.6974	1.2145	1.3634	1.5476	1.7959	2.2010	2.7181	3.1058	4.4370
12	0.6955	1.2089	1.3562	1.5380	1.7823	2.1788	2.6810	3.0545	4.3178
13	0.6938	1.2041	1.3502	1.5299	1.7709	2.1604	2.6503	3.0123	4.2208
14	0.6924	1.2001	1.3450	1.5231	1.7613	2.1448	2.6245	2.9768	4.1405
15	0.6912	1.1967	1.3406	1.5172	1.7531	2.1314	2.6025	2.9467	4.0728
16	0.6901	1.1937	1.3368	1.5121	1.7459	2.1199	2.5835	2.9208	4.0150
17	0.6892	1.1910	1.3334	1.5077	1.7396	2.1098	2.5669	2.8982	3.9651
18	0.6884	1.1887	1.3304	1.5037	1.7341	2.1009	2.5524	2.8784	3.9216
19	0.6876	1.1866	1.3277	1.5002	1.7291	2.0930	2.5395	2.8609	3.8834
20	0.6870	1.1848	1.3253	1.4970	1.7247	2.0860	2.5280	2.8453	3.8495
	⋮	⋮	⋮	⋮	⋮	⋮	⋮	⋮	⋮
30	0.6828	1.1731	1.3104	1.4774	1.6973	2.0423	2.4573	2.7500	3.6460
	⋮	⋮	⋮	⋮	⋮	⋮	⋮	⋮	⋮
40	0.6807	1.1673	1.3031	1.4677	1.6839	2.0211	2.4233	2.7045	3.5510
	⋮	⋮	⋮	⋮	⋮	⋮	⋮	⋮	⋮
50	0.6794	1.1639	1.2987	1.4620	1.6759	2.0086	2.4033	2.6778	3.4960
	⋮	⋮	⋮	⋮	⋮	⋮	⋮	⋮	⋮
60	0.6786	1.1616	1.2958	1.4582	1.6706	2.0003	2.3901	2.6603	3.4602
	⋮	⋮	⋮	⋮	⋮	⋮	⋮	⋮	⋮
∞	0.6745	1.1504	1.2816	1.4395	1.6449	1.9600	2.3264	2.5758	3.2905

APPENDIX E CHI-SQUARE PD

(For additional rows, see the Excel file Chi-Square Distribution under Distributions)

AREA TO THE RIGHT

ν	0.995	0.990	0.975	0.950	0.900	0.100	0.050	0.025	0.010	0.005
1	0.00	0.00	0.00	0.00	0.02	2.71	3.84	5.02	6.64	7.88
2	0.01	0.02	0.05	0.10	0.21	4.61	5.99	7.38	9.21	10.60
3	0.07	0.12	0.22	0.35	0.58	6.25	7.82	9.35	11.35	12.84
4	0.21	0.30	0.48	0.71	1.06	7.78	9.49	11.14	13.28	14.86
5	0.41	0.55	0.83	1.15	1.61	9.24	11.07	12.83	15.09	16.75
6	0.68	0.87	1.24	1.64	2.20	10.65	12.59	14.45	16.81	18.55
7	0.99	1.24	1.69	2.17	2.83	12.02	14.07	16.01	18.48	20.28
8	1.34	1.65	2.18	2.73	3.49	13.36	15.51	17.54	20.09	21.96
9	1.74	2.09	2.70	3.33	4.17	14.68	16.92	19.02	21.67	23.59
10	2.16	2.56	3.25	3.94	4.87	15.99	18.31	20.48	23.21	25.19
11	2.60	3.05	3.82	4.58	5.58	17.28	19.68	21.92	24.73	26.76
12	3.07	3.57	4.40	5.23	6.30	18.55	21.03	23.34	26.22	28.30
13	3.57	4.11	5.01	5.89	7.04	19.81	22.36	24.74	27.69	29.82
14	4.08	4.66	5.63	6.57	7.79	21.06	23.69	26.12	29.14	31.32
15	4.60	5.23	6.26	7.26	8.55	22.31	25.00	27.49	30.58	32.80
16	5.14	5.81	6.91	7.96	9.31	23.54	26.30	28.85	32.00	34.27
17	5.70	6.41	7.56	8.67	10.09	24.77	27.59	30.19	33.41	35.72
18	6.27	7.02	8.23	9.39	10.87	25.99	28.87	31.53	34.81	37.16
19	6.84	7.63	8.91	10.12	11.65	27.20	30.14	32.85	36.19	38.58
20	7.43	8.26	9.59	10.85	12.44	28.41	31.41	34.17	37.57	40.00
21	8.03	8.90	10.28	11.59	13.24	29.62	32.67	35.48	38.93	41.40
22	8.64	9.54	10.98	12.34	14.04	30.81	33.92	36.78	40.29	42.80
23	9.26	10.20	11.69	13.09	14.85	32.01	35.17	38.08	41.64	44.18
24	9.89	10.86	12.40	13.85	15.66	33.20	36.42	39.36	42.98	45.56
25	10.52	11.52	13.12	14.61	16.47	34.38	37.65	40.65	44.31	46.93
26	11.16	12.20	13.84	15.38	17.29	35.56	38.89	41.92	45.64	48.29
27	11.81	12.88	14.57	16.15	18.11	36.74	40.11	43.20	46.96	49.65
28	12.46	13.57	15.31	16.93	18.94	37.92	41.34	44.46	48.28	50.99
29	13.12	14.26	16.05	17.71	19.77	39.09	42.56	45.72	49.59	52.34
30	13.79	14.95	16.79	18.49	20.60	40.26	43.77	46.98	50.89	53.67
31	14.46	15.66	17.54	19.28	21.43	41.42	44.99	48.23	52.19	55.00
32	15.13	16.36	18.29	20.07	22.27	42.59	46.19	49.48	53.49	56.33
33	15.82	17.07	19.05	20.87	23.11	43.75	47.40	50.73	54.78	57.65
34	16.50	17.79	19.81	21.66	23.95	44.90	48.60	51.97	56.06	58.96
35	17.19	18.51	20.57	22.47	24.80	46.06	49.80	53.20	57.34	60.28

Appendix E: Chi-Square PD (Continued)

AREA TO THE RIGHT

ν	0.995	0.990	0.975	0.950	0.900	0.100	0.050	0.025	0.010	0.005
36	17.89	19.23	21.34	23.27	25.64	47.21	51.00	54.44	58.62	61.58
37	18.59	19.96	22.11	24.08	26.49	48.36	52.19	55.67	59.89	62.88
38	19.29	20.69	22.88	24.88	27.34	49.51	53.38	56.90	61.16	64.18
39	20.00	21.43	23.65	25.70	28.20	50.66	54.57	58.12	62.43	65.48
40	20.71	22.16	24.43	26.51	29.05	51.81	55.76	59.34	63.69	66.77
41	21.42	22.91	25.22	27.33	29.91	52.95	56.94	60.56	64.95	68.05
42	22.14	23.65	26.00	28.14	30.77	54.09	58.12	61.78	66.21	69.34
43	22.86	24.40	26.79	28.97	31.63	55.23	59.30	62.99	67.46	70.62
44	23.58	25.15	27.58	29.79	32.49	56.37	60.48	64.20	68.71	71.89
45	24.31	25.90	28.37	30.61	33.35	57.51	61.66	65.41	69.96	73.17
46	25.04	26.66	29.16	31.44	34.22	58.64	62.83	66.62	71.20	74.44
47	25.78	27.42	29.96	32.27	35.08	59.77	64.00	67.82	72.44	75.70
48	26.51	28.18	30.76	33.10	35.95	60.91	65.17	69.02	73.68	76.97
49	27.25	28.94	31.56	33.93	36.82	62.04	66.34	70.22	74.92	78.23
50	27.99	29.71	32.36	34.76	37.69	63.17	67.51	71.42	76.15	79.49
51	28.74	30.48	33.16	35.60	38.56	64.30	68.67	72.62	77.39	80.75
52	29.48	31.25	33.97	36.44	39.43	65.42	69.83	73.81	78.62	82.00
53	30.23	32.02	34.78	37.28	40.31	66.55	70.99	75.00	79.84	83.25
54	30.98	32.79	35.59	38.12	41.18	67.67	72.15	76.19	81.07	84.50
55	31.74	33.57	36.40	38.96	42.06	68.80	73.31	77.38	82.29	85.75
56	32.49	34.35	37.21	39.80	42.94	69.92	74.47	78.57	83.51	86.99
57	33.25	35.13	38.03	40.65	43.82	71.04	75.62	79.75	84.73	88.24
58	34.01	35.91	38.84	41.49	44.70	72.16	76.78	80.94	85.95	89.48
59	34.77	36.70	39.66	42.34	45.58	73.28	77.93	82.12	87.17	90.72
60	35.53	37.49	40.48	43.19	46.46	74.40	79.08	83.30	88.38	91.95
61	36.30	38.27	41.30	44.04	47.34	75.51	80.23	84.48	89.59	93.19
62	37.07	39.06	42.13	44.89	48.23	76.63	81.38	85.65	90.80	94.42
63	37.84	39.86	42.95	45.74	49.11	77.75	82.53	86.83	92.01	95.65
64	38.61	40.65	43.78	46.60	50.00	78.86	83.68	88.00	93.22	96.88
65	39.38	41.44	44.60	47.45	50.88	79.97	84.82	89.18	94.42	98.11
66	40.16	42.24	45.43	48.31	51.77	81.09	85.97	90.35	95.63	99.33
67	40.94	43.04	46.26	49.16	52.66	82.20	87.11	91.52	96.83	100.55
68	41.71	43.84	47.09	50.02	53.55	83.31	88.25	92.69	98.03	101.78
69	42.49	44.64	47.92	50.88	54.44	84.42	89.39	93.86	99.23	103.00
70	43.28	45.44	48.76	51.74	55.33	85.53	90.53	95.02	100.43	104.22

Workbook

Workbook

SECTION I: MATCHING TERMINOLOGY
SECTION II: FILL IN THE BLANK
SECTION III: CIRCLE ONE
SECTION IV: WORKED PROBLEMS

SECTION I: MATCHING TERMINOLOGY

A. Bias
B. Confounded
C. Descriptive
D. Double Blind
E. Individual
F. Inferential
G. Likert Scale
H. Lurking
I. Measure
J. Outlier
K. Parameter
L. Placebo Effect
M. Qualitative
N. Quantitative
O. Reliable
P. Seasonal Effect
Q. Simple Random Sample
R. Simulation
S. Statistic
T. Time Series
U. Treatment
V. Trend
W. Valid
X. Variability
Y. Variable
Z. Weight

1. _____ Describes a characteristic of an individual to be measured or observed.
2. _____ A consistent, repeated deviation of the sample statistic from the population parameter in the same direction when many samples are taken.
3. _____ A data value that falls outside the overall pattern of the graph.
4. _____ A graph in which the data are plotted over a period of time at regular intervals.
5. _____ A long-term upward or downward movement over time.
6. _____ A measure that is relevant or appropriate as a representation of that property.
7. _____ A measurement such that the random error is small.
8. _____ A numerical facsimile or representation of a real-world phenomenon.
9. _____ A numerical measure that describes an aspect of a **population**.
10. _____ A numerical measure that describes an aspect of a **sample**.
11. _____ A property of an individual given a numerical representation.
12. _____ A variable that has an important effect on the response variable and the relationship among the variables in a study but is not one of the explanatory variables studied either because it is unknown or not measured.
13. _____ A variable which describes an individual by placing the individual into a category or group.
14. _____ A variable which has a value or numerical measurement for which operations such as addition or averaging make sense.
15. _____ An experiment in which neither the subjects nor the people who work with them know which treatment each subject is receiving.
16. _____ Any specific experimental condition applied to the subjects.
17. _____ Changes over time that show a regular periodicity in the data where regular means over a fixed interval; the time between repetitions is called the period.
18. _____ Describes the spread in the values of the sample statistic when many samples are taken.
19. _____ Objects described by a set of data: person (animal), place, and thing. In a medical trial, the people in the study referred to as called **Subject**.

20. _____ Occurs when a subject receives no treatment, but (incorrectly) believes he or she is in fact receiving treatment and responds favorably.
21. _____ Sampling such that each individual has an equally likely chance of being selected as well as each group of size n has an equally likely chance of being selected.
22. _____ **Statistics** involve methods of organizing, picturing, and summarizing information from samples or population.
23. _____ **Statistics** involve methods of using information from a sample to draw conclusions regarding the population.
24. _____ Two variables such that their effects on the response variable cannot be distinguished from each other.
25. _____ Unlike a simple yes/no response, provides a scale that represents an ordinal scale such as Poor, Fair, Good, Excellent.
26. _____ Used to reduce bias, a **statistical adjustment** used to allow the more relevant information to have a greater influence on the mean.

SECTION II: FILL IN THE BLANK

1. **Population** is to **sample** as **parameter** is to ________________.
2. **Population** is to **sample** as ____________ is to **sample survey**.
3. **Skewed to the right** is when the mean is ____________ than the median and **skewed to the left** if the mean is ____________ than the median.
4. The difference between a **histogram** and a **bar chart** is that a **histogram** uses _________________ data and a **bar chart** uses ______________________ data.
5. The **distribution** of data includes exactly two pieces of information: the _____________________ and the ____.
6. A **confidence statement** is a _______________________________________ coupled with a ____.
7. The **margin of error** __________________ as the number of data increase.
8. One of principles of **experimental design** states that a good experiment has a comparative group by which we can compare the test group to a __________.
9. One of principles of **experiment design** states that a good sample must be selected at ______________.
10. One of principles of **experimental design** states that that a good experiment must be able to be _______________.
11. An additional principle of **experimental design** states that a good sample must be large enough; that is, for means a sample size of at least _____.
12. An additional principle of **experimental design** states that a good sample must be large enough; that is, for proportions a sample must consist of at least _____ in each cell.
13. A good sampling technique has _______ bias.
14. An experiment in which neither the subjects nor the people who work with them know which treatment each subject is receiving is a _______________ ________________ experiment.
15. An experiment in which the subjects alone do not know which treatment they are receiving is a ________________ experiment.

SECTION III: CIRCLE ONE

1. State the type of survey being preformed:
   a. A survey is done in which the sampling frame is first divided into groups based on gender and a sample of 10 are randomly taken from each.
   Convenience, Cluster, Systematic or **Stratified**
   b. A survey is done in which the sampling frame is first divided into groups based on area codes, 20 specified groups are selected at random and every individuals are included in the sample.
   Convenience, Cluster, Systematic or **Stratified**
   c. A survey is done in which every fifth individual is surveyed to obtain a sample of 50 individuals.
   Convenience, Cluster, Systematic or **Stratified**
   d. A survey is done in which individuals are asked to voluntarily call in and vote for who they believe will win in an election
   Convenience, Cluster, Systematic or **Stratified**

2. Determine whether the given value is a **statistics** and **parameter**.
   a. **Statistic** or **Parameter**: A sample of 30 widgets was selected and its average weight is computed to be 2.05 lb.
   b. **Statistic** or **Parameter**: In a study of the entire board of a Company Z consisted of 16 members, of which two hold executive positions.

3. Determine which of the four levels of measurement is most appropriate:
   a. **Nominal, Ordinal, Interval** or **Ratio** Zip Code
   b. **Nominal, Ordinal, Interval** or **Ratio** Evaluation of an restaurant on a five-point Likert scale
   c. **Nominal, Ordinal, Interval** or **Ratio** Temperature of a cup of coffee
   d. **Nominal, Ordinal, Interval** or **Ratio** Length of a piece of string

4. Determine which of the four levels of measurement is most appropriate:
   a. **Nominal, Ordinal, Interval** or **Ratio** Age of a tree
   b. **Nominal, Ordinal, Interval** or **Ratio** Time of Day
   c. **Nominal, Ordinal, Interval** or **Ratio** Social Security Number
   d. **Nominal, Ordinal, Interval** or **Ratio** A ranking of best liked ice cream flavors

5. Determine whether the given values are from a **discrete** or **continuous** data set.
   a. **Discrete** or **Continuous** The measure (miles) of the length of racing track.
   b. **Discrete** or **Continuous** The measure of the number of people in a family tree.

6. A research firm records all your information, makes several statistical summaries, both descriptive and inferential then shares this information with other research firms, but does not share personal information. Does the firm offer **anonymity, confidentiality,** or **neither**? If neither, explain.

7. Label each of the following as high or low bias and high or low variability off the center of the data:

a.

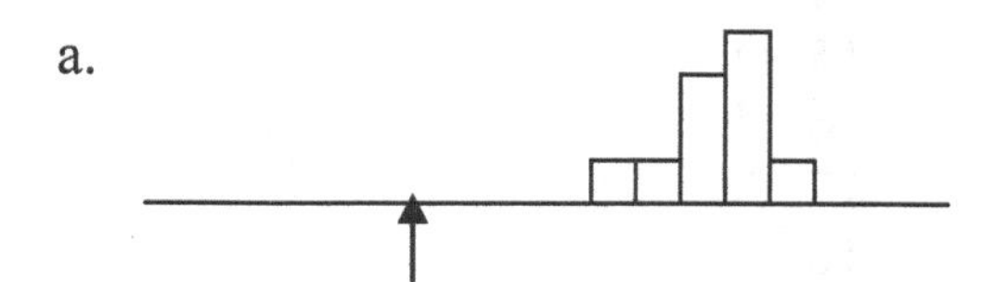

Bias: **Low** or **High**
Variability: **Low** or **High**

b.

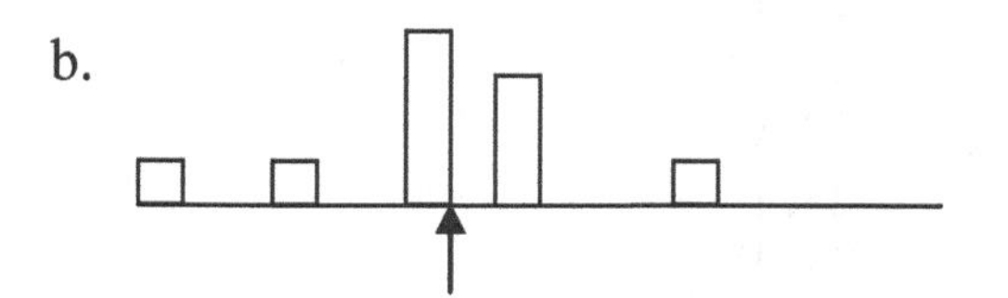

Bias: **Low** or **High**
Variability: **Low** or **High**

SECTION IV: WORKED PROBLEMS

1. A committee of four is to be selected from a group of ten individuals: A, B, C, D, E, F, G, H, I and J. Using the random set of digits 92630782401926795457 generate a random committee. Explain.
2. A committee of four is to be selected from a group of one hundred individuals. Using the random set of digits 92630782401926795457 generate a random committee. Explain.
3. Customers returned 36 coats at a large department store and only 12 to a smaller department store. The larger store sold 1100 coats this season, while the smaller store sold 200. When considering which store is a better investment, there are two **counts**, which in ratio form a single (return) **rate**.
   a. The large store had more coats returned than the smaller store, is this count a valid measure? Explain.
   b. The large store sold more coats then the smaller store, is this count a valid measure? Explain
   c. Compute the return rates. Are these valid measures? Explain.
4. A student missed 36 points on a Math exam and only missed 12 points on an English exam. The Math exam was out of a total of 360 points, while the English exam was out of 100. There are two counts, which in ratio form a single (return) rate.
   a. The student missed more points on the Math exam than on the English exam, is this count a valid measure to compare? Explain
   b. The Math exam was worth more points than the English exam, is this count a valid measure to compare? Explain
   c. Compute the percent missed. Are these valid measures? Explain.

KEY CHAPTER 1

SECTION I:

1. Y
2. A
3. J
4. T
5. V
6. W
7. O
8. R
9. K
10. S
11. I
12. H
13. M
14. N
15. D
16. U
17. P
18. X
19. E
20. L
21. Q
22. C
23. F
24. B
25. G
26. Z

SECTION II:

1. statistic
2. census
3. greater, less
4. quantitative, qualitative
5. outcomes, frequency of outcomes
6. degree of freedom, margin of error
7. decreases
8. control
9. random
10. replicated
11. 30
12. 5
13. low
14. double blind
15. single blind

SECTION III:

1. a. Stratified b. Cluster c. Systematic d. Convenience
2. a. Statistic b. Parameter
3. a. Nominal b. Ordinal c. Interval d. Ratio
4. a. Ratio b. Interval c. Nominal d. Ordinal
5. a. Continuous b. Discrete
6. Confidentiality
7. a. High Bias, Low Variability b. Low Bias, High Variability

SECTION IV:

1. There are multiple answers depending on coding and where you start in the set of random digits: let 0 represents A (0→A), 1→B, 2→C, 3→D, 4→E, 5→F, 6→G, 7→H, 8→I, and 9→J; then 9263 translates to J, C, G and D.

2. There are multiple answers depending on coding and where you start in the set of random digits: let 01 represents the first individual (01→P1), 02→P2... 99→P99, and 00→P100; then 92630782 is read 92 63 07 82 translates to the 7th, 63rd, 82nd and 92nd individual.

3. a) Invalid, no scale, from this information, we cannot conclude that customers are less satisfied with the large department store and more satisfied with the smaller store based on the fact that 36 is greater than 12. b) Valid, the scale; from this information we can conclude that more people purchased coats at the larger department store and less at a the smaller department store based on the fact that 1100 is greater than 200. c) 3.27%, 6%, valid since the total provides the scale needed for the first counts, we can now conclude that customers are more satisfied with the large department store and less satisfied with the smaller store based on the fact that $\frac{12}{200} = 0.06$ or 6% is greater than $\frac{36}{1100} = 0.03\overline{27}$ 3.27%.
4. a) Invalid, no scale, from this information, we cannot conclude that the student missed more information on the Math exam over the English Exam based on the fact that 36 is greater than 12. b) Valid, the scale, from this information we can conclude that the Math exam is worth more points than the English exam; 360 points is more than 100 points. c) Valid, $\frac{36}{360} = 0.10$ or 10% and $\frac{12}{100} = 0.12$ or 12%; hence, the student missed more information on the English exam than the Math exam

WORKBOOK CHAPTER 2: Graphics

SECTION I: MATCHING TERMINOLOGY

A. Bar chart
B. Box plot
C. Circle graph (Pie chart)
D. Contingency table
E. Dot plot
F. Frequency distribution
G. Frequency table
H. Histogram
I. Pareto chart
J. Probability distribution
K. Scatter plot
L. Seasonal Effect
M. Stem-and-leaf
N. Tree diagram
O. Trend

1. _____ One of the simplest ways to determine the distribution of numerical data – using a real number line, create a scale that includes the minimum and maximum data values, and then place a dot above each observed data point.
2. _____ A way of determining the distribution of numerical data constructed by breaking the observed data values into categories such as tens and hundreds (the **stem**) and then units digits or the remaining associated information (the **leaves**). This initial sort does give the overall **distribution**, but it is common practice to then sort the leaves. The **range** of a data set is the difference between the **minimum** and **maximum** value; or maximum minus minimum.
3. _____ A two-column table which outlines the various possible **outcomes** and the associated **frequencies** observed in a sample.
4. _____ A tabulation of the values that one or more variables take in a sample.
5. _____ A tabulation of the values that one or more variables take in a sample written in terms of **relative frequency**, **percentages** or **proportions**. If these values follow a formula, then this formula will be denoted as $\boldsymbol{f(x)}$.
6. _____ Representation of a frequency distribution of a qualitative variable by way of rectangles whose heights are proportional to relative frequencies placed over each category.
7. _____ The frequency distribution for a two-way statistical classification; that is a matrix of information where one factor is represented by the row and the second factor is represented by the column and the count of individuals that belong to exactly one cell within the matrix that is one row and one column.
8. _____ A bar chart such that the categories have been sorted according to frequency (in descending order).
9. _____ The frequency distribution represented by a circle is divided into categories $\mathbf{C_1, C_2, C_3, \ldots C_m}$ where the size of each partition is proportional to the relative frequency.
10. _____ A network diagram used to find and analyze the various outcomes in a multi-stage sampling.
11. _____ Representation of a frequency distribution by way of rectangles whose width represents the class width (class interval) and whose heights are proportional to relative frequencies.

12. _____ A line graph method of displaying data by grouping the data into quartiles. Recall, there are five quartiles, the **minimum, first quartile, median, third quartile** and the **maximum**, where a box is draw about the **interquartile range**.

13. _____ A graphical representation of a bivariate data using rectangular coordinate plane to display two variables for a set of data such that the explanatory variable is plotted on the horizontal axis and the response variable is plotted on the vertical axis.

14. _____ A **trend** is a long-term upward or downward movement over time.

15. _____ A **seasonal effect** is a pattern that changes over time and shows a regular periodicity in the data where regular means over a fixed interval of time; the time between repetitions is called the **period**.

SECTION II: FILL IN THE BLANK

1. **Skewed to the right** is when the mean is ____________ than the median and **skewed to the left** if the mean is ____________ than the median.
2. The difference between a **histogram** and a **bar chart** is that a **histogram** uses _________________ data and a **bar chart** uses ______________________ data.
3. The **distribution** of data includes exactly two pieces of information: the _____________________ and the ____.

SECTION III: MULTIPLE CHOICE

Determine whether the given values are from a **discrete** or **continuous** data set.

1. The measure (miles) of the length of racing track. a. Discrete b. Continuous
2. The measure of the number of people in a family tree. a. Discrete b. Continuous
3. The measure (count) of whole beans in a bean patch. a. Discrete b. Continuous
4. The measure time between commercials. a. Discrete b. Continuous

Determine which plot type is most appropriate.

5. Which plot can be used for a qualitative variable?
   a. Pie chart b. Histogram c. Stem-and-Leaf plot d. Box-and-Whisker plot
6. Which plot displays raw values of a data set of a quantitative variable
   a. Pie chart b. Histogram c. Stem-and-Leaf plot d. Box-and-Whisker plot
7. Which plot summarizes the five number summary of a data set?
   a. Pie chart b. Histogram c. Stem-and-Leaf plot d. Box-and-Whisker plot

SECTION IV: WORKED PROBLEMS: GRAPHICAL DISPLAYS

1. Draw a **bar chart** for the following information:

Group	Frequency
W	7
X	6
Y	5
Z	9

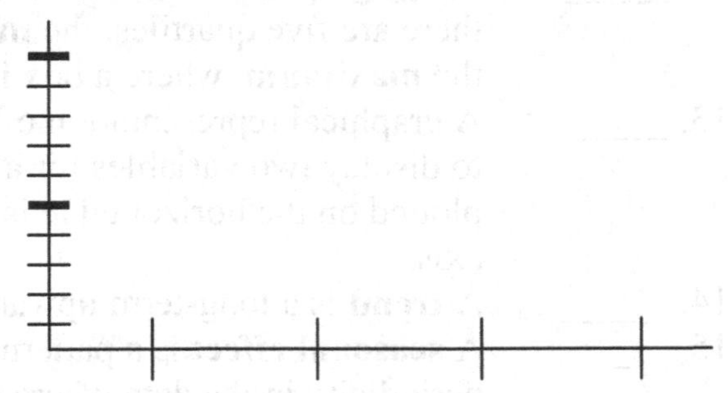

2. In an experiment, group preference is recorded for 20 individuals. Use the following information to draw a **pie chart**, include both the percentages and angles in degrees.

Group	Frequency	Percentage (%)	Degree (°)
A	5		
B	6		
C	4		
D	5		
TOTAL	20	100%	360°

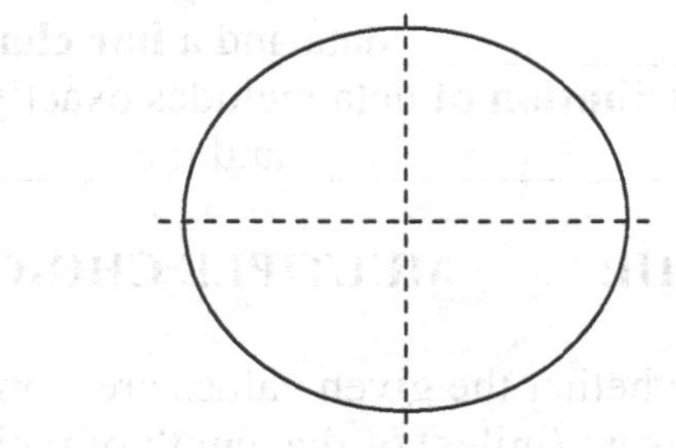

3. Identify the class width, class **midpoints**, and class **boundaries**. Complete the chart including the **relative frequencies** and the **cumulative frequencies**. Assume that the maximum data is 31.4 and the minimum data is 5.1. What is the class width with a tolerance of 1? ____________

Interval	Class Midpoints (Marks)	Frequency	Cumulative Frequency	Class Boundaries Lower	Upper	Relative Frequency (%)	Cumulative Relative Freq. (%)
5-11		8					
12-18		10					
19-25		19					
26-32		13					

4. Use the above information to draw a **histogram** of the information using the **class mark**.

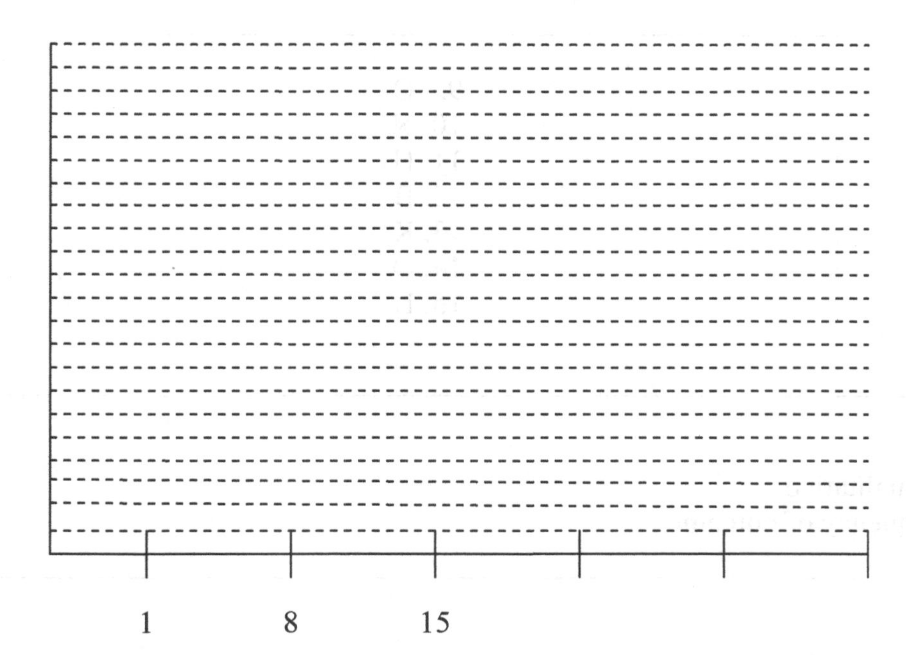

5. Use the below information to **estimate** the five-number summary. **Note: the O-give** is given in terms of **cumulative relative frequencies.** Note: as this is summarized data, these values will be approximations, round to the nearest integer.

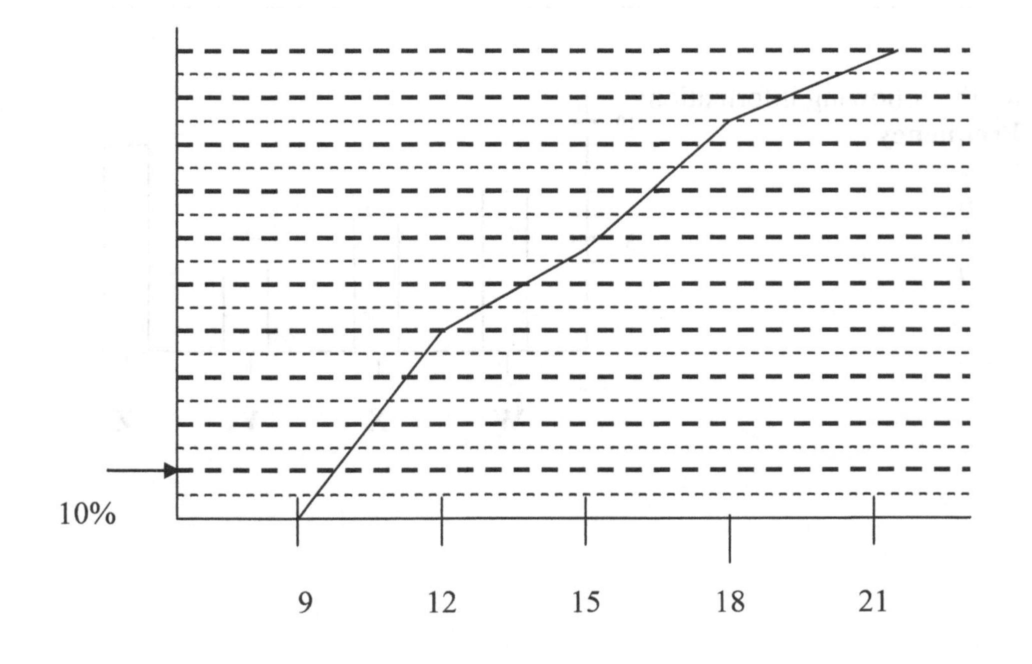

Min = ______

Q_1 = ________

Median = ___

Q_3 = ________

Max = ______

KEY CHAPTER 2

SECTION I:

1. E
2. M
3. G
4. F
5. J
6. A
7. D
8. I
9. C
10. N
11. H
12. B
13. K
14. O
15. L

SECTION II:

1. greater, less
2. quantitative, qualitative
3. outcomes, frequency of outcomes

SECTION III:

1. a. continuous
2. b. discrete
3. b. discrete
4. a. continuous
5. a. pie chart
6. c. stem-and-leaf plot
7. d. box-and-whisker plot

SECTION IV:

1. Draw a **bar chart** for the following information:

Group	Frequency
W	7
X	6
Y	5
Z	9

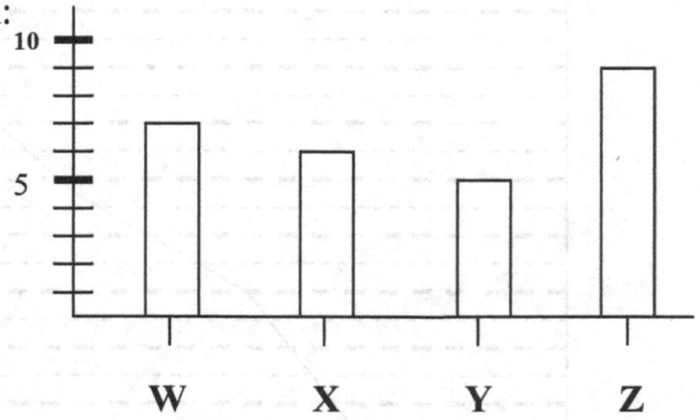

2. In an experiment, group preference is recorded for 20 individuals. Use the following information to draw a **pie chart**, include both the percentages and angles in degrees.

Group	Frequency	Percentage (%)	Degree (°)
A	5	25	90
B	6	30	108
C	4	20	72
D	5	25	90
TOTAL	**20**	**100%**	**360°**

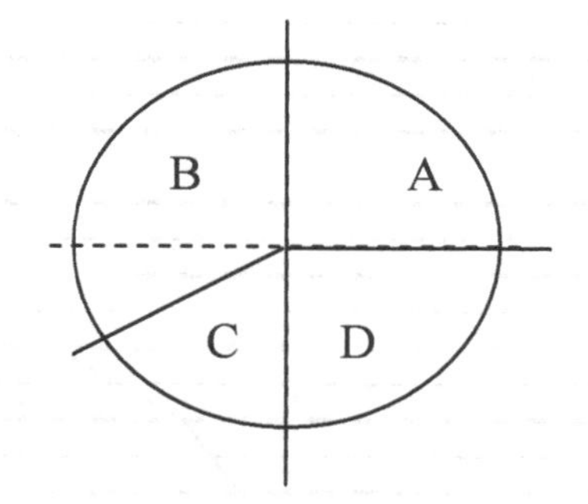

3. CW=7

Interval	Class Midpoints (Marks)	Frequency	Cumulative Frequency	Class Boundaries Lower	Upper	Relative Frequency (%)	Cumulative Relative Freq. (%)
5-11	8	8	8	4.5	11.5	16	16
12-18	15	10	18	11.5	18.5	20	36
19-25	22	19	37	18.5	25.5	38	74
26-32	29	13	50	25.5	32.5	26	100

4. Use the above information to draw a **histogram** of the information using the **class mark**.

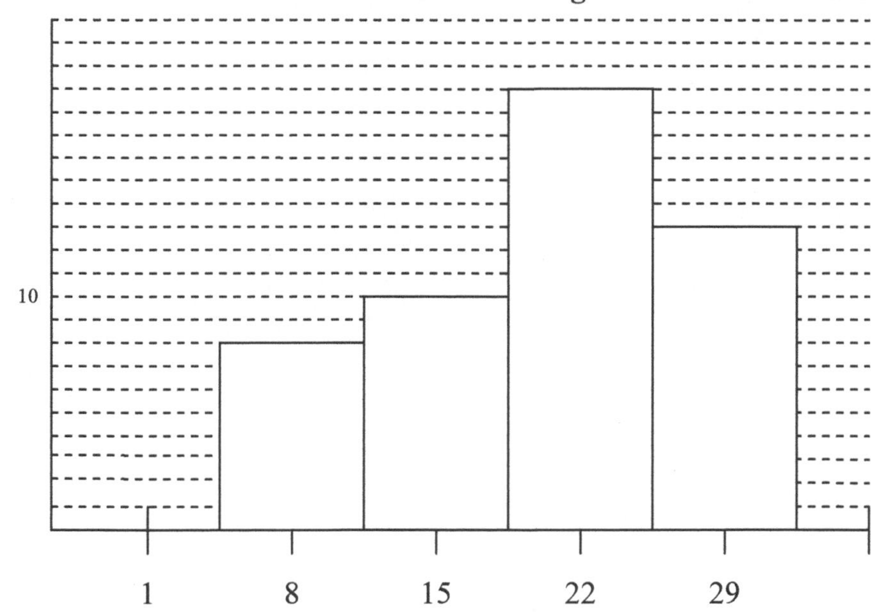

5. Use the below information to estimate the five-number summary. **Note: the O-give** is given in terms of **cumulative relative frequencies.**

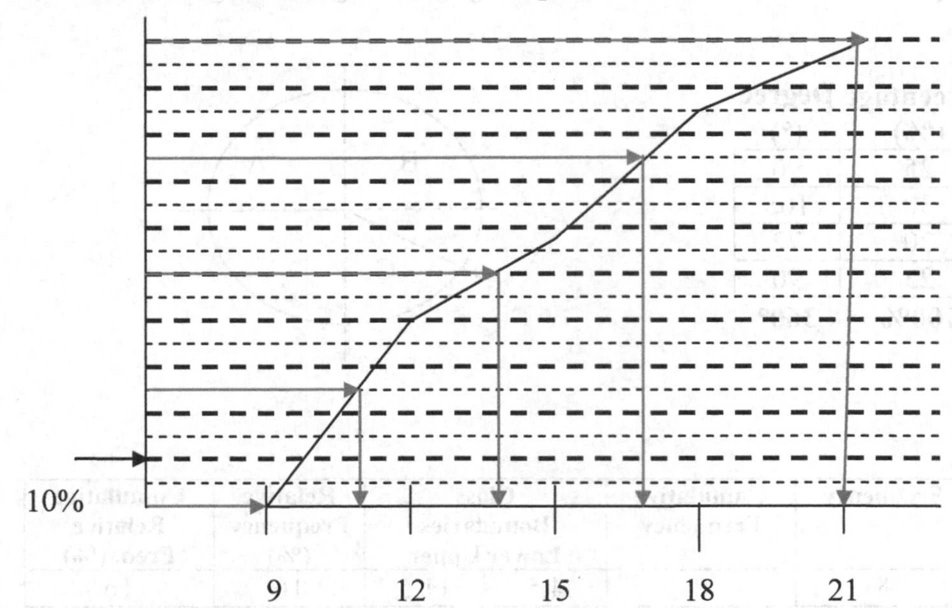

Min = 9

Q_1 = 11

Median = 14

Q_3 = 16

Max = 21

SECTION I: MATCHING TERMINOLOGY

A. Coefficient of variation
B. Deviation
C. Margin of error
D. Median
E. Mode
F. Range
G. Sample mean
H. Sample variance
I. Trimmed mean
J. Variance
K. Weighted mean

1. _____ The data value that occurs most frequently
2. _____ A data value such that 50% of the information lies to the left and 50% of the information lies to the right
3. _____ The sum of all data values divided by the total number of data values, denoted $\overline{x}$.
4. _____ The sum of the remaining data values once ***p*%** of the information from the upper data values and the lower data values, divided by the remaining number of data values.
5. _____ An estimate of the population mean by which more relevant information is counted more frequently then less relevant information; that is, some data points contribute more than others.
6. _____ A statistical measure of amount of random sampling error, denoted by the capital Greek letter Epsilon $\mathbf{E} = \left|\hat{\boldsymbol{\theta}} - \boldsymbol{\theta}\right|$
7. _____ A measure of differences between a set of data values and some fixed point such as the **mean.**
8. _____ The extent to which variation is possible; in a data set, this is defined to be the distance between the extremes, maximum minus minimum.
9. _____ Mean deviation-squared; that is, the squares of the differences between data point and mean, averaged. Also referred to as the mean square error.
10. _____ The averages of the square differences between a set of data values and the mean accounting the degree of freedom.
11. _____ A dimensionless measure, the ratio of the standard deviation to the mean; the coefficient of variation is an indication of the reliability of the measure, a measure of the dispersion of the data about the sample mean.

SECTION II: FILL IN THE BLANK

Given the data set: 2, 3, 7, 5, 3

1. What is the mode of the data set? _____
2. What is the sample mean of the data set? _____
3. What is the median of the data set? _____
4. What is the sample standard deviation of the data set? _____

SECTION III: MULTIPLE CHOICE

1. Which data set has the largest mean?
   a. {0, 2, 2} b. {0, 2, 3} c. {0, 2, 5} d. {100, 101, 102}
2. Which data set has the smallest variance?
   a. {0, 2, 2} b. {0, 2, 3} c. {0, 2, 5} d. {100, 101, 102}
3. Which one of the following measures of variation does not change when multiplying 20 to every value of the data set?
   a. Standard deviation b. Variance c. Range d. Coefficient of variation
4. Which of the three measures of central tendency may fail to exist?
   a. Mode b. Mean c. Median
5. Which of the three measures of central tendency is sensitive to changes in the data?
   a. Mode b. Mean c. Median

SECTION IV: WORKED PROBLEMS: STATISTICAL CALCULATIONS

1. Use the table of listed data below to find the **sample mean** $\bar{x}$, the **sum of squares** SS and **sample standard deviation** s of the data: (label each clearly)

Count (i)	x_i	$x_i - \bar{x}$	$(x_i - \bar{x})^2$
1	1		
2	3		
3	3		
4	5		
5	6		
6	6		
7	7		
8	7		
9	8		
10	9		
TOTALS			

2. Use the table of frequency data below to find the **mean** μ and **standard deviation** σ of the grouped (frequency) data:

Count (i)	x_i	f_i	$x_i f_i$	$x_i - \mu$	$(x_i - \mu)^2$	$(x_i - \mu)^2 f_i$
1	1	4				
2	2	3				
3	3	3				
4	5	6				
5	7	2				
TOTALS						

3. Use the table of listed data below to find the **mean** μ, the **sum of squares** SS and **standard deviation** σ of the data: (label each clearly)

Count (i)	x_i	$x_i - \mu$	$(x_i - \mu)^2$
1	11		
2	13		
3	13		
4	15		
5	16		
6	16		
7	17		
8	17		
9	18		
10	19		
TOTALS			

4. Use the table of frequency data below to find the **sample mean** $\bar{x}$, the **sum of squares** SS and **sample standard deviation** s of the data:

Count (i)	x_i	f_i	$x_i f_i$	$x_i - \bar{x}$	$(x_i - \bar{x})^2$	$(x_i - \bar{x})^2 f_i$
1	1	4				
2	2	3				
3	3	3				
4	5	6				
5	7	2				
TOTALS						

5. Use the table of listed data below to find the **sample mean** $\bar{x}$, the **sum of squares** SS and **sample standard deviation** s of the data: (label each clearly)

Count (i)	x_i	$x_i - \bar{x}$	$(x_i - \bar{x})^2$
1	1		
2	1		
3	2		
4	3		
5	4		
6	4		
7	5		
8	5		
9	6		
10	19		
TOTALS	50		

6. Given the information in questions 5, state the five number summary and draw the associated **box plot (box and whiskers)**.

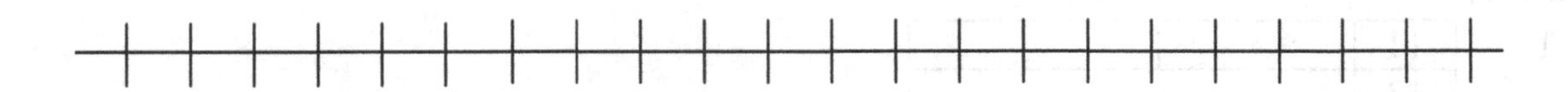

7. An **outlier** in a graph of data defined as an individual data point that falls outside the overall pattern of the graph. Using the information obtained in question 5 and 6, define and compare the outliers for the data set with summary statistics as follows:

   a. Defining an outlier as any observed data further than three standard deviations from the mean.
   b. Others define an outlier as any observed data outside the interval $Q_1 - 1.5 \times IQR$ and $Q_3 + 1.5 \times IQR$, where IQR is the **interquartile range**.

8. Computer the 25% **trimmed mean** given the data: 1, 1, 1, 2, 2, 2, 3, 4, 5, 5, 6, and 6.
9. Computer the 10% **trimmed mean** given the data: 14, 15, 21, 27, 29, 35, 39, 42, 57, and 58.
10. Computer the 25% **trimmed mean** given the data 73, 84, 89, 91; this statistic is equivalent to what commonly used statistic?
11. Compute the **weighted average** $\hat{\mu}$, for the following four test grades and respective weights. Grades: 69, 86, 91, 73; Weights: 1, 2, 2, 1.
12. Compute both the **standard mean,** $\hat{\mu}_1$, and (two **weighted averages**): the **linearly weighted mean,** $\hat{\mu}_2$, and the **trapezoidal mean,** $\hat{\mu}_3$, for the following four test grades and respective weights. Grades: 72, 85, 89, 71; (Linear weights: 1, 2, 3, 4 and Trapezoidal weights: 1, 2, 2, 1). Compare and discuss.
13. One may define an outlier as any observation outside the interval $Q_1 - 1.5 \times IQR$ and $Q_3 + 1.5 \times IQR$, where IQR is the interquartile range. Consider the following 10 observations that are listed in ascending order:

$$0, 9, 9, 9, 9, 11, 13, 13, 14, 28$$

   a. Find the five-number summary of the data.
   b. Define the outliers and identify the outliers based on the above criterion.

KEY CHAPTER 3

SECTION I:

1. E
2. D
3. G
4. I
5. K
6. C
7. B
8. F
9. J
10. H
11. A

SECTION II:

1. 3
2. 4
3. 3
4. 2

SECTION III:

1. d. {100, 101, 102}
2. d. {100, 101, 102}
3. d. Coefficient of variation
4. a. Mode
5. b. Mean

SECTION IV:

1. Use the table of listed data below to find the **sample mean** $\bar{x}$, the **sum of squares** SS and **sample standard deviation** s of the data: (label each clearly)

Count (i)	x_i	$x_i - \bar{x}$	$(x_i - \bar{x})^2$
1	1	-4.5	20.25
2	3	-2.5	6.25
3	3	-2.5	6.25
4	5	-0.5	0.25
5	6	0.5	0.25
6	6	0.5	0.25
7	7	1.5	2.25
8	7	1.5	2.25
9	8	2.5	6.25
10	9	3.5	12.25
TOTALS	55		56.5

$\bar{x} = \frac{55}{10} = 5.5$ $SS = 56.5$ $s = \sqrt{\frac{56.5}{10-1}} = 2.51$

2. Use the table of frequency data below to find the **mean** μ and **standard deviation** σ of the grouped (frequency) data:

Count (i)	x_i	f_i	$x_i f_i$	$x_i - \mu$	$(x_i - \mu)^2$	$(x_i - \mu)^2 f_i$
1	1	4	4	-2.5	6.25	25
2	2	3	6	-1.5	2.25	6.75
3	3	3	9	-0.5	0.25	0.75
4	5	6	30	1.5	2.25	13.5
5	7	2	14	3.5	12.25	24.5
TOTALS		18	63			70.5

$$\mu = \frac{63}{18} = 3.5 \qquad SS = 70.5 \qquad \sigma = \sqrt{\frac{70.5}{18}} = 1.98$$

3. Use the table of listed data below to find the **mean** μ, the **sum of squares** SS and **standard deviation** σ of the data: (label each clearly).

Count (i)	x_i	$x_i - \mu$	$(x_i - \mu)^2$
1	11	-4.5	20.25
2	13	-2.5	6.25
3	13	-2.5	6.25
4	15	-0.5	0.25
5	16	0.5	0.25
6	16	0.5	0.25
7	17	1.5	2.25
8	17	1.5	2.25
9	18	2.5	6.25
10	19	3.5	12.25
TOTALS	155		56.5

$$\mu = \frac{155}{10} = 15.5 \qquad SS = 56.5 \qquad \sigma = \sqrt{\frac{56.5}{10}} = 2.38$$

4. Use the table of frequency data below to find the **sample mean** $\bar{x}$, the **sum of squares** SS and **sample standard deviation** s of the data:

Count (i)	x_i	f_i	$x_i f_i$	$x_i - \bar{x}$	$(x_i - \bar{x})^2$	$(x_i - \bar{x})^2 f_i$
1	1	4	4	-2.5	6.25	25
2	2	3	6	-1.5	2.25	6.75
3	3	3	9	-0.5	0.25	0.75
4	5	6	30	1.5	2.25	13.5
5	7	2	14	3.5	12.25	24.5
TOTALS		18	63			70.5

$$\bar{x} = \frac{63}{18} = 3.5 \qquad SS = 70.5 \qquad s = \sqrt{\frac{70.5}{18-1}} = 2.04$$

5. Use the table of listed data below to find the **sample mean** $\bar{x}$, the **sum of squares** SS and **sample standard deviation** s of the data: (label each clearly)

Count (i)	x_i	$x_i - \bar{x}$	$(x_i - \bar{x})^2$
1	1	-4	16
2	1	-4	16
3	2	-3	9
4	3	-2	4
5	4	-1	1
6	4	-1	1
7	5	0	0
8	5	0	0
9	6	1	1
10	19	14	196
TOTALS	50		244

$\bar{x} = \dfrac{50}{10} = 5$ $\quad SS = 244$ $\quad s = \sqrt{\dfrac{244}{10-1}} = 5.21$

6. Given the information in questions 5, state the five number summary and draw the associated **box plot (box and whiskers)**.

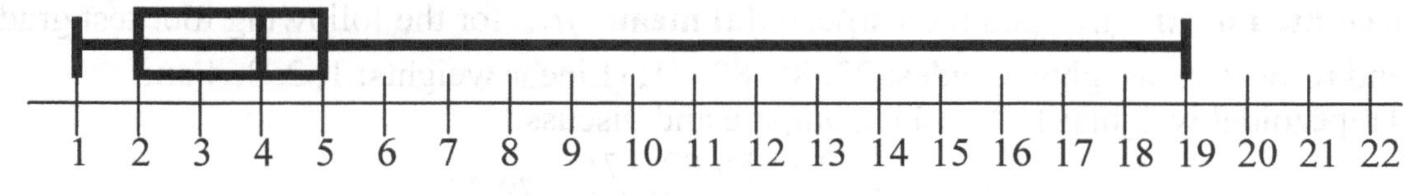

$Min = 1, Q_1 = 2, M = 4, Q_3 = 5, Max = 19$

7. An **outlier** in a graph of data defined as an individual data point that falls outside the overall pattern of the graph. Using the information obtained in question 5 and 6: define and compare the outliers for the data set with summary statistics as follows:

a) Defining an outlier as any observed data further than three standard deviations from the mean.

Outside the interval $(5 - 3 \times 5.21, 5 + 3 \times 5.21) \equiv (-10.62, 20.62)$ with no outliers

b) Others define an outlier as any observed data outside the interval $Q_1 - 1.5 \times IQR$ and $Q_3 + 1.5 \times IQR$, where IQR is the **interquartile range**.

Outside the interval $(2 - 1.5 \times 3, 5 + 1.5 \times 3) \equiv (-2.5, 9.5)$ with 19 as the outlier

8. Computer the 25% **trimmed mean** given the data: 1, 1, 1, 2, 2, 2, 3, 4, 5, 5, 6, and 6.

$$\hat{\mu} = \frac{2+2+2+3+4+5}{6} = 3$$

9. Computer the 10% **trimmed mean** given the data: 14, 15, 21, 27, 29, 35, 39, 42, 57, and 58.

$$\hat{\mu} = \frac{15+21+27+29+35+39+42+57}{8} = 33.125$$

10. Computer the 25% **trimmed mean** given the data 73, 84, 89, 91; this statistic is equivalent to what commonly used statistic?

$$\hat{\mu} = \frac{84+89}{2} = 86.5$$

11. Compute the **weighted average** $\hat{\mu}$, for the following four test grades and respective weights. Grades: 69, 86, 91, 73; Weights: 1, 2, 2, 1.

$$\hat{\mu} = \frac{69\times1+86\times2+91\times2+73\times1}{1+2+2+1} = 82.67$$

12. Compute both the **standard mean,** $\hat{\mu}_1$, and (two **weighted averages**): the **linearly weighted mean,** $\hat{\mu}_2$, and the **trapezoidal mean,** $\hat{\mu}_3$, for the following four test grades and respective weights. Grades: 72, 85, 89, 71; (Linear weights: 1, 2, 3, 4 and Trapezoidal weights: 1, 2, 2, 1). Compare and discuss.

$$\hat{\mu}_1 = \bar{x} = \frac{72+85+89+71}{4} = 79.25$$

$$\hat{\mu}_2 = \frac{72\times1+85\times2+89\times3+71\times4}{10} = 79.3$$

$$\hat{\mu}_3 = \frac{72\times1+85\times2+89\times2+71\times1}{6} = 81.8$$

The first two estimates show a C+; however, the third shows a B-.

13. One may define an outlier as any observation outside the interval $Q_1 - 1.5\times IQR$ and $Q_3 + 1.5\times IQR$, where IQR is the interquartile range. Consider the following 10 observations that are listed in ascending order:

0, 9, 9, 9, 9, 11, 13, 13, 14, 28

a. Find the five-number summary of the data.

$$Min = 0, Q_1 = 9, M = 10, Q_3 = 13, Max = 28$$

b. Define the outliers and identify the outliers based on the above criterion.

Outside the interval $(9 - 1.5\times 4, 13 + 1.5\times 4) \equiv (3,19)$ with 0 and 28 as the outlier

SECTION I: MATCHING TERMINOLOGY

A. Law of large number
B. Mutually Exclusive
C. Probability
D. Sample space

1) _____ The collection of all possible outcomes in an experiment.
2) _____ Two sets whose intersection is the empty set.
3) _____ A measure between 0 and 1 that describes the chances or likelihood that an event will occur.
4) _____ In the long run, as the sample size increases, the relative frequencies of outcomes approach to the theoretical probability. In general, as the sample size increases, the statistic approaches the parameter.

SECTION II: FILL IN THE BLANK

1) One **property of probability** states that the probability of the sample space is ______.
2) A second **property of probability** states that the probability of any event is between ____ and _____.
3) A third **property of probability** states that if mutually exclusive events which in __________ form the sample space, then the sum of the probability of the events is one.
4) Given $P(E) = 0.4281$, then $P(\overline{E}) =$ ________.
5) Let $n(E)$ be the number of outcomes in an event E. Given $n(E) = 14$ and $P(E) = 0.2$, then $n(\overline{E}) =$ ________.
6) Given $n(E) = x$ and $P(E) = \frac{x}{y}$, then $O(E) =$ ________.
7) If the events A and B are **mutually exclusive**, then $P(A \cup B) =$________________
8) If the events A and B are **not mutually exclusive**, then $P(A \cup B) =$________________
9) Given A and B are **dependent** than $P(A \cap B) =$ ___________.
10) Given A and B are **independent** than $P(A \cap B) =$ ____________________.
11) Given A and B are **independent** than $P(A|B) =$ ______.
12) Given A and B are **mutually exclusive** than $P(A \cap B) =$ ______.
13) Given A and B are **mutually exclusive** than $A \cap B =$ ______.
14) Given two independent random variables with $E(X_1) = \mu_1$, $Var(X_1) = \sigma_1^2$, $E(X_2) = \mu_2$, and $Var(X_2) = \sigma_2^2$; if we transform the data using the linear combination $Y = 3X_1 - 5X_2$, then $E(Y) =$ ________________ and $Var(Y) =$ ________________.

SECTION III: MULTIPLE-CHOICE QUESTIONS

1) In general, if any value a is **added** to each data, how would this affect the **mean** and **standard deviation**?
   a. Increase the **mean** by a value of a and the **deviation** by a multiple of $\sqrt{a}$
   b. It would increase the **mean** and the **deviation** by a multiple of a
   c. Increase the **mean** by a value of a but does not affect the **deviation**

2) In general, if each data were **multiplied** by any positive value m, how would this affect the mean?
   a. Increase the **mean** by a multiple of m
   b. Increase the **mean** by a value of m
   c. Increase the **mean** by a multiple of $\sqrt{m}$

3) In general, if each data were **multiplied** by any positive value m, how would this affect the **standard deviation**?
   a. Increase the **standard deviation** by a multiple of m^2
   b. Increase the **standard deviation** by a multiple of $\sqrt{m}$
   c. Increase the **standard deviation** by a multiple of m

4) In general, if each data were **multiplied** by any positive value m, how would this affect the **variance**?
   a. Increase the **variance** by a multiple of m^2
   b. Increase the **variance** by a multiple of $\sqrt{m}$
   c. Increase the **variance** by a multiple of m

5) Which one can be a probability distribution?

(a)

X	1	2	3
$P(X)$	0.1	0.7	0.4

(b)

X	1	2	3
$P(X)$	0.1	-0.2	0.3

(c)

X	1	2	3
$P(X)$	0.1	0.3	0.6

(d)

X	1	2	3
$P(X)$	0.9	-0.2	0.3

6) How many different ways are possible when three positions (supervisor, coordinator, secretary) are filled from total 100 candidates?
   (a) ${}_{100}P_3$ (b) ${}_{100}C_3$ (c) 100! (d) 3^{100}

7) How many different groups are possible when selecting three secretaries from 100 candidates?
   (a) ${}_{100}P_3$ (b) ${}_{100}C_3$ (c) 100! (d) 3^{100}

SECTION IV: WORKED PROBLEMS

1) In a survey of 100 individuals who use one of two brands of detergent, 61 used brand **A**, 52 used brand **B**, and 29 used both brands **A** and **B**.

   a. What proportion (probability) used either brand **A** or brand **B**.

   b. What proportions use neither of these two brands?

2) An urn contains 7 red, 8 orange, and 8 yellow balls.

   a. What is the conditional probability that the second ball is red given the first ball was red without replacement?

   b. What is the probability that two yellow balls are drawn in succession when chosen without replacement?

   c. What is the probability that two yellow balls are drawn in succession when chosen with replacement?

3) Given three women and five men, what is the probability of two women and one man are selected to form a three-member committee?

4) Parts are purchased from three different companies; 42% from company A, 33% from company B and the rest from the company C. The proportion of defectives found in general is 1%, 2% and 3%, respectively.

   a. Construct the associated **tree diagram**.

   b. Find the probability that the part was from company A and it was **not** defective when a part was randomly selected.

   c. Find the probability that the part is **defective**.

   d. What is the probability that the part is from **company A** given it is **defective**?

5) In an experiment, there are two boxes of marbles – in the first box (***H***), there are three white and one black marble and in the second box (***T***), there are two white and two black marbles; an unfair coin is tossed: if a head appears uppermost, then a marble is selected from the first box; otherwise, a marble is selected from the second box. If the probability of a head is 0.4, complete the following.

a. Draw the tree diagram that illustrates the above experiment, a box is selected, followed by a single marble is selected from that box.

b. State the sample space.

c. Give the associated probability distribution.

d. Illustrate or explain how a twenty-sided die might be used to simulate this experiment.

$$S = \{1, 2, 3, 4, 5, 6, 7, 8, 9, 10, 11, 12, 13, 14, 15, 16, 17, 18, 19, 20\}$$

e. What assumption justifies using a fair twenty-sided die to simulated this?

6) Consider a small population consisting of 60 students enrolled in STA4321 course. All 60 students are cross-classified by two classification variables: (1) **Gender** and (2) **Eye color**.

	Male	**Female**	**TOTAL**
Brown	6	9	15
Blue	10	10	20
Green	11	14	25
TOTAL	27	33	60

a. Find the probability that a student selected at random is a male or has blue eye color.

b. Find the probability that a student selected at random has green eye color given that the student is a female.

KEY CHAPTER 4

SECTION I:

1. D
2. B
3. C
4. A

SECTION II:

1. 1
2. 0, 1
3. union
4. 0.5719
5. 56
6. $x: (y - x)$
7. $P(A) + P(B)$
8. $P(A) + P(B) - P(A \cap B)$
9. $P(A) \times P(B|A)$ or $P(B) \times P(A|B)$
10. $P(A) \times P(B)$
11. $P(A)$
12. 0
13. $\emptyset$
14. $3\mu_1 - 5\mu_2$, $9\sigma_1^2 + 25\sigma_2^2$

SECTION III:

1. c. Increase the **mean** by a value of a but does not affect the **deviation**
2. a. Increase the **mean** by a multiple of m
3. c. Increase the **standard deviation** by a multiple of m
4. a. Increase the **variance** by a multiple of m^2
5. c. Sum to 1 with no negatives
6. a. Permutations
7. b. Combinations

SECTION IV:

1. a. $P(A \cup B) = \frac{61}{100} + \frac{52}{100} - \frac{29}{100} = 0.84$

   b. $P(\bar{A} \cap \bar{B}) = 1 - 0.84 = 0.16$

2. a. $P(R|R) = \frac{6}{22} = 0.2727$

   b. $P(Y \cap Y) = \frac{8}{23} \times \frac{7}{22} = 0.1107$

   c. $P(Y \cap Y) = \frac{8}{23} \times \frac{8}{23} = 0.1059$

3. $P(2W \text{ and } 1M) = \frac{C(3,2) \times C(5,1)}{C(8,3)} = 0.2679$

4. a.

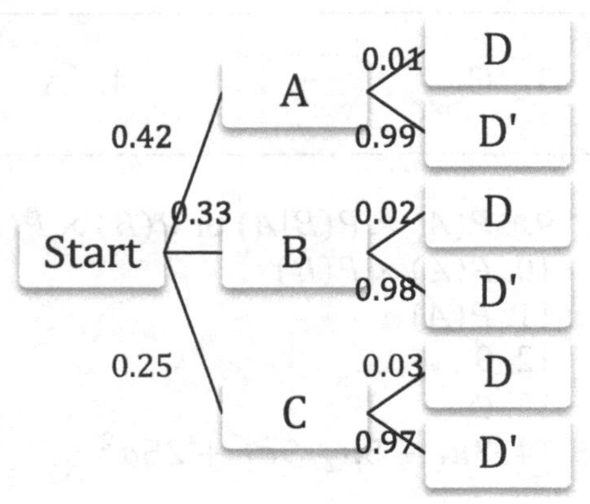

b. $P(A \cap \overline{D}) = 0.42 \times (0.99) = 0.4158$

c. $P(D) = 0.42 \times 0.01 + 0.33 \times 0.02 + 0.25 \times 0.03 = 0.0183$

d. $P(A|D) = \frac{0.42 \times 0.01}{0.0183} = 0.2295$

5. a.

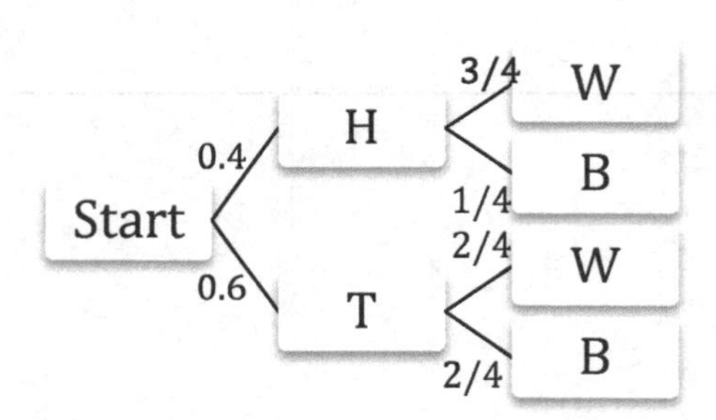

b. $S = \{HW, HB, TW, TB\}$

c. $P(HW) = 0.4 \times \frac{3}{4} = 0.3, P(HB) = 0.4 \times \frac{1}{4} = 0.1,$

$P(TW) = 0.6 \times \frac{1}{2} = 0.3, P(TB) = 0.6 \times \frac{1}{2} = 0.3.$

d. Note: there are many possible answers.

$$S = \{\overbrace{1, 2, 3, 4, 5, 6}^{HW}, \overbrace{7, 8}^{HB}, \overbrace{9, 10, 11, 12, 13, 14}^{\text{TW}}, \overbrace{15, 16, 17, 18, 19, 20}^{\text{TB}}\}$$

e. Matching probability structures

6. a. $P(M \cup B) = \frac{27}{60} + \frac{20}{60} - \frac{10}{60} = \frac{37}{60} = 0.6167$

b. $P(G|F) = \frac{14}{33} = 0.4242$

SECTION I: MATCHING TERMINOLOGY

A. Binomial experiment
B. Geometric experiment
C. Poisson experiment
D. Law of large number
E. Mutually Exclusive
F. Probability
G. Sample space

1) _____ The collection of all possible outcomes in an experiment.
2) _____ Consists of a number of independent trials repeated under identical conditions. On each trial, there are two possible outcomes; however, "success" is only found on the last try.
3) _____ Two sets whose intersection is the empty set.
4) _____ A measure between 0 and 1 that describes the chances or likelihood that an event will occur.
5) _____ In the long run, as the sample size increases, the relative frequencies of outcomes approach to the theoretical probability. In general, as the sample size increases, the statistic approaches the parameter.
6) _____ Consists of a number of independent trials repeated under identical conditions. On each trial, there are two possible outcomes where one outcome is a rare event; a discrete version of the exponential distribution.
7) _____ Consists of a number of independent trials repeated under identical conditions. On each trial, there are two possible outcomes.

SECTION II: FILL IN THE BLANK

1) In a **Binomial probability distribution** with $n = 100$ and $p = 0.04$; then using normal approximation to the binomial we have $\mu =$ _______ and $\sigma^2 =$ _________.
2) In a **Binomial probability distribution** with $n = 20$ and $p = 0.4$; then using normal approximation to the binomial we have $\mu =$ _______ and $\sigma^2 =$ _________.
3) In a **Binomial probability distribution** with $n = 10$ and $p = 0.4$; the probability of exactly four successes: $P(4) =$ __________.
4) In a **Poisson probability distribution** with $\lambda = 4$; then we have $\mu =$ _______ and $\sigma^2 =$ _________.
5) In a **Poisson probability distribution** with $\lambda = 4$; the probability of exactly four: $P(4) =$ __________.
6) In a **Geometric probability distribution** with $p = 0.04$; then we have $\mu =$ _______ and $\sigma^2 =$ _________.
7) In a **Geometric probability distribution** with $p = 0.04$; the probability of success on the fourth try: $P(4) =$ __________.

SECTION III: MULTIPLE-CHOICE QUESTIONS

1) Ten fair coins are shaken in a cup then poured out onto a table top. Which of the following distributions has the highest probability off occurrence:
(a) 0 H 10 T (b) 7 H 3 T (c) 5 H 5 T (d) All equally likely

2) Let n be the number of the Florida bar exams to take until the first pass. What distribution does n follow?
(a) Binomial (b) Geometric (c) Poisson (d) Normal

3) Let x be the number of the flaws in a yard of fabric. What distribution does x follow?
(a) Binomial (b) Geometric (c) Poisson (d) Normal

4) Which one is a discrete distribution?
(a) Binomial (b) Normal (c) Chi-square (d) Student's t

5) Which one is a continuous distribution?
(a) Geometric (b) Poisson (c) Normal (d) Binomial

6) Let n be the number of the CPA exams to take until the first pass. What distribution does n follow?
(a) Binomial (b) Geometric (c) Poisson (d) Normal

7) Suppose that 100 people take the CPA exam. Let p be the probability that a person passes the exam. Let r be the number of people who pass the CPA exam. What distribution does r follow?
(a) Binomial (b) Geometric (c) Poisson (d) Normal

SECTION IV: WORKED PROBLEMS:

1) Given the following information, determine the **expected value** and **variance**.

x_i	p_i	$x_i p_i$	$x_i - \mu$	$(x_i - \mu)^2$	$(x_i - \mu)^2 p_i$
2	0.15				
4	0.30				
5	0.30				
8	0.25				

2) A company purchases large shipments of lemons and uses this acceptance sampling plan: randomly select and test 500 lemons, then accept the whole batch if there is less than two found to be rotten bitter; that is, at most one lemon is bad. If a particular shipment actually has a 1.5% rate of defects:

a. Using the binomial probability distribution is the probability that this whole shipment is accepted?

b. What is the expected value of the number of bad lemons?

c. What is the standard deviation of the number of bad lemons?

3) Given the mean number of errors a typist makes on average is 3.4 words per page.
a. Find the probability that there are at least one error on a given page.

b. Find the expected value of the number of errors on a page and the variance of the number of errors on a page.

4) Given that the probability of success is 2% and each trial is independent and identically distributed.
a. Find the probability of finding success on the third trial.

b. Find the expected value of the number of trials needed to find success and the variance in the numbers of trials one needs to find success.

KEY CHAPTER 5

SECTION I:

1. G
2. B
3. E
4. F
5. D
6. C
7. A

SECTION II:

1. $\mu = 100 \times 0.04 = 4$ and $\sigma^2 = 100 \times 0.04 \times 0.96 = 3.84$
2. $\mu = 10 \times 0.4 = 4$ and $\sigma^2 = 10 \times 0.4 \times 0.6 = 2.4$
3. $P(4) = C(10,4) \times 0.4^4 \times 0.6^6 = 0.2508$
4. $\mu = \lambda = 4$ and $\sigma^2 = \lambda = 4$
5. $P(4) = \frac{4^4 e^{-4}}{4!} = 0.195367$
6. $\mu = \frac{1}{0.04} = 25$ and $\sigma^2 = \frac{1-p}{p^2} = 24.49$
7. $P(4) = 0.04 \times 0.96^3 = 0.0354$

SECTION III:

1. c
2. b
3. c
4. a
5. c
6. b
7. a

SECTION IV:

1. $\mu = 5, \sigma^2 = 3.9$

x_i	p_i	$x_i p_i$	$x_i - \mu$	$(x_i - \mu)^2$	$(x_i - \mu)^2 p_i$
2	0.15	0.3	-3	9	1.35
4	0.30	1.2	-1	1	0.3
5	0.30	1.5	0	0	0
8	0.25	2	3	9	2.25

2. a. $P(Accepted)$
   $= C(500,0) \times 0.015^0 \times 0.985^{500} + C(500,1) \times 0.015^1 \times 0.985^{499} = 0.0045$

   b. $\mu = 500 \times 0.015 = 7.5$

   c. $\sigma = \sqrt{500 \times 0.015 \times 0.985} = 2.72$
3. a. $P(x \geq 1) = 1 - P(0) = 1 - \frac{3.4^0 e^{-3.4}}{0!} = 0.9666$ b. $\mu = 3.4 = \sigma^2$
4. a. $P(3) = 0.02 \times 0.98^2 = 0.0192$ b. $\mu = 50, \sigma^2 = 49.49$

SECTION I: MATCHING TERMINOLOGY

A. Central Limit Theorem
B. Continuous Probability Distribution
C. Normal Probability Distribution
D. Sampling Distribution
E. Standard Error
F. Standard Normal

1. _____ A random variable which can assume an infinitely large number of values associated with the points on a line interval, and the probability of which is spread continuously over these points,
2. _____ A continuous random variable X such that the probability distribution is given by the following function:

$$f(x) = \frac{1}{\sigma\sqrt{2\pi}} e^{-\frac{(x-\mu)^2}{2\sigma^2}}, -\infty < x < \infty, -\infty < \mu < \infty, 0 < \sigma^2 < \infty$$

3. _____ A continuous random variable X such that the probability distribution is given by the following function:

$$f(z) = \frac{1}{\sqrt{2\pi}} e^{-\frac{z^2}{2}}, -\infty < z < \infty, \mu = 0, \sigma^2 = 1$$

4. _____ a probability distribution of a sample statistic based on all possible simple random samples of the ***same size*** from the same population.
5. _____ The standard deviation of the statistic. That is, given a parameter, θ, in descriptive statistics, there is an estimate called a statistic denoted by, $\hat{\theta}$, where $E(\hat{\theta}) = \theta$ the standard error is $\sigma_{\hat{\theta}} = \sqrt{V(\hat{\theta})}$, where $V(\hat{\theta})$ is the variance of the statistic.
6. _____ For means, as the sample size n increase, the probability distribution of the sample mean $\bar{X}$ approaches a normal probability distribution with mean μ and variance $\frac{\sigma^2}{n}$.

SECTION II: FILL IN THE BLANK

1) In any **symmetrical** and **bell-shaped** distribution (namely the normal probability distribution), the **empirical rule** states approximately
   a. _____% of the observed data fall within one standard deviation of the mean
   b. _____% of the observed data fall within two standard deviation of the mean
   c. _____% of the observed data fall within three standard deviation of the mean

2) The **points of inflection** (the change in concavity or cupping) in a normal probability curve occur at _____________ and _______________.

3) If the random variable X has a **normal distribution** with **mean** μ and **standard deviation** σ, then the transformed z-score: $Z = \dfrac{X - \mu}{\sigma}$ has a normal distribution with **mean** of _____ and **standard deviation** of _____. This transformed distribution is called the **standard normal distribution**.

4) If the random variable X has a **normal distribution** with **mean** μ and **standard deviation** σ, the **sampling distribution** for means, $\overline{X}$, the standard normal random variable, Z, is given by $Z =$ ________________.

5) For the **sampling distribution** for proportions, where x is the observed number of successes, n trials and p is the true population proportion.

a) To using **normal approximation** to the **binomial**, we need a count of at least ___ in each category; that is, $\boldsymbol{np} \geq$____ and $\boldsymbol{n(1-p)} \geq$___.

b) State the mean proportion $\mu_{\hat{p}}$ and standard error for proportions $\sigma_{\hat{p}}$ and define $\hat{p}$ and the z-score z for the approximate normal random variable both with and without correction for continuity, where x is the observed number of successes, n trials and p is the true population proportion.

$\mu_{\hat{p}} =$ _______

$\sigma_{\hat{p}} =$ _______

$\hat{p} =$ _______

$z =$ ________ $z =$ ________

c) Give alternative forms for the mean, the standard deviation of the population proportion (normal approximate to the binomial) and the associated z-score both with and without correction for continuity.

$\mu =$ ________

$\sigma =$ ________

$z =$ ________ $z =$ ________

SECTION III: MULTIPLE-CHOICE QUESTIONS

1) **Normal probability distribution** is more appropriately called what?
a. Standard Normal b. Gaussian c. Poisson

Assume that $F(x)$ is the cumulative normal probability distribution.

[1]	**QQ** Plot mapping $F^{-1}(p_i)$ versus x_i
[2]	**PP** Plot mapping $F(x_i)$ versus p_i
[3]	**Standard Z-Score** mapping x_i versus $z_i = \frac{x_i - \mu}{\sigma}$
[4]	**Percent Change** mapping x_i versus $z_i = \frac{x_i - \mu}{\mu}$

2) Which graph(s) described above **normalize** the data, just with two different scales?
a. [1] & [2] b. [1] & [3] c. [2] & [3] d. [3] & [4]

3) Which graph(s) described above are used to determine if the data is normal?
a. [1] & [2] b. [1] & [3] c. [2] & [3] d. [3] & [4]

4) Comparing Scores: A students take three tests graded as follows:
Test 1: a score of 18 of a test with a mean of 16 and a standard deviation of 6
Test 2: a score of 44 on a test with a mean of 38 and a standard deviation of 14
Test 3: a score of 95 on a test with mean of 87 and a standard deviation of 36

Which is the higher relative score?
a. Test 1 b. Test 2 c. Test 3

5) Comparing Scores: A students take three tests graded as follows:
Test 1: a score of 36 of a test with a mean of 32 and a standard deviation of 12
Test 2: a score of 44 on a test with a mean of 50 and a standard deviation of 12
Test 3: a score of 32 on a test with mean of 29 and a standard deviation of 12

Which is the lower relative score?
a. Test 1 b. Test 2 c. Test 3

6) What type of "**out of control**" signal is illustrated (circle control issue)

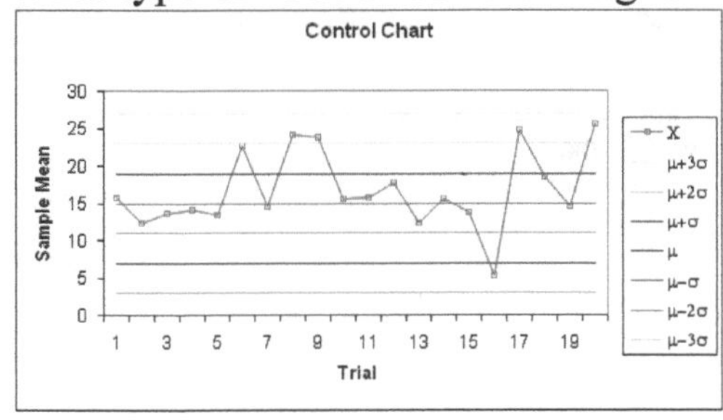

a. Signal I

b. Signal II

c. Signal III

7) What type of "**out of control**" signal is illustrated (circle control issue)

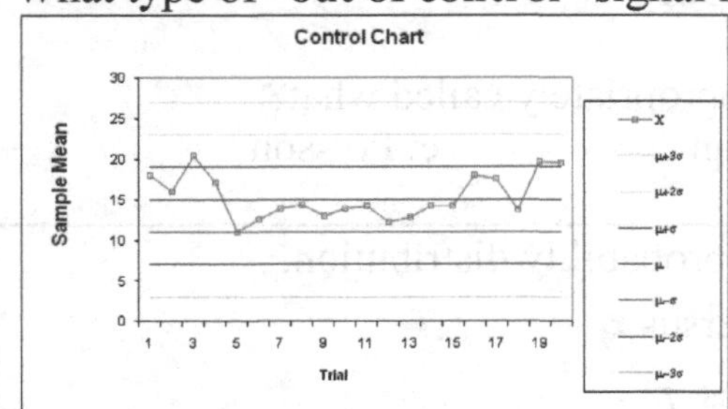

a. Signal I

b. Signal II

c. Signal III

8) What type of "**out of control**" signal is illustrated (circle control issue)

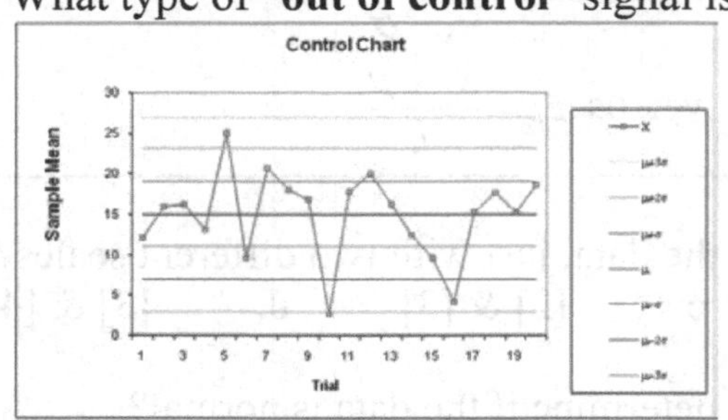

a. Signal I

b. Signal II

c. Signal III

9) Which binomial distribution can be well approximated by a normal distribution?

(a) $Binomial(n = 100, p = 0.01)$ (b) $Binomial(n = 100, p = 0.999)$

(c) $Binomial(n = 20, p = 0.5)$ (d) $Binomial(n = 10, p = 0.5)$

SECTION IV: WORKED PROBLEMS:

1) State the three common schemes for "**out of control**" in order and compute the associated probabilities (show work).

2) Which of the following QQ plots shown in the figures below indicate that the data is **normal** and which is not? Explain.

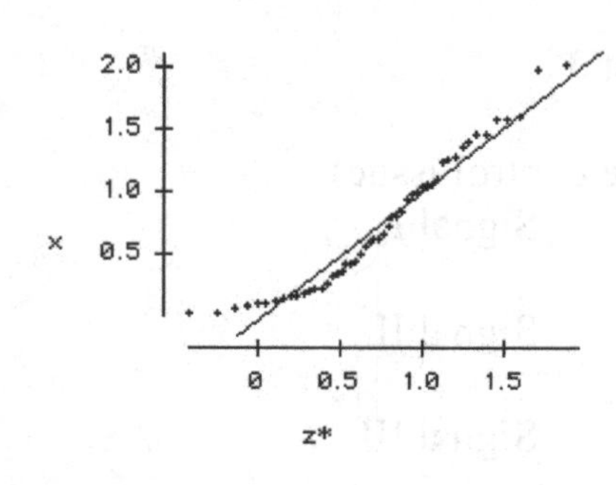

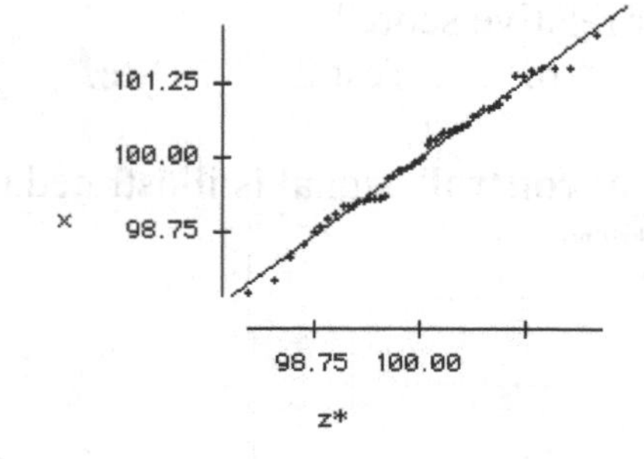

3) Given the following QQ-plot and the associated histogram, can we assume normality? Construct the associated box-plots.

a.

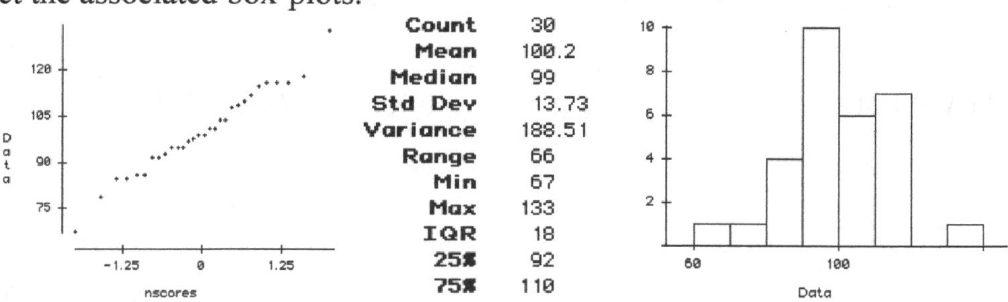

b.

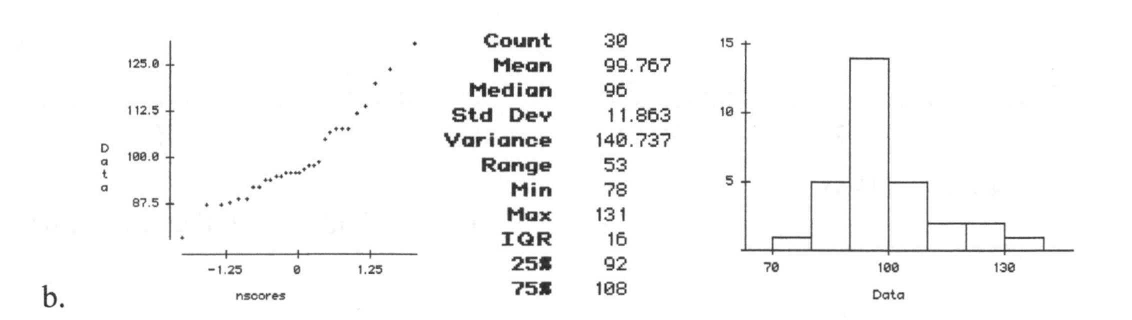

c.

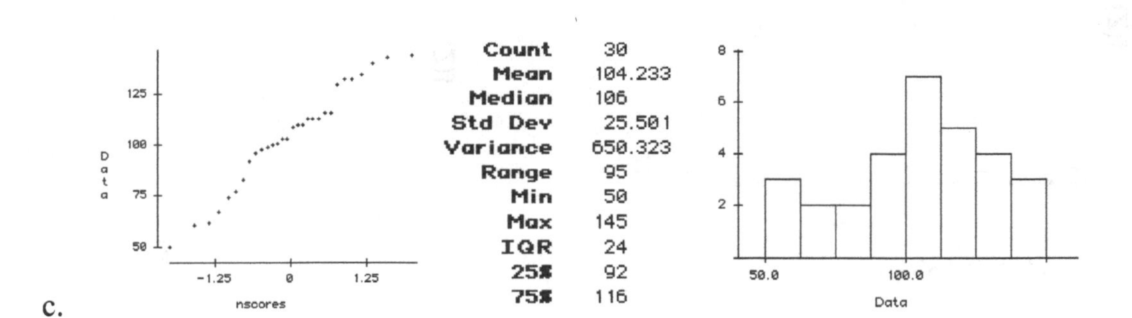

4) Given that the **population mean** is 100 and the **standard deviation** is 15, convert the following intervals in terms of the data into intervals in terms of **standard score**.

a. $X \geq 90$
b. $80 \leq X \leq 125$
c. $X \leq 135$

5) Given that the **population mean** is 190 and the **standard deviation** is 36 on a continuous **normally distributed** scale. Find the following.

a. $P(X \le 194)$

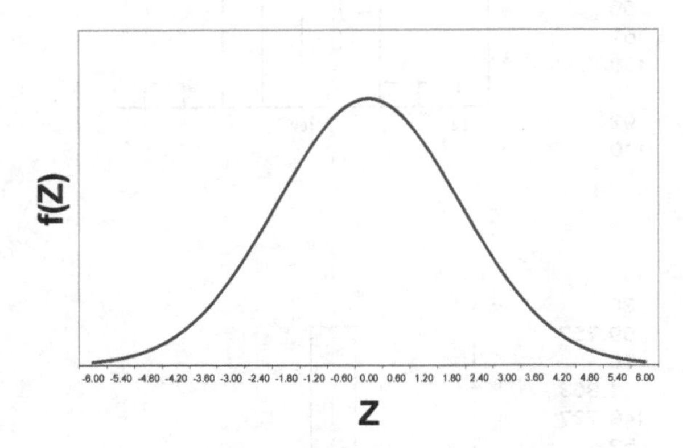

b. $P(140 \le X \le 194)$

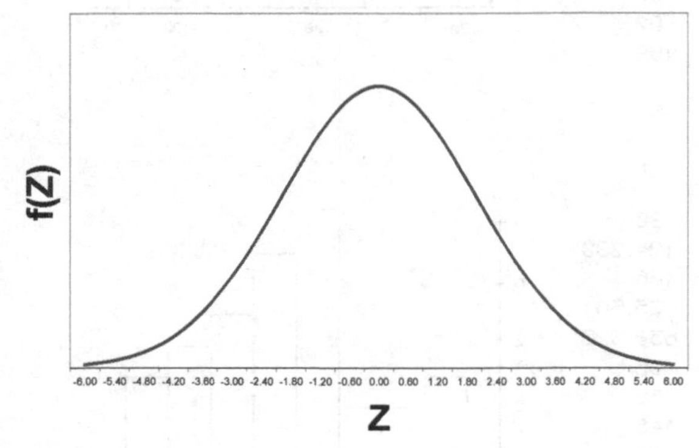

c. $P(X \ge 180)$

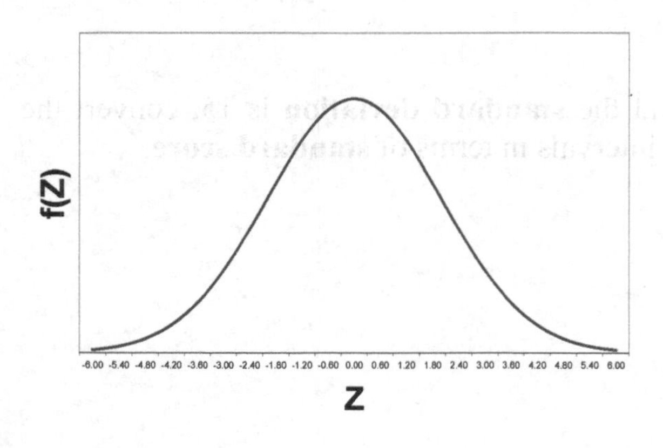

d. $P(X \le 120)$

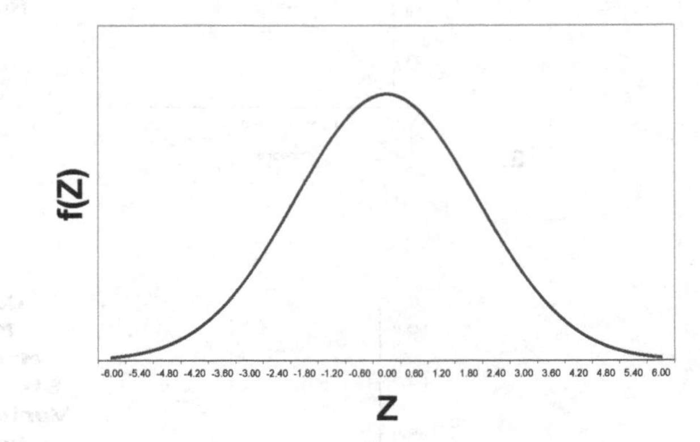

e. Find a such that $P(X \le a) = 0.9$

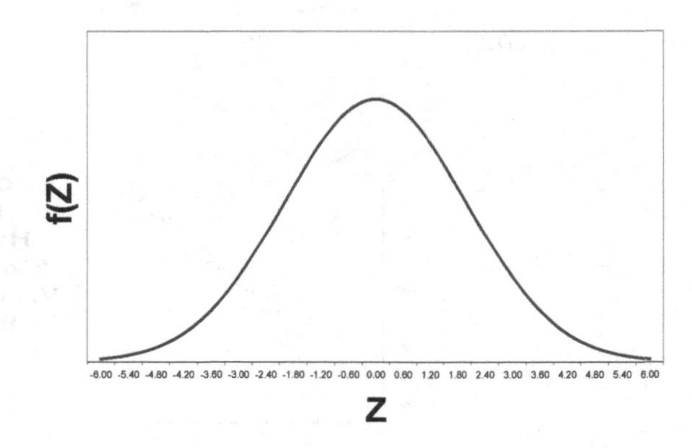

f. Find a such that $P(X \ge a) = 0.95$

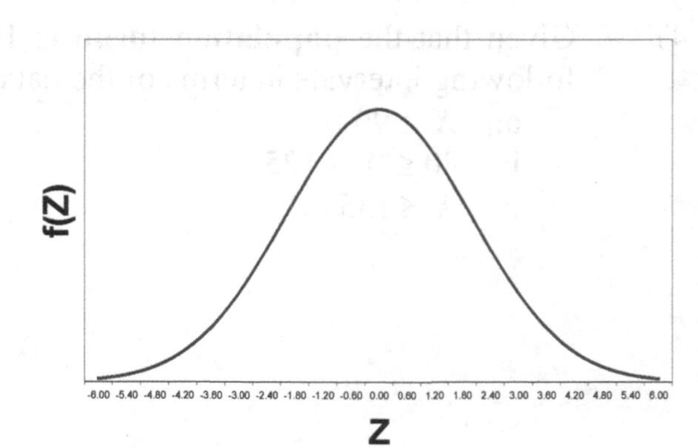

6) Given that the **population mean** is 95 and the **standard deviation** is 10 on a continuous **normally distributed** scale. Find the following.

a. $P(X \leq 97)$

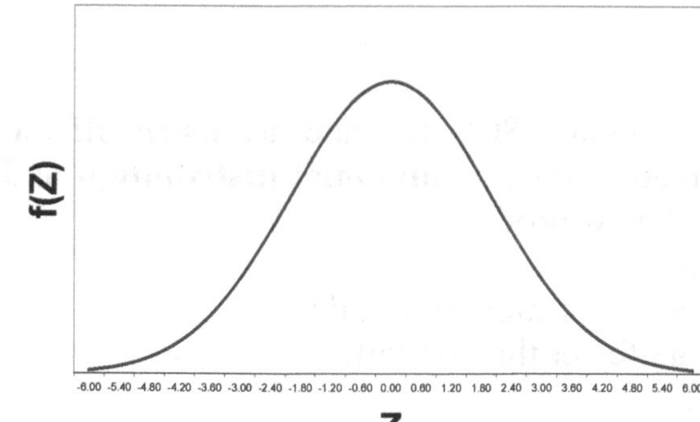

d. $P(X \geq 80)$

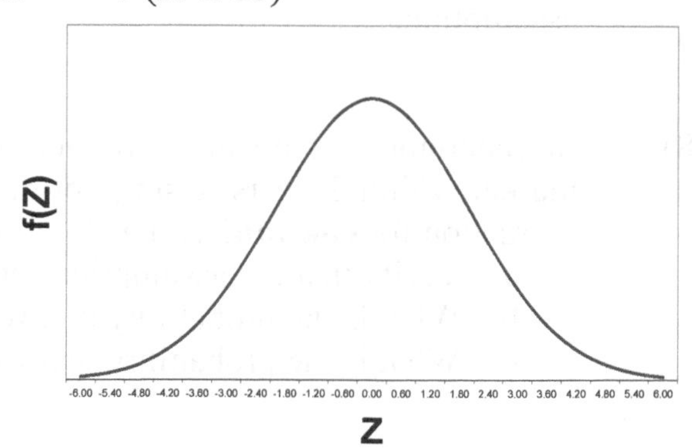

b. 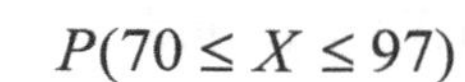 $P(70 \leq X \leq 97)$

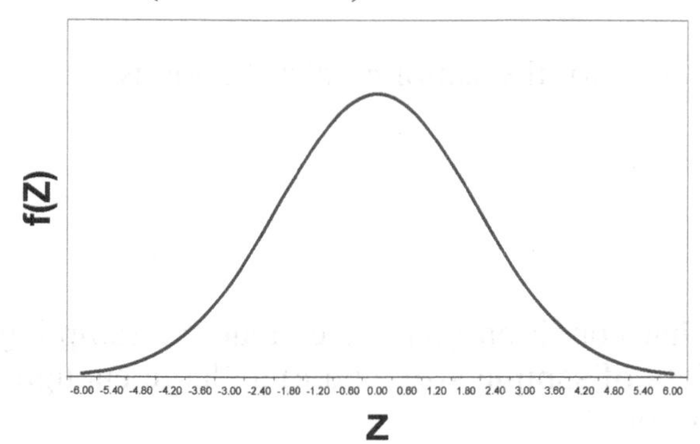

e. $P(X \leq 60)$

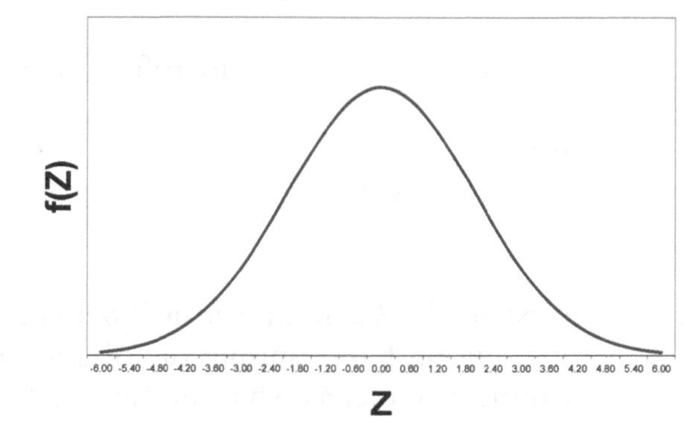

c. $P(70 \leq X \leq 80)$

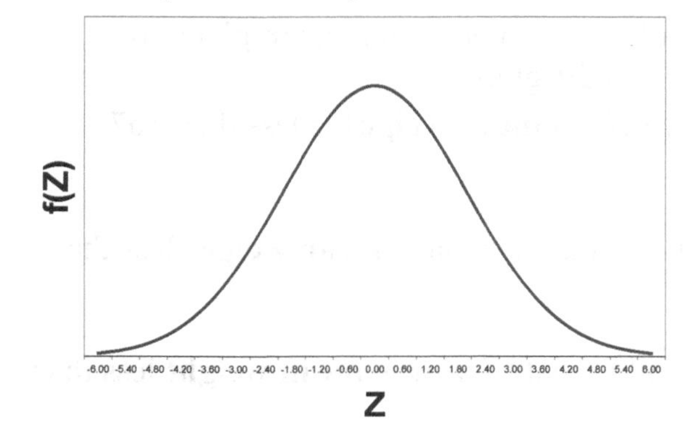

f. $P(X \geq a) = 0.75$

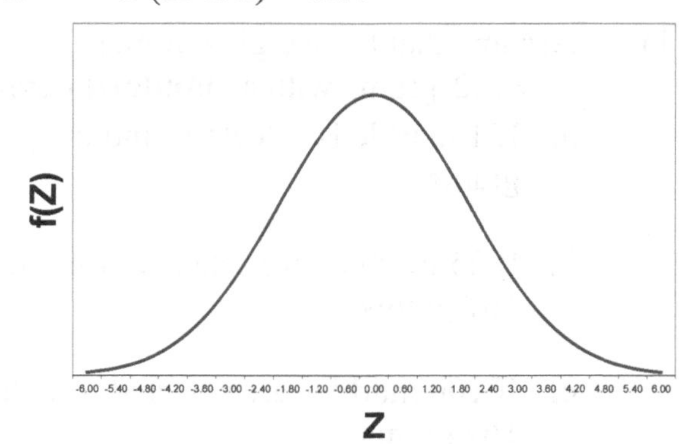

7) Given $n = 100$ and $p = 0.97$, a) find $P(\text{at least } 98)$, first using the indicated **binomial probability** by using the formula $P(X = r) = \binom{n}{r} p^r (1-p)^{n-r}$, and b) then estimate the indicated probability by using the **normal distribution** both with and without correction for **continuity**. Compare and discuss these probabilities. Finally, c) discuss the assumptions.

8) In economics, of all new products put on the market, 80% fail and are taken off the market within 2 years. Using normal approximation for this **binomial distribution** and correction for **continuity**, if a store introduces 75 new product,

a. Verify that the assumptions are satisfied.
b. What is the probability that within 2 years 54 or more will fail?
c. What is the probability that within 2 years fewer than 62 fail?

9) Given that $E(X) = \mu$, $V(X) = \sigma^2$ and $\bar{x} = \dfrac{\sum_{i=1}^{n} x_i}{n}$, **prove** $\mu_{\bar{x}} = E(\overline{X}) = \mu$ and $\sigma_{\bar{x}}^2 = V(\overline{X}) = \dfrac{\sigma^2}{n}$, and therefore the standard error for the sampling distribution is $SE = \sigma_{\bar{x}} = \dfrac{\sigma}{\sqrt{n}}$.

10) a) State the **Central Limit Theorem**. b) What condition guarantees that the sampling distribution has a normal distribution regardless of sample size; and c) a "large enough" sample size means what for means? for proportions?

11) Assume that the weights of marbles are normally distributed with a **mean** given by $\mu = 172$ grams with a **standard deviation** of $\sigma = 29$ grams.

a. If 1 marble is selected, find the probability that its **mean weight** is less than 167 grams.

b. If 25 marbles are selected, find the probability that they have **mean weight** less than 167 grams.

c. If 100 marbles are selected, find the probability that they have **mean weight** less than 167 grams.

d. Discuss the difference in these probabilities.

KEY CHAPTER 6

SECTION I:

1. B
2. C
3. F
4. D
5. E
6. A

SECTION II:

1. a. 68 b. 95 c. 99.7
2. $\mu - \sigma, \mu + \sigma$
3. 0, 1
4. $z = \frac{\bar{x}-\mu}{\sigma/\sqrt{n}}$
5. a. 5, 5, 5

   b. $\mu_{\hat{p}} = p$, $\sigma_{\hat{p}} = \sqrt{\frac{p(1-p)}{n}}$, $\hat{p} = \frac{x}{n}$

$$z = \frac{\hat{p} - p}{\sqrt{\frac{p(1-p)}{n}}} \qquad z = \frac{\left(\hat{p} \pm \frac{0.5}{n}\right) - p}{\sqrt{\frac{p(1-p)}{n}}}$$

c) $\mu = np$, $\sigma = \sqrt{n(1-p)}$

$$z = \frac{x - \mu}{\sigma} \qquad z = \frac{(x \pm 0.5) - \mu}{\sigma}$$

SECTION III:

1. b
2. d
3. a
4. b
5. b
6. c
7. b
8. a
9. c

SECTION IV:

1. State the three common schemes for "**out of control**" in order and compute the associated probabilities (show work).

Signal I: a single point that falls beyond three-standard deviation above or below the mean.

Probability of Signal I

The probability of signal 1 is the probability that the data is further than three-standard deviations above the mean or three-standard deviation below the mean; since 99.87% of the data lie to the left of positive three-standard deviation (see z-chart), the probability of lying above positive three-standard deviation is 0.13%. Hence, by symmetry, the probability of signal 1 is $2 \times 0.0013 = 0.0026$ or approximately 0.003. By the empirical rule, this is 1-0.997=0.003.

Signal II: A run of nine consecutive points on one side of the center line; that is, the mean.

Probability of Signal II

The probability of signal 2 is the probability that the nine consecutive data points fall to the left of the center line (the mean) or to the right of the center line; since 50% of the data lie the left of the mean, using the multiplication principle the probability of nine consecutive points lying to the left is $(0.5)^9 = 0.001953125$. Hence the probability of nine consecutive points lying to the left of the mean or to the right of the mean is $2\times(0.5)^9 = 0.00390625$ or approximately 0.004.

Signal III: at least two out of three points on the same side of the mean, fall beyond two-standard deviation above or below the center line (or mean).

Probability of Signal III

The probability of signal 3 is the probability that two out of three or three out of three consecutive data values lie further than two-standard deviation from the mean on the same side; hence since the probability of one data point further than two-standard deviations from the mean on one side is 0.023 (or approximately 0.025 using the empirical rule. Hence, at least two out of three is a binomial probability:

$$\left.\begin{array}{l} P(\text{At least 2 out of 3 two - standard deviations above}) \\ = {}_3C_2(0.023)^2(0.977)^1 + {}_3C_3(0.023)^3(0.977)^0 \approx 0.002 \end{array}\right] \Rightarrow P(\text{Signal 3}) \approx 0.004$$

2. Since the z-scores are linearly related to the data; that is, $z = \dfrac{x-\mu}{\sigma}$ or $z = \dfrac{x}{\sigma} - \dfrac{\mu}{\sigma}$ with a slope $m = \dfrac{1}{\sigma}$ and intercept $b = -\dfrac{\mu}{\sigma}$. The second data illustrates data that is normally distributed since that data versus the associated z-scores z^* forms a line, whereas the first data set is not exactly linearly related to the associated z-scores z^* as indicated by the curving away from the regression line.

3. (a) Yes, the graph is approximately a straight line (as well as the mean equal the median – which is not decisive, but necessary.) Moreover, the histogram has a clear mode and is symmetric with a gap that indicates variability. In fact, the data was simulated using normal distribution with mean 100 and standard deviation 15. (b) No, there is a bow in the line. Moreover, there is a skew in the data as indicated by the relationship between the mean and the mode. Furthermore, there is a clear mode; however, this data has less variability and a lean in the histogram – the data is skewed right. In fact, the data was simulated using a Weibull (skewed) distribution. (c) No, not exactly. This QQ-plot can be misleading in that is does appear to be a straight line, but the histogram is heavier in the tails, that is, there are smaller differences between the observed frequencies, so while there is symmetry and the mean approximately equals the mode, this is not enough to assume normality. In fact, this was simulated using uniform probability distribution [50,150]. Moreover, consider the box-plot. The first distribution is more symmetrically balance (an indication of normality), the second has an outlier (an indication of skew) and the third is not as clear.

4. a) $\dfrac{X-\mu}{\sigma} \geq \dfrac{90-100}{15}$ ➔ $z \geq -0.67$

   b) $\dfrac{80-100}{15} \leq \dfrac{X-\mu}{\sigma} \leq \dfrac{125-100}{15}$ ➔ $-1.33 \leq z \leq 1.67$

   c) $\dfrac{X-\mu}{\sigma} \leq \dfrac{135-100}{15}$ ➔ $z \leq 2.33$

5. Given that the **population mean** is 190 and the **standard deviation** is 36 on a continuous **normally distributed** scale. Find the following.

a. $P(X \le 194)$

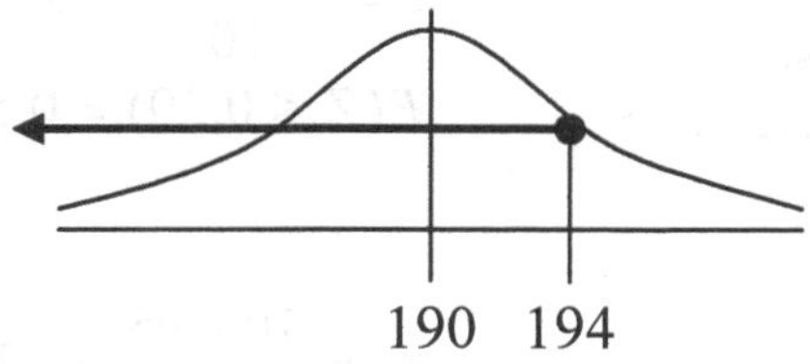

$z = \frac{194-190}{36} = 0.11$

$P(Z \le 0.11) = 0.5438$

190 194

b. $P(140 \le X \le 194)$

$z_1 = \frac{140-190}{36} = -1.39$

$P(Z \le 0.11) = 0.5438$

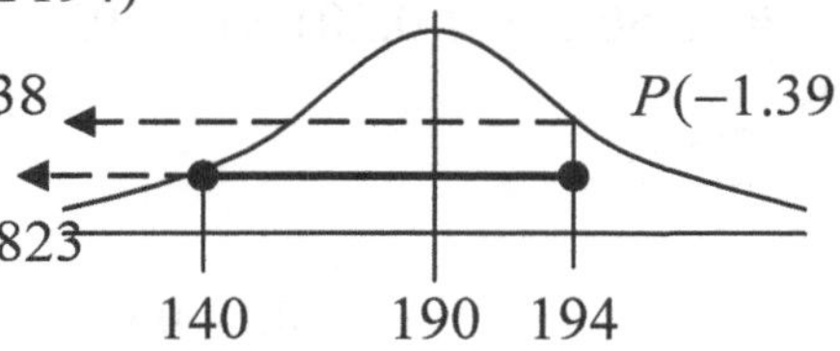

$P(-1.39 \le Z \le 0.11) = 0.5438 - 0.0823$

$= 0.4615$

$P(Z \le -1.39) = 0.0823$

140 190 194

c. $P(X \ge 180)$

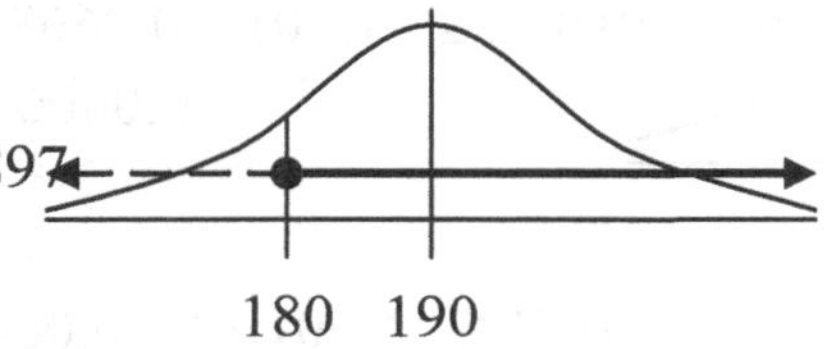

$z = \frac{180-190}{36} = -0.28$

$P(Z \le -0.28) = 0.3897$

$P(Z \ge -0.28) = 1 - 0.3897$

180 190

$= 0.6103$

OR by symmetry, $P(Z \ge -0.28) = P(Z \le 0.28) = 0.6103$

d. $P(X \le 120)$

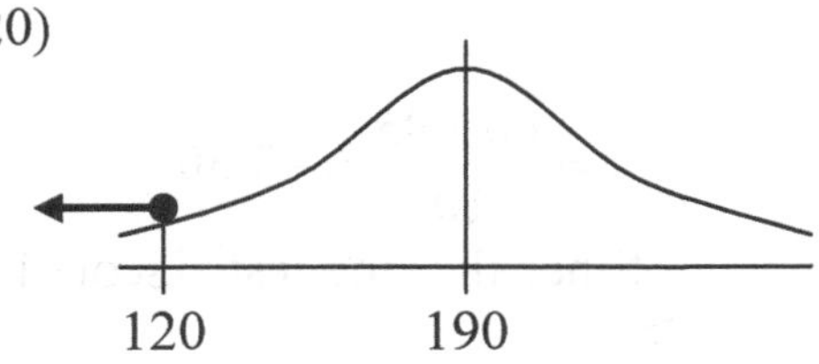

$z = \frac{120-190}{36} = -1.94$

$P(Z \le -1.94) = 0.0262$

120 190

e. Find a such that $P(X \le a) = 0.9$

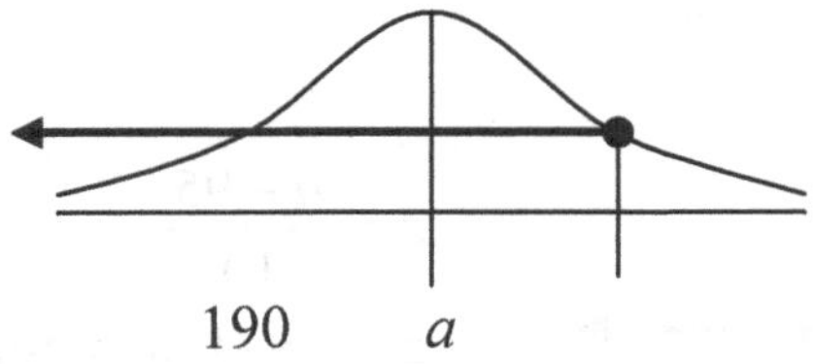

$z = \frac{a-190}{36}$

$z \approx 1.285$

$a = 190 + 1.285(36) = 236.26$

190 a

f. Find a such that $P(X \ge a) = 0.95$

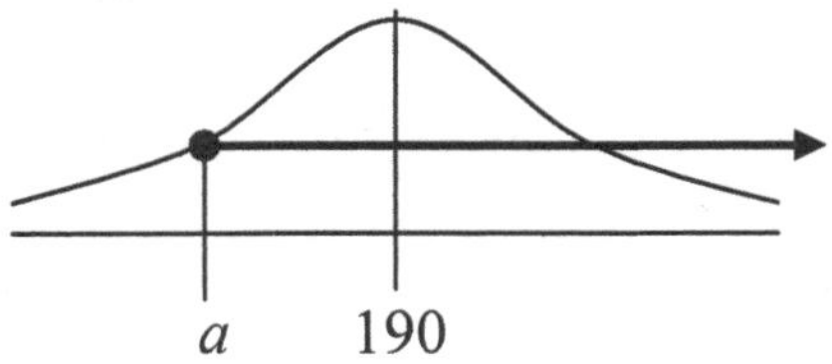

$z = \frac{a-190}{36}$

$z \approx -1.645$

$a = 190 - 1.645(36) = 130.78$

a 190

6. Given that the **population mean** is 95 and the **standard deviation** is 10 on a continuous **normally distributed** scale. Find the following.

a. $P(X \le 97)$

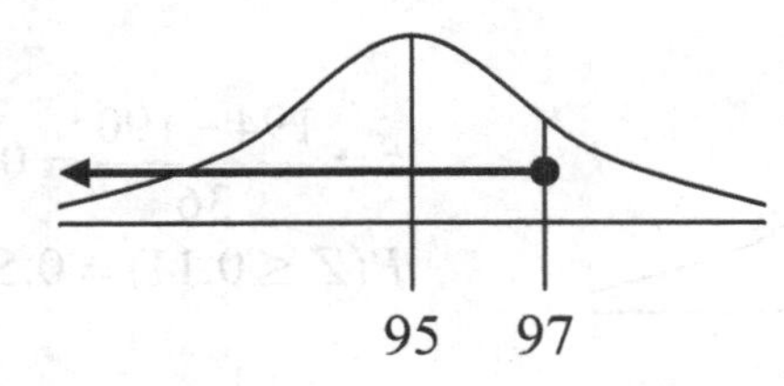

$$z = \frac{97-95}{10} = 0.20$$

$P(Z \le 0.20) = 0.5793$

b. $P(70 \le X \le 97)$

$P(Z \le 0.20) = 0.5793$

$P(Z \le -2.50) = 0.0062$

70 95 97

$$z_1 = \frac{70-95}{10} = -2.50$$

$P(-2.50 \le Z \le 0.20) = 0.5793 - 0.0062$
$= 0.5731$

c. $P(70 \le X \le 80)$

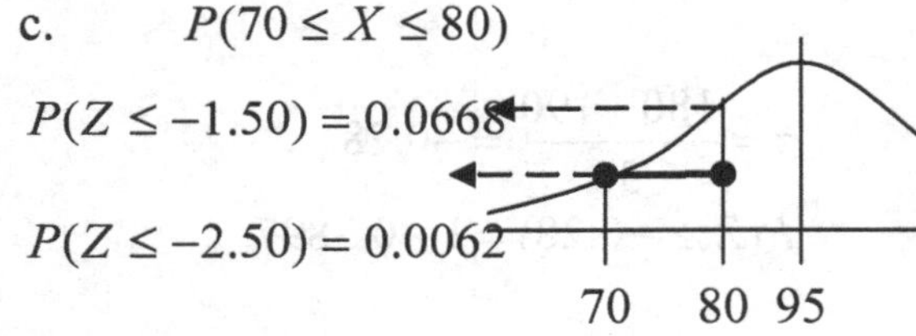

$$z_2 = \frac{80-95}{10} = -1.50$$

$P(-2.50 \le Z \le -1.50) = 0.0668 - 0.0062$
$= 0.0606$

d. $P(X \ge 80)$

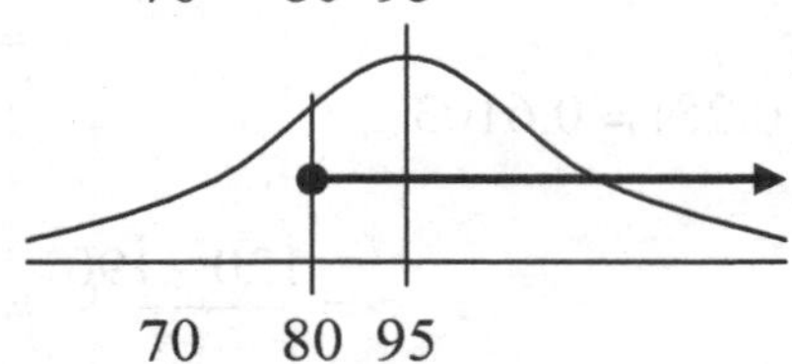

$P(Z \ge -1.50) = 1 - 0.0668 = 0.9332$

e. $P(X \le 60)$

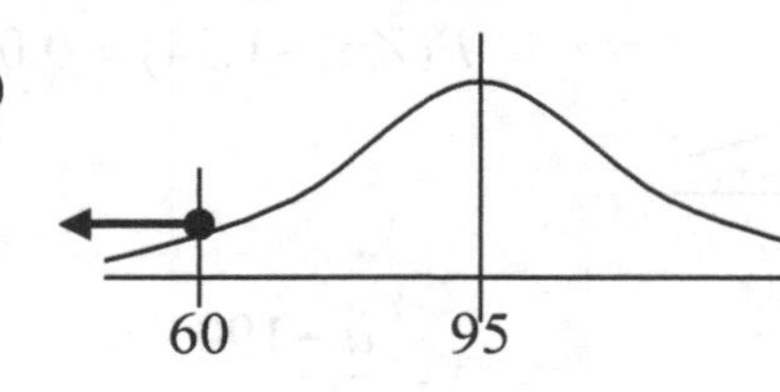

$$z = \frac{60-95}{10} = -3.50$$

Since the smallest z-score is –3.49,

$P(Z \le -3.50) < 0.0002$

OR Using a calculator, $P(Z \le -3.50) \approx 0.0002$

f. $P(X \ge a) = 0.75$

$z_{0.75} \approx 0.675$ below

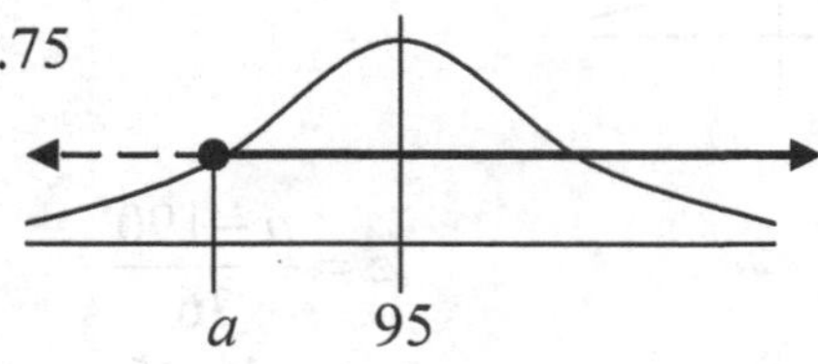

$$z = \frac{a-95}{10}$$

$z_{0.25} \approx -0.675$ for 75% above

$a = 95 - 0.675(10) = 88.25$

7. a) The assumptions are not satisfied, while $\mu = 0.97 \times 100 = 97 \geq 5$, $n(1-p) = 100(1-0.97) = 3 < 5$

$$P(\text{at least } 98) = \binom{100}{98}(0.97)^{98}(0.03)^{2} + \binom{100}{99}(0.97)^{99}(0.03)^{1} + \binom{100}{100}(0.97)^{100}(0.03)^{0} = =0.4198$$

Given $\mu = 0.97 \times 100 = 97$ and $\sigma = \sqrt{100 \times 0.97 \times 0.03} \approx 1.706$.
Hence, without correction for continuity,
$P(\text{at least } 98) = P(x \geq 98) = P(z \geq 0.586) = 1 - 0.7224 = 0.2776$ and
With correction for continuity, $P(\text{at least } 98) = P(x \geq 97.5) = P(z \geq 0.293) = 1 - 0.6141 = 0.3859$

With the assumptions violated, even with correction for continuity the estimated probability is too low and with the correction for continuity, the estimated probability is still too low; both estimates yield an inaccurate approximation of the binomial probability distribution. This technique would yield an even better approximation had the number of trial been increased.

8. a. $np = 75 \times 0.80 = 60 > 5$ and $n(1-p) = 75 \times 0.20 = 15 > 5$
Given $\mu = 0.80 \times 75 = 60$ and $\sigma = \sqrt{75 \times 0.80 \times 0.20} \approx 3.464$, (b.) without using correction for continuity below, $P(X \geq 54) = P(Z \geq -1.73) = 0.9584$ and with correction for continuity below, $P(X \geq 53.5) = P(Z \geq -1.88) = 0.9697$ (c.) without using correction for continuity above $P(X \leq 61) = P(Z \leq 0.29) = 0.6136$,using correction for continuity above, $P(X \leq 61.5) = P(Z \leq 0.43) = 0.6675$.

9. $$\mu_{\bar{x}} = E(\bar{X} = \bar{x}) = E\left(\frac{\sum_{i=1}^{n} x_i}{n}\right) = \frac{1}{n}E\left(\sum_{i=1}^{n} x_i\right) = \frac{1}{n}\sum_{i=1}^{n} E(x_i) = \frac{1}{n}\sum_{i=1}^{n} \mu = \frac{1}{n}(n\mu) = \mu .$$

Furthermore,

$$V(\bar{X} = \bar{x}) = V\left(\frac{\sum_{i=1}^{n} x_i}{n}\right) = \frac{1}{n^2}V\left(\sum_{i=1}^{n} x_i\right) = \frac{1}{n^2}\sum_{i=1}^{n} V(x_i) = \frac{1}{n^2}\sum_{i=1}^{n} \sigma^2 = \frac{1}{n^2}(n\sigma^2) = \frac{\sigma^2}{n}, \text{ and}$$

hence, the standard error $SE = \sigma_{\bar{x}} = \sqrt{V(\bar{X})} = \sqrt{\frac{\sigma^2}{n}} = \frac{\sigma}{\sqrt{n}}$ **QED**

10. a) The Central Limit Theorem states regardless of the population distribution of x (the data's distribution), as the sample size increases the sampling distribution (for $\bar{x}$) will approach a normal probability distribution. Note: the mean of the sampling distribution is the population mean and the variance of the sampling distribution is inversely proportional to the sample size. b) If the data's distribution is normally distributed, then the sampling distribution is normal regardless of the sample size. c) Furthermore, "large enough" to assume the sampling distribution is normal for means is $n \geq 30$ and for proportions, at least five in each category; that is, $np > 5$ and $n(1-p) > 5$

11. a. 0.4316 b. 0.1943 c. 0.0423

d. The large the same size, the more confident we are in the point estimate $\bar{x}$, hence if our sample size is 1, a sample mean of 167, given the true mean is 172 is more likely then in a sample of 25. If our sample size is 25, we would expect an even more accurate estimate of the population mean and therefore the probability of a sample mean of 167 is less likely. Similarly, if our sample size is 100, more than enough information to estimate the population mean which we know is 172, the probability of obtaining a sample mean of 167 is extremely unlikely as illustrate the by relative low probability

SECTION I: MATCHING TERMINOLOGY

A. Critical Statistic
B. Degree of confidence
C. Interval Estimate
D. Level of significance
E. Margin of Error
F. Point Estimate

1. _____ Probability of rejecting a true null hypothesis; that is, the alpha value or risk you are willing to take probabilistically speaking.
2. _____ A statistical estimate of the population parameter.
3. _____ $(1-\alpha)\%$, the desired probabilistic level at which the obtained interval that will contain the population parameter
4. _____ The magnitude of difference between the statistic (point estimate) and the parameter (true state of nature), $|\hat{\theta} - \theta|$.
5. _____ An open interval centered about the point estimate, $\hat{\theta}$.
6. _____ The standard score associated with a given degree of confidence or level of significance.

SECTION II: FILL IN THE BLANK

1. Suppose that a random variable X has a normal distribution with a mean μ and standard deviation σ. The sample mean $\bar{X}$ follows a __________ distribution with a mean of ______ and a variance of _______________.
2. Suppose that a random variable X has a normal distribution with a mean μ and standard deviation σ. However, in a fixed sample of size n, the standard deviation is unknown; let sample mean $\bar{X}$ and s be the sample standard deviation, then the test statistic $\frac{\bar{x}-\mu}{s/\sqrt{n}}$ follows a ___________ distribution with __________ degree(s) of freedom.

SECTION III: MULTIPLE-CHOICE QUESTIONS

1. Which one is **NOT** true for a normal distribution?
   (a) Symmetric about median (b) Bimodal
   (c) Mean=mode (d) Bell -shaped (Mound)
2. Which one is **NOT** true for a Student's t distribution?
   (a) Symmetric about zero (b) Thicker tail than a standard normal
   (c) As the degree of freedom decreases, the distribution gets closer to $\boldsymbol{N(0,1)}$
   (d) Unimodal
3. The maximal margin of error when constructing a 95% CI for a normal population mean was 0.5 from sample size 200. How many observations are necessary to make the maximal margin of error 0.25 at the same confidence level?
   (a) 100 (b) 400 (c) 800 (d) 1000
4. The maximal margin of error when constructing a 99% CI for a normal population mean was 25 from sample size 200. How many observations are necessary to make the maximal margin of error 5 at the same confidence level?
   (a) 5000 (b) 225 (c) 299 (d) 1000

SECTION IV: WORKED PROBLEMS:

1. The Packaging Company produces boxes out of cardboard and has a specified weight of 8 oz. A random sample of 40 boxes yielded a sample mean of 7.5 oz. Given the standard deviation is 1.4 oz, give a 95% confidence interval. Clearly label the **point estimate**, the **critical statistic**, the **margin of error**, the **confidence interval** and the **interpretation** (confidence statement).

2. The Soda Company produces soda in bottles labeled 32 oz. A random sample of 50 bottles yielded a sample mean of 31.8 oz. Given the standard deviation is 0.6 oz, give a 90% confidence interval. Clearly label the **point estimate**, the **critical statistic**, the **margin of error**, the **confidence interval** and the **interpretation** (confidence statement).

3. Based on the 77th Annual Report of the New Mexico Department of Game and Fish, a researcher wished to estimate how much mountain lions weigh in New Mexico. A random sample of 6 wild mountain lions (18 months or older) where captured, weighed, tagged and released; the weights recorded in pounds were 60, 64, 68, 104, 122, and 128 yielding a sample mean of 91.0 lbs and a sample standard deviation of 30.7, give a 90% confidence interval. Clearly label the **point estimate**, the **critical statistic**, the **margin of error**, the **confidence interval** and the **interpretation** (confidence statement).

4. The following is based on information from *The Wolf in the Southwest: The Making of an Endangered Species*. Before 1918, the proportion of female wolves in the general population of all southwestern wolves was about 50%. However, after 1918, southwestern cattle ranchers began a widespread effort to destroy wolves. In a recent sample of 34 wolves, there were only 10 females. At the 0.01 level of significance, do these data indicate that the population proportion of female wolves is now less than 50% in the region? Clearly label the **point estimate**, the **critical statistic**, the **margin of error**, the **confidence interval** and the **interpretation** (confidence statement).

5. In the population, 38.8% are type A personality, in a random sample of 1000, only 426 where type A personality. Using normal approximation at the $\alpha = 0.05$ significance level, give a 95% confidence interval. Clearly label the **point estimate**, the **critical statistic**, the **margin of error**, the **confidence interval** and the **interpretation** (confidence statement).

6. When computing the confidence interval for proportions, if this interval contains either zero or one, then the sample size is not large enough and the validity of the hypothesis testing should be question. Given examples, both valid and invalid, and explain why they are valid or invalid.

7. A sociologist is studying marriage customs in a rural community in Denmark. A random sample of 35 women who have been married was used to determine the age of the woman at the time of her first marriage. The sample standard deviation of these ages was 2.3 years. The sociologist wants to estimate the population's mean age of a woman at the time of her first marriage. How many more women should be included in the sample to be 95% confident that the sample mean $\bar{x}$ of the age is within 0.25 year of the population mean μ.

8. A random sample of medical files used to estimate the proportion p of all people who have blood type B. If you have no preliminary estimate for p, how many medical files should you include in a random sample in order to be 85% sure that the point estimate $\hat{p}$ within a distance of 0.05 from p; that is, the (percent) error is 5%.

9. In the previous question, if it is estimated that 11.1% of the population have blood type B, how many medical files should you include in a random sample in order to be 90% sure that the point estimate $\hat{p}$ within a distance of 0.03 from p; that is, the (percent) error is 3%.

KEY CHAPTER 7

SECTION I:

1. D
2. F
3. B
4. E
5. C
6. A

SECTION II:

1. normal, $\mu, \frac{\sigma^2}{n}$
2. $t, n-1$

SECTION III:

1. b
2. c - it is as the sample size increases that the t-distribution approaches the standard normal probability distribution
3. c
4. a

SECTION IV:

1. $n = 40, \bar{x} = 7.5, \sigma = 1.4$

Step 1: $c = 0.95$ $\Rightarrow \alpha = 1 - 0.95 = 0.05$

Step 2: Since $\sigma = 1.4$ is known, $n = 40 \geq 30$ and hence the underlying sampling distribution is the standard normal distribution, **critical statistics**: $z_{\alpha/2} = 1.96$; $\hat{\theta} = \bar{x} = 7.5$ and **margin of error** $E = 1.96 \frac{1.4}{\sqrt{40}} \approx 0.4338$.

Step 3: $x_L = 7.5 - 0.4338 = 7.0661$ and $x_U = 7.5 + 0.4438 = 7.9339$, the interval estimate (**confidence interval**) is $(7.0661, 7.9339)$.

Step 4: **Interpretation**: We are 95% confident that the true mean is 7.5 oz with a 0.4338 oz margin of error; that is, we are 95% confident that the true mean is between 7.0661 and 7.9339. Hence, the company appears to be shorting the customer.

Step 5: The standard deviation was known to be 1.4 and the sample size was large enough, $n = 40 \geq 30$, we assumed standard normal probability distribution.

2. $n = 50$, **point estimate:** $\bar{x} = 31.8$ oz., $\alpha = 0.10$ and $\sigma = 0.6$ oz.

Step 1: $\alpha = 0.10 \quad \Rightarrow c = 1 - 0.10 = 0.90$

Step 2: While $\sigma = 0.6$ is known, $n = 50 \geq 30$ and hence the underlying sampling distribution is the standard normal distribution, **critical statistics:** $z_{\alpha c/2} = 1.645$; $\hat{\theta} = \bar{x} = 31.8$ and **margin of error** $\text{E} = 1.645 \frac{0.6}{\sqrt{50}} \approx 0.140$.

Step 3: $x_L = 31.8 - 0.140 = 31.66$ and $x_U = 31.8 + 0.140 = 31.94$, the interval estimate (**confidence interval**) is $(31.66, 31.94)$.

Step 4: **Interpretation**: We are 90% confident that the true mean is 31.8 oz with a 0.14 oz margin of error; that is, we are 90% confident that the true mean is between 31.66 and 31.94. Hence, the company appears to be shorting the customer.

Step 5: The standard deviation was known to be 0.6 and the sample size was large enough, $n = 50 \geq 30$, we assumed standard normal probability distribution.

3. $n = 6$, **point estimate:** $\bar{x} = 91.0$ lbs, $s = 30.7$, $\alpha = 0.10$, $\mu = 95$ lbs.

Step 1: $\alpha = 0.10 \quad \Rightarrow c = 1 - 0.10 = 0.90$

Step 2: As σ is unknown, we can estimate the standard deviation as $s = 30.7$. Moreover, wiith $n = 6$, the underlying probability distribution is Student's t-distribution with $\nu = 6 - 1 = 5$, **critical statistics:** $t_{\nu,c} = 2.015$; $\hat{\theta} = \bar{x} = 91.0$ and **margin of error** $\text{E} = 2.015 \frac{30.7}{\sqrt{6}} \approx 25.25$.

Step 3: $x_L = 91.0 - 25.25 = 65.75$ and $x_U = 91.0 + 25.25 = 116.25$, the interval estimate (**confidence interval**) is $(65{,}75{,}116.25)$.

Step 4: **Interpretation**: We are 90% confident that the true mean weight of a mountain lion is 91.0 lb with a 25.25 lb margin of error; that is, we are 90% confident that the true mean is between 65.75 lb and 116.25 lb.

Step 5: The standard deviation was unknown and estimated to be 30.7 and the sample size is rather small, $n = 6 < 30$, we assumed a bell-shaped symmetric distribution, Student's t-distribution with $\nu = 6 - 1 = 5$ degrees of freedom.

4. $p = 50\%$, $n = 34$, $x = 10$ and $\alpha = 0.01$

Step 1: $\alpha = 0.01 \quad \Rightarrow c = 1 - 0.01 = 0.99$

Step 2: Since $n\hat{p} = x = 10 > 5$ and $n(1-\hat{p}) = n - x = 34 - 10 = 24 > 5$, there is enough information to use the normal approximation to the binomial; **critical statistics:** $z_c = 2.576$; **point estimate:** $\hat{\theta} = \hat{p} = \frac{10}{34} \approx 0.2941$ and **margin of error** $\text{E} = 2.576\sqrt{\frac{\frac{10}{34}\left(1-\frac{10}{34}\right)}{34}} \approx 0.2013$.

Step 3: $x_L = 0.2941 - 0.2013 = 0.0928$ and $x_U = 0.2941 + 0.2014 = 0.4954$, the interval estimate (**confidence interval**) is $(0.0928, 0.4954)$.

Step 4: **Interpretation**: We are 99% confident that the true proportion is 29.41% with a 20.14% margin of error; that is, we are 99% confident that the true proportion of female wolves is between 9.28% and 49.54%. Hence, the wolves female population has been significantly reduced and is now less than 50% (as 50% is not contained in our confidence interval).

Step 5: The standard deviation was estimated using standard statistical methods as the sample size was large enough with at least five in each category to use a standard normal approximate of the binomial probability distribution.

5. $p = 38.8\%$, $n = 1000$, $x = 426$ and $\alpha = 0.05$

Step 1: $\alpha = 0.05 \quad \Rightarrow c = 1 - 0.05 = 0.95$

Step 2: Since $n\hat{p} = x = 426 > 5$ and $n(1-\hat{p}) = n - x = 1000 - 426 = 574 > 5$, there is enough information to use the normal approximation to the binomial; $z_c = 1.96$; $\hat{\theta} = \hat{p} = \frac{426}{1000} \approx 0.426$ and margin of error $\text{E} = 1.96\sqrt{\frac{0.426(1-0.426)}{1000}} \approx 0.0306$.

Step 3: $x_L = 0.426 - 0.0306 = 0.3954$ and $x_U = 0.426 + 0.0306 = 0.4566$, the interval estimate is $(0.3954, 0.4566)$.

Step 4: We are 95% confident that the true proportion is 42.6% with a 3.06% margin of error; that is, we are 95% confident that the true proportion of people with type A personality is between 39.54% and 45.66%. Hence, the percent of the population with type A personality not 38.8% (as 38.8% is not contained in our confidence interval).

Step 5: The standard deviation was estimated using standard statistical methods as the sample size was large enough with at least five in each category to use a standard normal approximate of the binomial probability distribution.

6. Answers will vary: if zero is included this causes negatives to be included which imply that proportions can be negative, a fallacy. If one is included this causes values greater than one to be included which imply that proportions can be greater than one, a fallacy.

For example, (0,0.15) does not include zero and therefore is plausible, since $0 < p < 0.15$; however, the interval (-0.0001,0.15), which contains zero; that is, $-0.0001 < p < 0.15$, also contains a negative number, say –0.00001 and hence you are stating you are confident that a probability (or proportion) could be negative. You cannot win a negative number of games, no matter how many games you play. This is a contradiction to the principles of probability.

On the other hand, the interval (0.84,1) does not include one and all included values are between zero and one and are therefore plausible. However, the interval (0.84,1.00001) contains one and therefore contains a number greater than one, say 1.000001, which implies you are confident that a probability (or proportion) could be greater than one. This also is contradicts the principles of probability. You cannot have more green M&Ms in a bag than there are M&M in the bag.

7. $n \geq \left(\frac{1.96 \times 2.3}{0.25}\right)^2 \approx 325.15$, therefore a minimum of 326 women are needed **OR** an additional 291 women.

8. $n \geq \frac{1}{4}\left(\frac{1.44}{0.05}\right)^2 = 207.36$, hence 208 medical files.

9. $n \geq 0.111(1-0.111)\left(\frac{1.645}{0.03}\right)^2 \approx 296.7$, hence 297 medical.

SECTION I: MATCHING TERMINOLOGY

A. Alpha value
B. Beta value
C. Power
D. *p-value*
E. Type I Error
F. Type II Error

1. _____ Probability of rejecting a true null hypothesis; that is, the level of significance.
2. _____ Rejecting a true null hypothesis
3. _____ Failing to reject a false null hypothesis
4. _____ Probability of failing to reject a false null hypothesis
5. _____ The probability of correctly detecting a false null hypothesis
6. _____ The probability of the observed value or something more extreme under the assumption that the null hypothesis is true. That is, the probability of a standard score at least as extreme as the observed test statistic.

SECTION II: FILL IN THE BLANK

1. An event is considered ________________ if the event is highly unlikely to occur by chance.
2. The null hypothesis is rejected when the probability of the observed value or something more extreme is __________ than the specified level of significance.

SECTION II: MULTIPLE-CHOICE QUESTIONS

1. Suppose that we perform a hypothesis testing at 2% level of significance. For which ***p-value*** of the following we fail to reject the null hypothesis?
   (a) ***p-value***=0.001 (b) ***p-value*** =0.005 (c) ***p-value*** =0.01 (d) ***p-value*** =0.05
2. Suppose that we perform a hypothesis testing at 0.1% level of significance. For which ***p-value*** of the following we reject the null hypothesis?
   (a) ***p-value*** =0.001 (b) ***p-value*** =0.005 (c) ***p-value*** =0.0001 (d) ***p-value*** =0.05
3. Suppose that we perform a hypothesis testing at 0.1% level of significance. For which ***p-value*** of the following would you use a randomized test?
   (a) ***p-value*** =0.001 (b) ***p-value*** =0.005 (c) ***p-value*** =0.01 (d) ***p-value*** =0.05

SECTION IV: WORKED PROBLEMS:

1. The Packaging Company produces boxes out of cardboard and has a specified weight of 8 oz. A random sample of 40 boxes yielded a sample mean of 7.5 oz. Given the standard deviation is 1.4 oz, test the hypothesis that the boxes are less than the specified 8 oz at the 5% level of significance. Clearly state the **null hypothesis**, the **alternative hypothesis**, the **test statistic**, the **critical statistic**, the ***p-value*** and the **decision** (significance statement).

2. A professional employee in a large corporation receives an average of $\mu = 41.7$ e-mails per day. Most of these e-mails are from other employees in the company. Because of the large number of e-mails, employees find themselves distracted and are unable to concentrate when they return to their tasks. In an effort to reduce distraction caused by such interruptions, one company established a priority list that all employees were to use before sending an email. One month after the new priority list was put in place, a random sample of 45 employees showed that an average of $\bar{x} = 36.2$ e-mails per day. The computer server through which the e-mail is routed showed that $\sigma = 18.5$. Has the policy had any effect? Use a 5% level of significance to test the claim that there has been a change (either way) in the average number of e-mails received per day per employee. Clearly state the **null hypothesis**, the **alternative hypothesis**, the **test statistic**, the **critical statistic**, the ***p-value*** and the **decision** and **interpretation** (significance statement).

3. The Soda Company produces soda in bottles labeled 32 oz. A random sample of 50 bottles yielded a sample mean of 31.8 oz. Given the standard deviation is 0.6 oz, test the hypothesis that the bottles contain an amount less than the specified 32 oz at the 10% level of significance. Clearly state the **null hypothesis**, the **alternative hypothesis**, the **test statistic**, the **critical statistic**, the ***p-value*** and the **decision** (significance statement).

4. Based on the 77th Annual Report of the New Mexico Department of Game and Fish, a researcher wished to estimate how much mountain lions weigh in New Mexico. A random sample of 6 wild mountain lions (18 months or older) where captured, weighed, tagged and released; the weights recorded in pounds were 60, 64, 68, 104, 122, and 128 yielding a sample mean of 91.0 lbs and a sample standard deviation of 30.7, test the hypothesis that the weight is 95 lbs (either way) at the 10% level of significance. Clearly state the **null hypothesis**, the **alternative hypothesis**, the **test statistic**, the **critical statistic**, the ***p-value*** and the **decision** and **interpretation** (significance statement).

5. In the population, 38.8% are type A personality, in a random sample of 1000, only 426 where type A personality. Using normal approximation at the $\alpha = 0.05$ significance level, test the hypothesis that the proportion is greater than the assumed 38.8% at the 5% level of significance. Clearly state the **null hypothesis**, the **alternative hypothesis**, the **test statistic**, the **critical statistic**, the ***p-value*** and the **decision** and **interpretation** (significance statement).

6. The following is based on information from *The Wolf in the Southwest: The Making of an Endangered Species*. Before 1918, the proportion of female wolves in the general population of all southwestern wolves was about 50%. However, after 1918, southwestern cattle ranchers began a widespread effort to destroy wolves. In a recent sample of 34 wolves, there were only 10 females. At the 0.01 level of significance, do these data indicate that the population proportion of female wolves is now less than 50% in the region? Clearly state the **null hypothesis**, the **alternative hypothesis**, the **test statistic**, the **critical statistic**, the ***p-value*** and the **decision** and **interpretation** (significance statement).

KEY CHAPTER 8

SECTION I:

1. A
2. E
3. F
4. B
5. C
6. D

SECTION II:

1. significant
2. less

SECTION III:

1. d
2. c
3. a

SECTION IV:

1. $\mu = 8$, $n = 40$, $\bar{x} = 7.5$, $\sigma = 1.4$, $\alpha = 0.05$

Step 1: The **null hypothesis** is that the population mean is 8.
Shorthand: $H_0 : \mu = 8$
Alternatively, (the **alternative hypothesis** is) the population is different from 8.
Shorthand: $H_1 : \mu < 8$

Step 2: $\alpha = 0.05$

Step 3: Critical statistic: $z_\alpha = -1.645$ and **test statistic:** $z = \dfrac{7.5 - 8}{1.4/\sqrt{40}} = -2.26$,

Step 4: Based on the critical statistic and test statistic found in the third step, graphically illustrate the critical regions (acceptance and rejection regions) and the *p-value*.

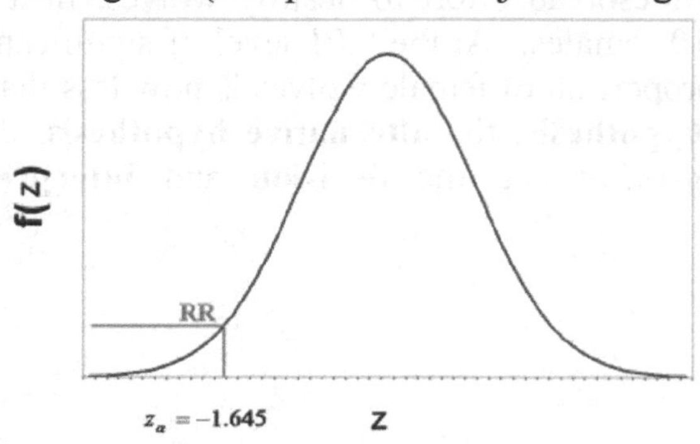

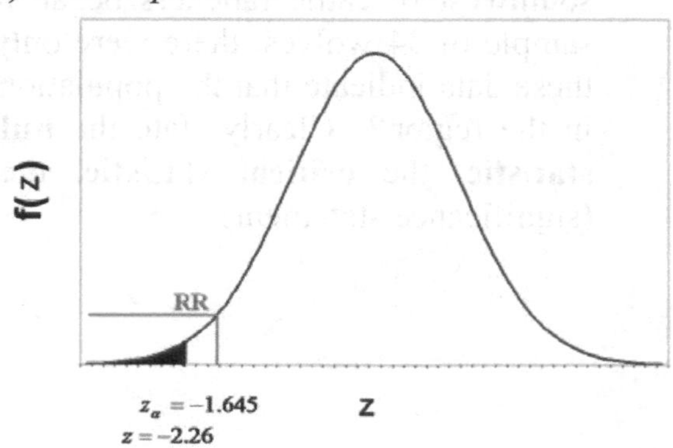

Step 5: *p-value* = 0.0119

Step 6: **Decision:** Reject the null hypothesis.

Step 7: **Interpretation:** At the 5% level of significance, there is sufficient evidence to reject the null hypothesis. That is, the mean is less than the hypothesized 8.

Step 8: The standard deviation was known to be 1.4 and the sample size was large enough, $n = 40 \geq 30$, we assumed standard normal probability distribution. Here we have also argued the weaker statement.

2. $\mu = 41.7$, $n = 45$, $\bar{x} = 36.2$, $\sigma = 18.5$, $\alpha = 0.05$

Step 1: The **null hypothesis** is that the population mean is 41.7.
Shorthand: $H_0 : \mu = 41.7$
Alternatively, (the **alternative hypothesis** is) the population is different from 41.7.
Shorthand: $H_1 : \mu \neq 41.7$

Step 2: $\alpha = 0.05$

Step 3: **Critical statistic:** $z_{\alpha/2} = -1.96$ and **test statistic:** $z = \dfrac{36.2 - 41.7}{18.5/\sqrt{45}} = -1.99$,

Step 4: Based on the critical statistic and test statistic found in the third step, graphically illustrate the critical regions (acceptance and rejection regions) and the *p-value*.

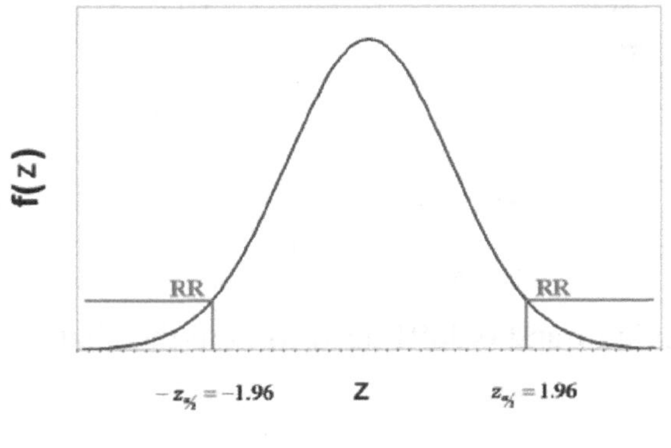

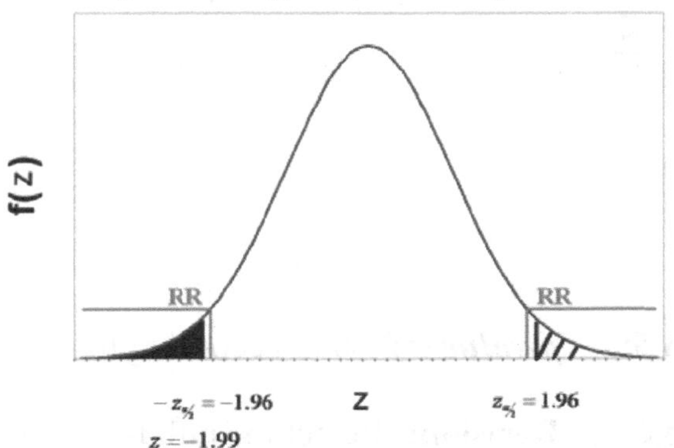

Step 5: *p-value* = 0.0466 =2(0.023295397) according to the calculator or
=2(1-0.9767) using the chart

Step 6: **Decision:** Reject the null hypothesis.

Step 7: **Interpretation:** At the 5% level of significance, there is sufficient evidence to reject the null hypothesis. That is, the mean number of e-mails is no longer 41.7.

Step 8: The standard deviation was known to be 18.5 and the sample size was large enough, $n = 45 \geq 30$, we assumed standard normal probability distribution. Here we have also argued the weaker statement. After considering the confidence interval and the two-tail hypothesis, there should be enough information to argue the stronger statement that the mean number of e-mails is not just different, but in fact less.

3. $\mu = 32$ oz., $n = 50$, $\bar{x} = 31.8$ oz., $\alpha = 0.10$ and $\sigma = 0.6$ oz.

Step 1: The **null hypothesis** is that the population mean is 32.
Shorthand: $H_0 : \mu = 32$
Alternatively, (the **alternative hypothesis** is)the population is less than 32; we will argue as the customers.
Shorthand: $H_1 : \mu < 32$

Step 2: $\alpha = 0.10$

Step 3: **Critical statistic:** $z_\alpha = -1.28$
Note: this is not $z_{\alpha/2}$ because this is a one-tail test.

Test statistic: $z = \dfrac{31.8 - 32}{0.6/\sqrt{50}} = -2.36 \qquad |-2.36| > |-1.28|$

Step 4: Based on the critical statistic and test statistic found in the third step, graphically illustrate the critical regions (acceptance and rejection regions) and the *p-value*.

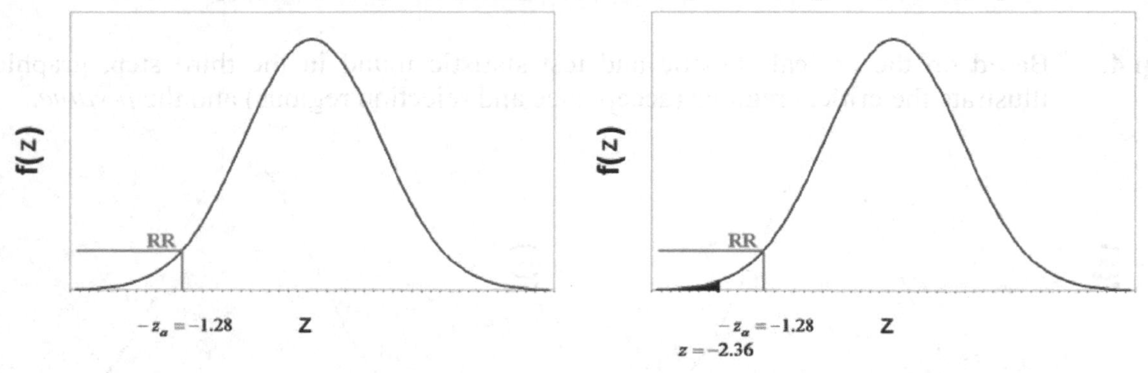

Step 5: ***p-value*** = 0.0092 according to the calculator and 0.0091 according to the chart

Step 6: **Decision:** Reject the null hypothesis.

Step 7: **Interpretation:** At the 10% level of significance, there is sufficient evidence to reject the null hypothesis. That is, the mean number of ounces is significantly less than 32.

Step 8: The standard deviation was known to be 0.6 and the sample size was large enough, $n = 50 \geq 30$, we assumed standard normal probability distribution. Here we have also argued the stronger statement. After considering the confidence interval and the one-tail hypothesis, there should be enough information to argue that the machine is consistently filling the cans with less than the stated 32 oz.

4. $n = 6$, $\bar{x} = 91.0$ lbs, $s = 30.7$, $\alpha = 0.10$, $\mu = 95$ lbs.

Step 1: The **null hypothesis** is that the population mean is 95.
Shorthand: $H_0 : \mu = 95$
Alternatively, (the **alternative hypothesis** is)the population is different from 95.
Shorthand: $H_1 : \mu \neq 95$

Step 2: $\alpha = 0.10$

Step 3: **Critical statistic:** $t_{\nu,\alpha/2} = 2.015$ and **test statistic:** $t = \frac{91.0 - 95.0}{30.7/\sqrt{6}} = -0.32$,

Step 4: Based on the critical statistic and test statistic found in the third step, graphically illustrate the critical regions (acceptance and rejection regions) and the *p-value*.

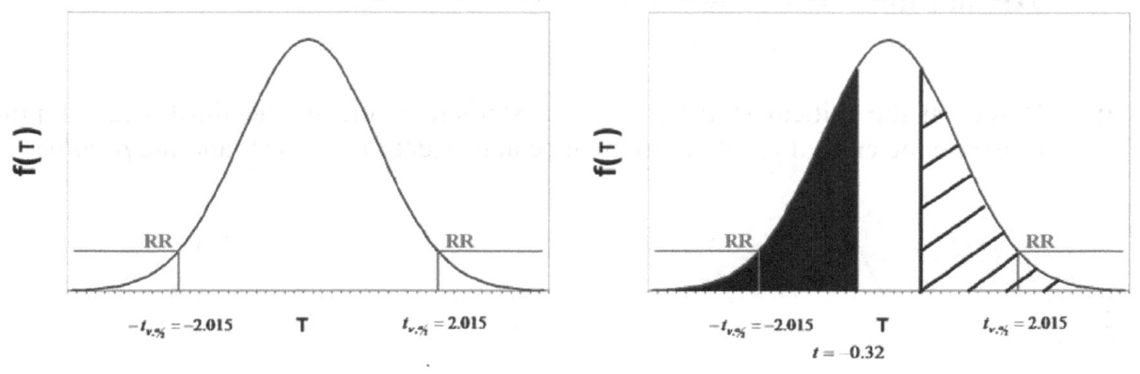

Step 5: ***p-value*** $= 0.7625$ using the calculator; using the chart the best estimation is ***p-value*** > 0.500 since $0.32 < 0.727$, hence for a two-tail test

Step 6: **Decision:** Fail to reject the null hypothesis.

Step 7: **Interpretation:** At the 10% level of significance, there is insufficient evidence to reject the null hypothesis. That is, the mean weight of a lion is approximately 95.

Step 8: The standard deviation was unknown and estimated to be 30.7 and the sample size was rather small, $n = 6 < 30$, we assumed Student's t-distribution with $\nu = 6 - 1 = 5$. Here we have also argued the weaker statement. After considering the confidence interval and the two-tail hypothesis, there does not appear to be enough information to argue the stronger statement that the mean weight is less than 95 (as it very well could be).

5. $p = 38.8\%$, $n = 1000$, $x = 426$ and $\alpha = 0.05$

Step 1: The **null hypothesis** is that the population proportion is 38.8%.
Shorthand: $H_0 : p = 0.388$
Alternatively, (the **alternative hypothesis** is) the population is not 38.8% (as not direction was given, suggested or implied).
Shorthand: $H_1 : p \neq 0.388$

Step 2: $\alpha = 0.05$

NOTE: The assumptions for normal approximation to the binomial are satisfied: $np = 388 \geq 5$ and $n(1-p) = 612 \geq 5$.

Step 3: **Critical statistic:** $z_{\alpha/2} = \pm 1.96$

Test statistic: $z = \dfrac{0.426 - 0.388}{\sqrt{\frac{0.388(1-0.388)}{1000}}} = 2.47$

Step 4: Based on the critical statistic and test statistic found in the third step, graphically illustrate the critical regions (acceptance and rejection regions) and the *p-value*.

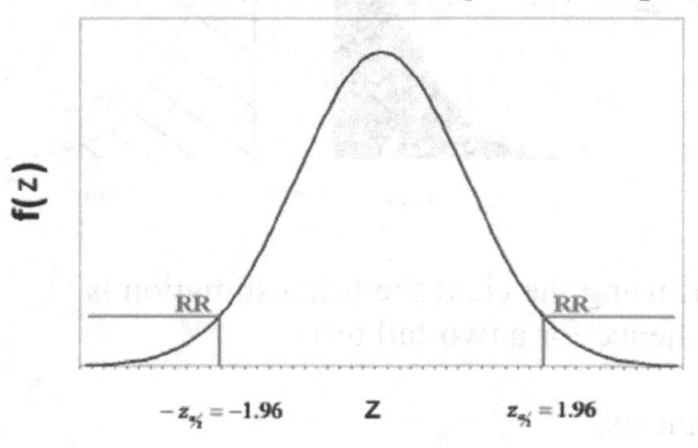

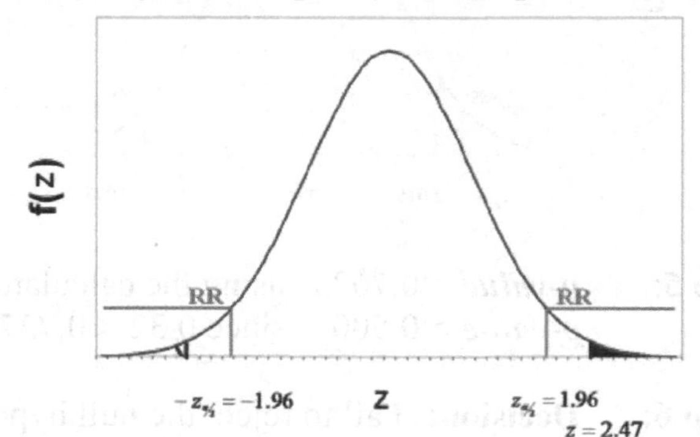

Step 5: *p-value* = 0.0137

Step 6: **Decision:** Reject the null hypothesis.

Step 7: **Interpretation:** At the 5% level of significance, there is sufficient evidence to reject the null hypothesis. That is, the mean proportion of type A personalities is significantly different than 38.8%.

Step 8: The standard deviation was estimated using standard statistical methods as the sample size was large enough with at least five in each category to use a standard normal approximate of the binomial probability distribution. Here we have also argued the weaker statement. After considering the confidence interval and the two-tail hypothesis, there should be enough information to argue the stronger statement that the proportion is not just different than 33.8%, but in fact greater than 38.8%.

6. $p = 50\%$, $n = 34$, $x = 10$ and $\alpha = 0.01$

Step 1: The **null hypothesis** is that the population proportion is 50%.
Shorthand: $H_0 : p = 0.50$
Alternatively, (the **alternative hypothesis** is) the population is less than 50%,
Shorthand: $H_1 : p < 0.50$

Step 2: $\alpha = 0.01$

NOTE: The assumptions for normal approximation to the binomial are satisfied: $np = 17 \geq 5$ and $n(1-p) = 17 \geq 5$.

Step 3: **Critical statistic:** $-z_\alpha = -2.326$

Note: this is not $z_{\alpha/2}$ because this is a one-tail test.

Test statistic: $z = \dfrac{\frac{10}{34} - 0.5}{\sqrt{\frac{0.5(1-0.5)}{34}}} = -2.40$

Step 4: Based on the critical statistic and test statistic found in the third step, graphically illustrate the critical regions (acceptance and rejection regions) and the *p-value*.

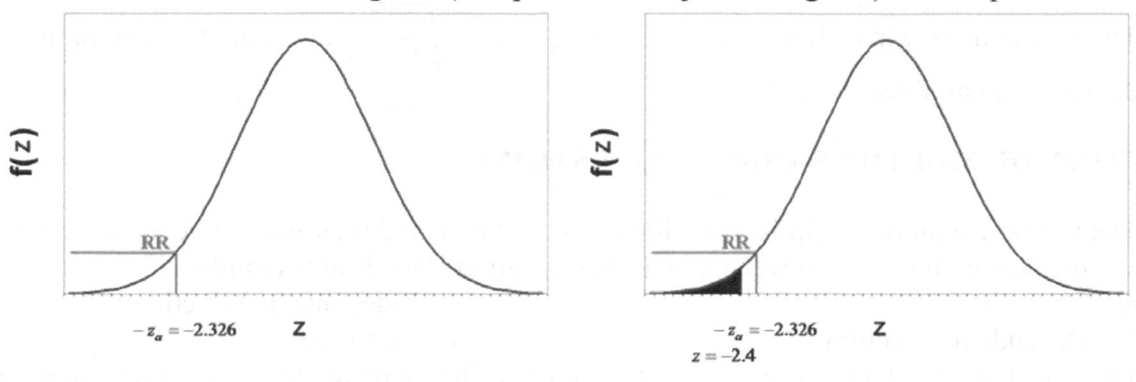

Step 5: *p-value* = 0.0082

Step 6: **Decision:** Reject the null hypothesis.

Step 7: **Interpretation:** At the 1% level of significance, there is sufficient evidence to reject the null hypothesis. That is, the mean proportion of female wolves is significantly less than 50%.

Step 8: The standard deviation was estimated using standard statistical methods as the sample size was large enough with at least five in each category to use a standard normal approximate of the binomial probability distribution.

SECTION I: MATCHING TERMINOLOGY

A. Dependent Selection
B. Heterogeneous
C. Homogeneous
D. Independent Selection

1. _____ Sample data drawn from one population is completely unrelated to the selection of sample data from the other population. For example, compare two sample means for the first exam of the semester, one from a mass lecture course and one from a night course (not a mass lecture.)
2. _____ Data gathered in two different samples in such a way that there is a matching of the first sample data drawn and a corresponding data value in the second sample data. For example, compare two sample means, one for the first exam of the semester and the second for the second exam of the semester, match via the student taking each test.
3. _____ Equal in Variance
4. _____ Unequal in Variance

SECTION II: FILL IN THE BLANK

1. In estimating the standard error, use the _________ variance, $s_p^2 = \sqrt{\frac{(n_1-1)s_1^2+(n_2-1)s_2^2}{n_1+n_2-2}}$, when the data is homogeneous.
2. The standard error in differences of means, $\sigma_{\bar{x}_1-\bar{x}_2} = \sqrt{\frac{\sigma_1^2}{n_1}+\frac{\sigma_2^2}{n_2}}$, is under the assumption that the random variables, x_1 and x_2 are ___________________________.

SECTION III: MULTIPLE-CHOICE QUESTIONS

1. The measurement of height is taken for a group of men and their wives to determine if there is a difference in height between men and their wives. This is an example of
   a. Clustering
   b. Dependent Selection
   c. Independent Selection
   d. Stratified
2. The test scores are taken from two mass lectures with two different instructors to determine if there is a difference in scores between the two mass lectures. This is an example of
   a. Clustering
   b. Dependent Selection
   c. Independent Selection
   d. Stratified

SECTION IV: WORKED PROBLEMS:

1. Given two independent random variables x_1 and x_2 such that $E(\bar{x}_1)=\mu_1$, $E(\bar{x}_2)=\mu_2$, $V(\bar{x}_1)=\frac{\sigma_1^2}{n_1}$ and $V(\bar{x}_2)=\frac{\sigma_2^2}{n_2}$, define the parameter for difference of means as $\theta=\mu_1-\mu_2$ and the statistic for difference of means as $\hat{\theta}=\bar{x}_1-\bar{x}_2$, assuming these

random variables are independent, **prove** $E(\hat{\theta}) = \mu_1 - \mu_2$, $V(\hat{\theta}) = \frac{\sigma_1^2}{n_1} + \frac{\sigma_2^2}{n_2}$ and hence $\sigma_{\hat{\theta}} = \sqrt{\frac{\sigma_1^2}{n_1} + \frac{\sigma_2^2}{n_2}}$.

2. Fred and George bowled twenty-five games in a friendly rivalry with the following given in the following chart. Assuming the score are normally distributed random variables, who is the better bowler and why.

FRED x	f	**GEORGE** y	f
139	4	137	7
142	5	154	5
155	8	160	6
166	5	177	4
230	3	182	3
TOTALS	25	TOTALS	25

3. (a) In the journal *Mental Retardation*, an article reported the results of a peer-tutoring program to help mildly mentally retarded children learn to read. In the experiment, the mildly mentally retarded children randomly divided into two groups: the experimental group received peer tutoring along with the regular instruction and the control group received regular instruction with no peer tutoring. There were $n_1 = n_2 = 30$ children in each group. For the experimental group, the mean score was $\bar{x}_1 = 344.5$ with sample standard deviation $s_1 = 49.1$. For the control group, the mean score was $\bar{x}_2 = 354.2$ with sample standard deviation $s_2 = 50.9$. Use a 5% level of significance to test the hypothesis that there was no difference (either way) in scores between the two groups.

   (b) Compare the (non-pooled) test statistic to four decimals and the pooled test statistic $t = \frac{(x_1 - x_2)}{s\sqrt{\frac{1}{n_1} + \frac{1}{n_2}}}$ to four decimals, where $s = s_p = \sqrt{\frac{(n_1 - 1)s_1^2 + (n_2 - 1)s_2^2}{n_1 + n_2 - 2}}$. Discuss the effect of using the pooled statistic with degree of freedom $\nu = n_1 + n_2 - 2$ and the non-pooled statistic with degree of freedom $\nu = \min(n_1 - 1, n_2 - 1)$ with respect to your conclusion or decision.

4. In a poll, it was found that 148 out of 250 men voted yes on an amendment and 133 out of 280 women voted yes on the same amendment. Use a 1% level of significance to test the hypothesis that there was no difference (**either way**) in the proportion of men and women.

5. A random sample of $n_1 = 378$ hotel guests was taken one year ago and it was fount that $x_1 = 194$ requested nonsmoking rooms. Recently, a random sample of $n_2 = 516$ hotel guests showed that $x_2 = 320$ requested nonsmoking rooms. Do these data indicate that

the proportion of hotel guests requesting non-smoking rooms has increased? Use a 1% level of significance.

6. The following is based on information taken form *Winter Wind Studies in Rocky Mountains National Park*. At five weather stations on Trail Ridge Road, the peak wind gusts (in miles per hour) in January and April recorded below. Does this information indicate that the peak wind gusts are higher in January than in April using mean differences; that is, at the 0.01 significance level, use hypothesis testing of mean differences where $\hat{\mu}_d = \bar{d}$ and $\hat{\sigma}_d = s_d$.

Weather Station	January	April	Difference
1	139	104	35
2	122	113	9
3	126	100	26
4	64	88	-24
5	78	61	17
Mean	$\bar{x}_1 = 105.8$	$\bar{x}_2 = 93.2$	$\bar{d} = 12.6$
Sample Deviation	$s_1 = 32.76$	$s_2 = 20.12$	$s_d = 22.66$

7. Consider the test average and final for five students. Does this information indicate that the final grades are **higher** than the score on the final; that is, at the 0.05 significance level, use hypothesis testing of mean differences where $\hat{\mu}_d = \bar{d}$ and $\hat{\sigma}_d = s_d$.

Student	Test Average	Final	Difference
1	75	87	12
2	71	81	10
3	84	79	-5
4	64	82	18
5	76	69	-7
Mean	$\bar{x}_1 = 74$	$\bar{x}_2 = 79.6$	$\bar{d} = 5.6$
Sample Deviation	$s_1 = 7.3$	$s_2 = 6.6$	$s_d = 11.0$

KEY CHAPTER 9

SECTION I:

1. D
2. A
3. C
4. B

SECTION II:

1. pooled
2. independent

SECTION III:

1. b
2. c

SECTION IV:

1. **Detailed Proof:**

Given $E(x_1) = \mu_1$, $V(x_1) = \sigma_1^2$, $E(x_2) = \mu_2$, $V(x_2) = \sigma_2^2$, then this is the **long version**

$$E(\hat{\theta}) = E(\bar{x}_1 - \bar{x}_2) = E\left(\frac{\sum_{i=1}^{n_1} x_{1i}}{n_1} - \frac{\sum_{i=1}^{n_2} x_{2i}}{n_2}\right) = E\left(\frac{\sum_{i=1}^{n_1} x_{1i}}{n_1}\right) + (-1)E\left(\frac{\sum_{i=1}^{n_2} x_{2i}}{n_2}\right)$$

$$= \frac{1}{n_1}E\left(\sum_{i=1}^{n_1} x_{1i}\right) - \frac{1}{n_2}E\left(\sum_{i=1}^{n_2} x_{2i}\right) = \frac{1}{n_1}\sum_{i=1}^{n_1} E(x_{1i}) - \frac{1}{n_2}\sum_{i=1}^{n_2} E(x_{2i})$$

$$= \frac{1}{n_1}\sum_{i=1}^{n_1} \mu_1 - \frac{1}{n_2}\sum_{i=1}^{n_2} \mu_2 = \frac{1}{n_1}(n_1\mu_1) - \frac{1}{n_2}(n_2\mu_2) = \mu_1 - \mu_2$$

$$V(\hat{\theta}) = V(\bar{x}_1 - \bar{x}_2) = V\left(\frac{\sum_{i=1}^{n_1} x_{1i}}{n_1} - \frac{\sum_{i=1}^{n_2} x_{2i}}{n_2}\right) = V\left(\frac{\sum_{i=1}^{n_1} x_{1i}}{n_1}\right) + (-1)^2 V\left(\frac{\sum_{i=1}^{n_2} x_{2i}}{n_2}\right)$$

$$= \frac{1}{n_1^2}V\left(\sum_{i=1}^{n_1} x_{1i}\right) + \frac{1}{n_2^2}V\left(\sum_{i=1}^{n_2} x_{2i}\right) = \frac{1}{n_1^2}\sum_{i=1}^{n_1} V(x_{1i}) + \frac{1}{n_2^2}\sum_{i=1}^{n_2} V(x_{2i})$$

$$= \frac{1}{n_1^2}\sum_{i=1}^{n_1} \sigma_1^2 + \frac{1}{n_2^2}\sum_{i=1}^{n_2} \sigma_2^2 = \frac{1}{n_1^2}(n_1\sigma_1^2) + \frac{1}{n_2^2}(n_2\sigma_2^2) = \frac{\sigma_1^2}{n_1} + \frac{\sigma_2^2}{n_2}$$

Therefore, $\sigma_{\hat{\theta}} = \sqrt{V(\hat{\theta})} = \sqrt{\frac{\sigma_1^2}{n_1} + \frac{\sigma_2^2}{n_2}}$

Given $E(\bar{x}_1) = \mu_1$, $V(\bar{x}_1) = \frac{\sigma_1^2}{n_1}$, $E(\bar{x}_2) = \mu_2$, $V(\bar{x}_2) = \frac{\sigma_2^2}{n_2}$, then this is the **short version** is

$$E(\hat{\theta}) = E(\bar{x}_1 - \bar{x}_2) = E(\bar{x}_1) + (-1)E(\bar{x}_2) = \mu_1 - \mu_2,$$

$$V(\hat{\theta}) = V(\bar{x}_1 - \bar{x}_2) = V(\bar{x}_1) + (-1)^2 V(\bar{x}_2) = \frac{\sigma_1^2}{n_1} + \frac{\sigma_2^2}{n_2}, \text{ and hence}$$

$$\sigma_{\hat{\theta}} = \sqrt{V(\hat{\theta})} = \sqrt{\frac{\sigma_1^2}{n_1} + \frac{\sigma_2^2}{n_2}}$$

2. $\bar{x}_F = 161.04$, $s_F = 27.72$, $\bar{x}_G = 157.72$, $s_G = 16.28$, $n_1 = n_2 = 25$ and $\alpha = 0.05$, assuming normal distribution.

CI:

Step 1: $\alpha = 0.05 \quad \Rightarrow c = 1 - 0.05 = 0.95$

Step 2: Since data is given to be normally distributed and the variances are assumed (more specifically, that the data is a census); $z_{\alpha/2} = 1.96$; $\hat{\theta} = \bar{x}_F - \bar{x}_G \approx 3.32$ and margin of error $\text{E} = 1.96\sqrt{\frac{27.72^2}{25} + \frac{16.28^2}{25}} \approx 12.6$.

Step 3: $x_L = 3.32 - 12.6 = -9.26$ and $x_U = 3.32 + 12.6 = 15.92$, the interval estimate is $(-9.26, 15.92)$.

Step 4: We are 95% confident that the true difference of means is 3.32 with a 12.6 point margin of error; that is, we are 95% confident that the true difference between Fred and George is between -9.26 (George is better) and 15.92 (Fred is better). Hence, the there is no significant difference between Fred and George on average. However, George's sample standard deviation is lower and hence, George is more consistent – George is the better bowler, as there is no significant difference between their means and George is more consistent.

Step 5: The standard deviations were unknown and sample size was rather small, $n = 25 < 30$; however, as the data's distribution is given to be normally distributed, we can assume the standard normal distribution. Here we have also argued the weaker statement and after considering the confidence interval and the two-tail hypothesis, there does not appear to be enough information to argue that there is a better bowler based on means alone.

HT:

Step 1: The null hypothesis is that there is no difference of means.

Shorthand: $H_0 : \mu_F - \mu_G = 0$

Alternatively, there is a difference of proportions.

Shorthand: $H_1 : \mu_F - \mu_G \neq 0$

Step 2: $\alpha = 0.05$

Step 3: $z_{\alpha/2} = 1.96$ and $z = \dfrac{161.04 - 157.72}{\sqrt{\dfrac{27.72^2}{25} + \dfrac{16.28^2}{25}}} = 0.52$

Step 4: Based on the critical statistic and test statistic found in the third step, graphically illustrate the critical regions (acceptance and rejection regions) and the *p-value*.

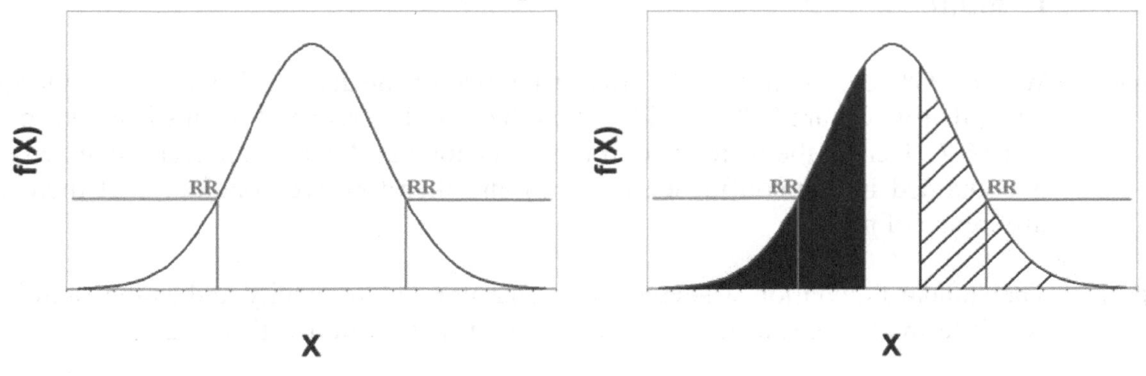

Step 5: *p-value* = 0.6031 $\qquad p - \text{value} >> \alpha$

Step 6: Fail to reject the null hypothesis.

Step 7: At the 5% level of significance, there is insufficient evidence to reject the null hypothesis. That is, the difference of means is not significantly different than 0. That is, there is no significant difference between Fred and George on average.

Step 8: The standard deviation was unknown and estimated assuming heterogeneity; the sample size was a little small, $n_1 = n_2 = 25$; however, it is given that the data's distribution is normally distributed. George is the better bowler, as there is no significant difference between their means and George is more consistent.

3. (a) $n_1 = n_2 = 30$, $\bar{x}_1 = 344.5$, $s_1 = 49.1$, $\bar{x}_2 = 354.2$, $s_2 = 50.9$ and $\alpha = 0.05$.

CI:

Step 1: $\alpha = 0.05 \quad \Rightarrow c = 1 - 0.05 = 0.95$

Step 2: While $n_1 = n_2 = 30$, there is not enough information to use the normal probability distribution as the standard deviations are unknown and, assuming heterogeneity, are estimated with $\nu = 30 - 1 = 29$ degrees of freedom; hence,
$t_{\nu,c} = 2.045$; $\hat{\theta} = \bar{x}_2 - \bar{x}_2 = 354.2 - 344.5 = 9.7$ and margin of error

$$\text{E} = 2.045\sqrt{\frac{49.1^2}{30} + \frac{50.9^2}{30}} \approx 26.4.$$

Step 3: $x_L = -9.7 - 26.4 = -36.1$ and $x_U = -9.7 + 26.4 = 16.7$, the interval estimate is $(-36.1, 16.7)$.

Step 4: We are 95% confident that the true difference of means is 9.7 with a 26.4 margin of error; that is, we are 95% confident that the true difference of means is between -36.1 and 16.7. Hence, the difference of means is not significantly different than zero (as 0 is contained in our confidence interval) and therefore we conclude that there is no difference of means.

Step 5: The standard deviation was estimated assuming heterogeneity and as the sample size is a little small, we selected to use Student's t-distribution with $\nu = 29$..

HT:

Step 1: The null hypothesis is that there is no difference of means.
Shorthand: $H_0 : \mu_2 - \mu_1 = 0$
Alternatively, there is a difference of proportions.
Shorthand: $H_1 : \mu_2 - \mu_1 \neq 0$

Step 2: $\alpha = 0.05$

Step 3: $\nu = 29$, $t_{\nu,\alpha/2} = \pm 2.045$ and $t = \dfrac{(344.5 - 354.2) - 0}{\sqrt{\dfrac{49.1^2}{30} + \dfrac{50.9^2}{30}}} = -0.75$.

Step 4: Based on the critical statistic and test statistic found in the third step, graphically illustrate the critical regions (acceptance and rejection regions) and the *p-value*.

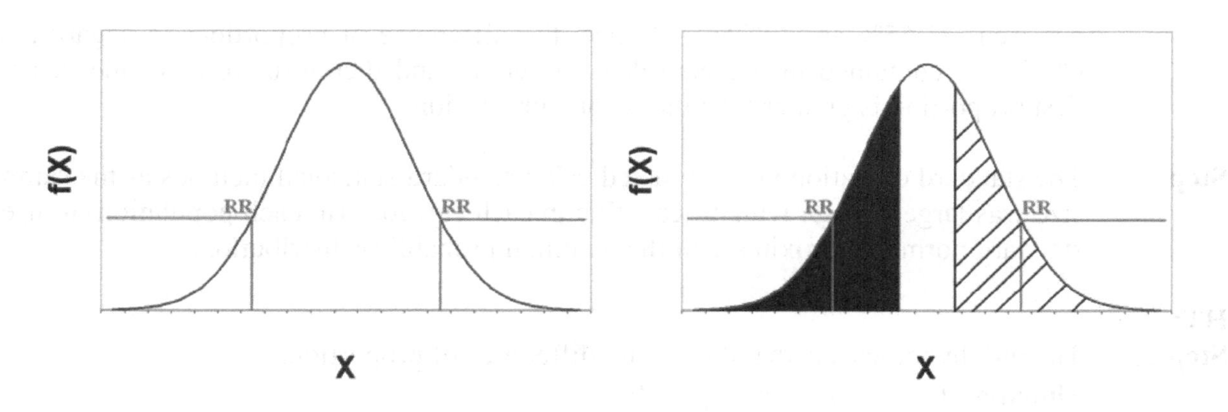

Step 5: *p-value* $= 0.4556$ $\qquad p - \text{value} >> \alpha$

Step 6: Fail to reject the null hypothesis.

Step 7: At the 5% level of significance, there is insufficient evidence to reject the null hypothesis. That is, the difference of means is not significantly different than 0.

Step 8: The standard deviation was unknown and estimated assuming heterogeneity; the sample size was a little small, $n = 30$; hence, we assumed Student's t-distribution with $\nu = 30 - 1 = 29$. Here we have also argued the weaker statement. After considering the confidence interval and the two-tail hypothesis, there does not appear to be enough information to argue the stronger statement that the difference of means is less than 0.

(b) Non-pooled: $t = -0.7512$, $\nu = 29$ Pooled: $s_p = 50.008$, $t = -0.7512$, $\nu = 58$

4. $x_1 = 148$, $n_1 = 250$, $x_2 = 133$, $n_2 = 280$ and $\alpha = 0.01$

CI:

Step 1: $\alpha = 0.01 \quad \Rightarrow c = 1 - 0.01 = 0.99$

Step 2: Since $n_1 \hat{p}_1 = 148 > 5$, $n_1(1 - \hat{p}_1) = 250 - 148 = 102 > 5$, $n_2 \hat{p}_2 = 133 > 5$, $n_2(1 - \hat{p}_2) = 280 - 133 = 147 > 5$, there is enough information to use the normal approximation to the binomial; $z_c = 2.576$; $\hat{\theta} = \hat{p}_2 - \hat{p}_1 = \frac{148}{250} - \frac{133}{280} \approx -0.117$ and margin of error $E = 2.576\sqrt{\frac{0.592(1-0.592)}{250} + \frac{0.475(1-0.475)}{280}} \approx 0.0995$.

Step 3: $x_L = -0.117 - 0.0995 = -0.2165$ and $x_U = -0.117 + 0.0995 = -0.0175$, the interval estimate is $(-0.2165, -0.0175)$.

Step 4: We are 99% confident that the true difference of proportion is -11.7% with a 9.95% margin of error; that is, we are 99% confident that the true difference of proportion is between -21.65% and -1.75%. Hence, the difference of proportions is negative (as 0% is not contained in our confidence interval) and therefore we conclude that the first proportion is greater than the second proportion.

Step 5: The standard deviation was estimated using standard statistical methods as the sample size was large enough with at least five in each category (in each population) to use a standard normal approximate of the binomial probability distribution.

HT:

Step 1: The null hypothesis is that there is no difference of proportion.

Shorthand: $H_0 : p_2 - p_1 = 0$

Alternatively, there is a difference of proportions.

Shorthand: $H_1 : p_2 - p_1 \neq 0$

Step 2: $\alpha = 0.01$

Step 3: $z_{\alpha/2} = \pm 2.576$ and under the assumption that the null hypothesis is true,

$$\bar{p} = \frac{148+133}{250+280} \approx 0.53 \text{, and hence, } z = \frac{-0.117}{\sqrt{\frac{0.53(1-0.53)}{250} + \frac{0.53(1-0.53)}{280}}} = -2.694$$

Step 4: Based on the critical statistic and test statistic found in the third step, graphically illustrate the critical regions (acceptance and rejection regions) and the *p-value*.

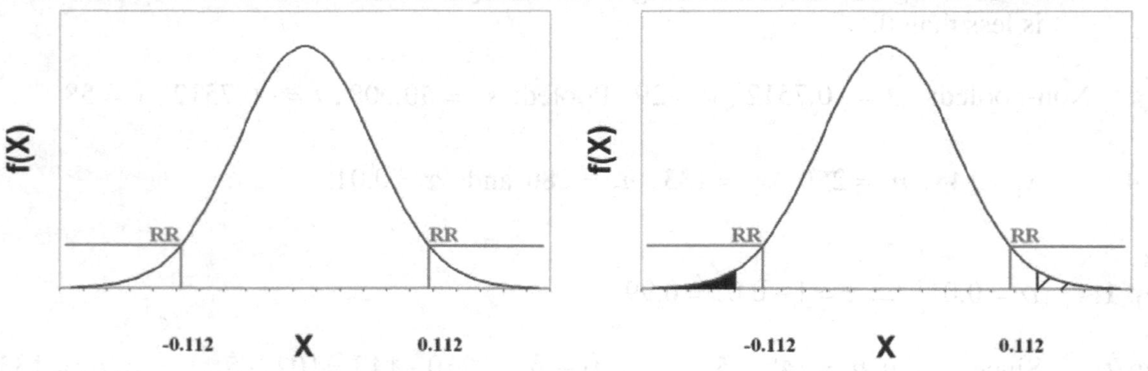

Step 5: *p-value* = 0.0071

Step 6: Reject the null hypothesis.

Step 7: At the 1% level of significance, there is sufficient evidence to reject the null hypothesis. That is, the difference of proportion is significantly different than 0.

Step 8: The standard deviation was estimated using standard statistical methods as the sample size was large enough with at least five in each category to use a standard normal approximate of the binomial probability distribution. Here we have also argued the weaker statement. After considering the confidence interval and the two-tail hypothesis, there should be enough information to argue the stronger statement that the difference of proportion is not zero, but that the first proportion is greater than the second proportion.

5. $x_1 = 194$, $n_1 = 378$, $x_2 = 320$, $n_2 = 516$ and $\alpha = 0.01$

CI:

Step 1: $\alpha = 0.01 \quad \Rightarrow c = 1 - 0.01 = 0.99$

Step 2: Since $n_1\hat{p}_1 = 194 > 5$, $n_1(1-\hat{p}_1) = 378 - 194 = 184 > 5$, $n_2\hat{p}_2 = 320 > 5$, $n_2(1-\hat{p}_2) = 516 - 320 = 196 > 5$, there is enough information to use the normal approximation to the binomial; $z_c = 2.576$; $\hat{\theta} = \hat{p}_2 - \hat{p}_1 = \frac{320}{516} - \frac{194}{378} \approx 0.1069$ and margin of error $\text{E} = 2.576\sqrt{\dfrac{0.62(1-0.62)}{516} + \dfrac{0.51(1-0.51)}{378}} \approx 0.0861$.

Step 3: $x_L = 0.1069 - 0.0861 = 0.0208$ and $x_U = 0.1069 + 0.0861 = 0.1930$, the interval estimate is $(0.0208, 0.1930)$.

Step 4: We are 99% confident that the true difference of proportion is 10.69% with a 8.61% margin of error; that is, we are 99% confident that the true difference of proportion is between 2.08% and 19.30%. Hence, the difference of proportions is positive (as 0% is not contained in our confidence interval) and therefore we conclude that the first proportion is less than the second proportion.

Step 5: The standard deviation was estimated using standard statistical methods as the sample size was large enough with at least five in each category (in each population) to use a standard normal approximate of the binomial probability distribution.

HT:

Step 1: The null hypothesis is that there is no difference of proportion.

Shorthand: $H_0 : p_2 - p_1 = 0$

Alternatively, there is a difference of proportions.

Shorthand: $H_1 : p_2 - p_1 > 0$

Step 2: $\alpha = 0.01$

Step 3: $z_\alpha = 2.81$ and under the assumption that the null hypothesis is true,

$$\bar{p} = \frac{194 + 320}{378 + 516} \approx 0.575, \text{ and hence, } z = \frac{0.1069}{\sqrt{\frac{0.575(1-0.575)}{378} + \frac{0.575(1-0.575)}{516}}} = 3.19$$

Step 4: Based on the critical statistic and test statistic found in the third step, graphically illustrate the critical regions (acceptance and rejection regions) and the *p-value*.

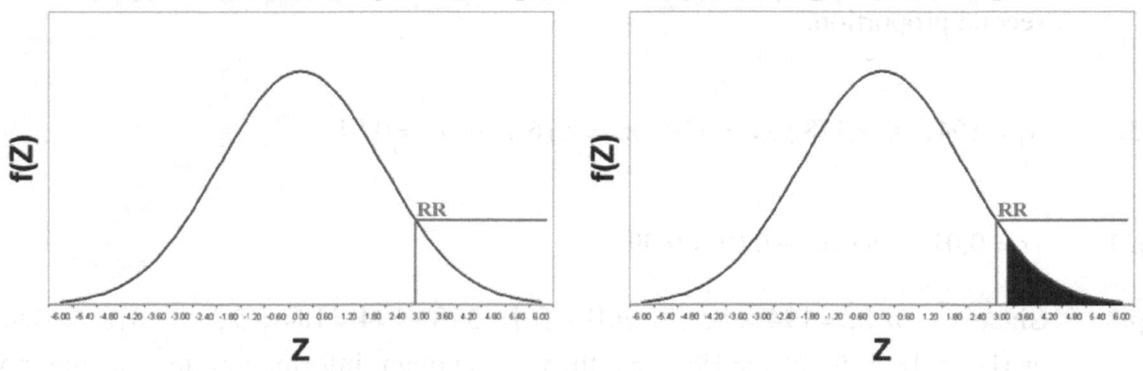

Step 5: *p-value* = 0.000687 using the calculator and 0.0007 using the chart (illustrated on chart above) $p-\text{value} < \alpha$

Step 6: Reject the null hypothesis.

Step 7: At the 1% level of significance, there is sufficient evidence to reject the null hypothesis. That is, the difference of proportion is significantly different than 0.

Step 8: The standard deviation was estimated using standard statistical methods as the sample size was large enough with at least five in each category to use a standard normal approximate of the binomial probability distribution. This is consistent with the confidence interval, there is enough information to that the first proportion is less than the second proportion. These data indicate that the proportion of hotel guests requesting non-smoking rooms has increased.

6. $\mu_d = 0$, $n = 5$, $\bar{d} = 12.6$, $\alpha = 0.01$ and $s_d = 22.66$.

CI:

Step 1: $\alpha = 0.01 \quad \Rightarrow c = 1 - 0.01 = 0.99$

Step 2: While σ_d is unknown, $n = 5$ and hence the we will use Student's t-distribution with $\nu = 5 - 1 = 4$, $t_{\nu,c} = 4.604$; $\hat{\theta} = \bar{d} = 12.6$ and margin of error

$$\text{E} = 4.604\frac{22.66}{\sqrt{5}} \approx 46.66$$

Step 3: $x_L = 12.6 - 46.66 = -34.06$ and $x_U = 12.6 + 46.66 = 59.26$, the interval estimate is $(-34.06, 59.257)$.

Step 4: We are 99% confident that the true mean is 12.6 with a 44.66 margin of error; that is, we are 99% confident that the true mean is between -34.06 and 59.26. Hence, there appears to be no mean difference or at least there is insufficient information to discern a difference.

Step 5: The standard deviation was unknown and estimated to be 46.66 and the sample size was rather small, $n = 5 < 30$, we assumed Student's t-distribution with $\nu = 5 - 1 = 4$ degrees of freedom.

HT:

Step 1: The null hypothesis is that the population mean difference is 0.

Shorthand: $H_0 : \mu_d = 0$

Alternatively, the mean difference is greater than 0; as $d = x_J - x_A$ and $\mu_J > \mu_A$.

Shorthand: $H_1 : \mu_d > 0$

Step 2: $\alpha = 0.01$

Step 3: $t_\alpha = 3.74$ Note: this is not $t_{\nu,\alpha/2}$ because this is a one-tail test.

$$t = \frac{12.6 - 0}{22.66/\sqrt{5}} = 1.24$$

Step 4: Based on the critical statistic and test statistic found in the third step, graphically illustrate the critical regions (acceptance and rejection regions) and the *p-value*.

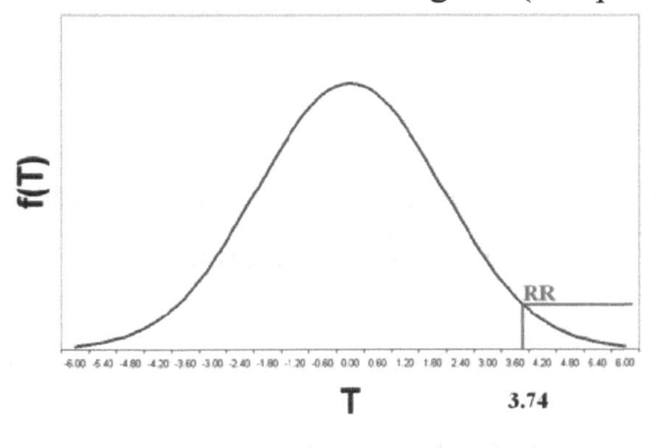

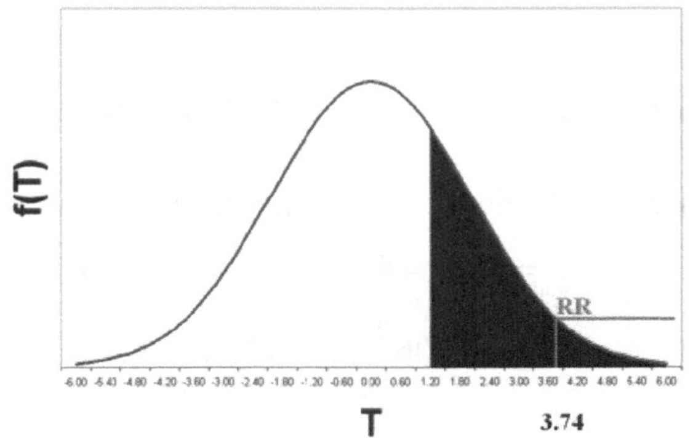

Step 5: *p-value* = 0.1408 using the calculator or since on the student t-distribution chart assuming 4 degrees of freedom, $0.741 < 1.24 < 1.344$, hence for a one-tail test (see top of chart – but realize in reverse order; that is as the t-statistic increase the probability decrease) we have $0.25 > p\text{-value} > 0.125$ or more appropriately $0.125 < p\text{-value} < 0.25$; this is a good enough estimate to make a decision.

Step 6: Accept (fail to reject) the null hypothesis.

Step 7: At the 1% level of significance, there is insufficient evidence to reject the null hypothesis. That is, the mean difference in temperature between April and January is not significantly different than zero.

Step 8: The standard deviation was unknown and estimated to be 22.66 and the sample size was rather small, $n = 5 < 30$, we assumed Student's t-distribution with $\nu = 5 - 1 = 4$ degrees of freedom.

7. Consider the test average and final for five students. Does this information indicate that the final grades are **higher** than the score on the final; that is, at the 0.05 significance level, use hypothesis testing of mean differences where $\hat{\mu}_d = \bar{d}$ and $\hat{\sigma}_d = s_d$.

Student	Test Average	Final	Difference
1	75	87	12
2	71	81	10
3	84	79	-5
4	64	82	18
5	76	69	-7
Mean	$\bar{x}_1 = 74$	$\bar{x}_2 = 79.6$	$\bar{d} = 5.6$
Sample Deviation	$s_1 = 7.3$	$s_2 = 6.6$	$s_d = 11.0$

Information: $\mu_d = 0$, $n = 5$, $\bar{d} = 5.6$., $\alpha = 0.05$ and $s_d = 11.0$.

CI:

Step 1: $\alpha = 0.05 \quad \Rightarrow c = 1 - 0.05 = 0.95$

Step 2: While σ_d is unknown, $n = 5$ and hence the we will use Student's t-distribution with $\nu = 5 - 1 = 4$, $t_{\nu,c} = 2.5706$; $\hat{\theta} = \bar{d} = 5.6$ and margin of error $\text{E} = 2.5706\frac{11.0}{\sqrt{5}} \approx 12.65$

Step 3: $x_L = 5.6 - 12.65 = -7.05$ and $x_U = 5.6 + 12.65 = 18.25$, the interval estimate is $(-7.05, 18.25)$.

Step 4: We are 95% confident that the true mean is 5.6 with a 12.65 margin of error; that is, we are 95% confident that the true mean is between -7.05 and 18.25. Hence, there appears to be no mean difference or at least there is insufficient information to discern a difference.

Step 5: The standard deviation was unknown and estimated to be 11.06 and the sample size was rather small, $n = 5 < 30$, we assumed Student's t-distribution with $\nu = 5 - 1 = 4$ degrees of freedom.

HT:

Step 1: The null hypothesis is that the population mean difference is 0.
Shorthand: $H_0 : \mu_d = 0$
Alternatively, the mean difference is greater than 0.
Shorthand: $H_1 : \mu_d > 0$

Step 2: $\alpha = 0.05$

Step 3: $t_\alpha = 2.015$ Note: this is not $t_{v,\alpha/2}$ because this is a one-tail test.

$$t = \frac{5.6 - 0}{11.0/\sqrt{5}} = 1.14$$

Step 4: Based on the critical statistic and test statistic found in the third step, graphically illustrate the critical regions (acceptance and rejection regions) and the *p-value*.

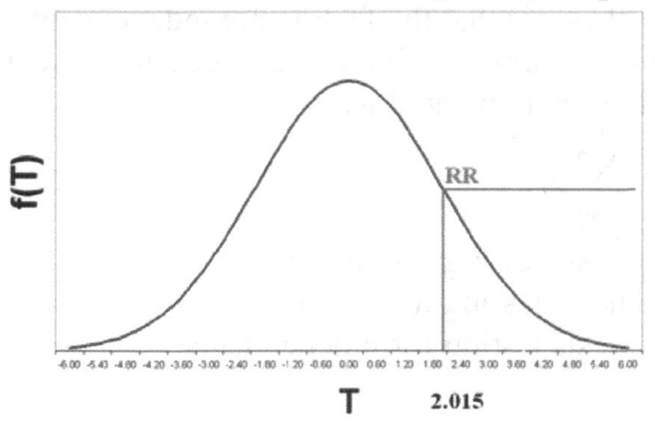

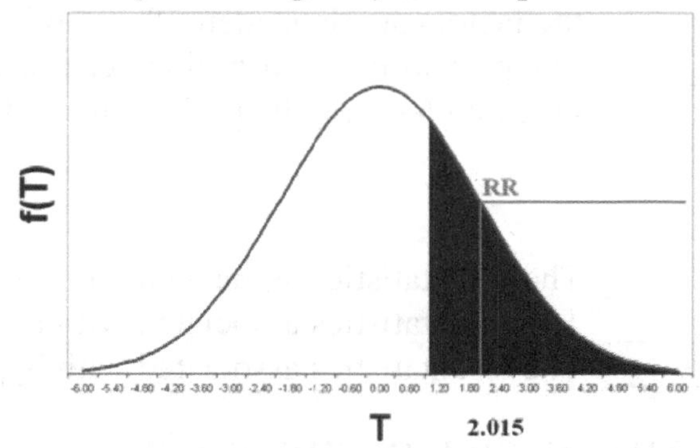

Step 5: *p-value* = 0.1408 using the calculator or since on the student t-distribution chart assuming 4 degrees of freedom, $0.741 < 1.24 < 1.344$, hence for a one-tail test (see top of chart – but realize in reverse order; that is as the t-statistic increase the probability decrease) we have $0.25 > p\text{-value} > 0.125$ or more appropriately $0.125 < p\text{-value} < 0.25$; this is a good enough estimate to make a decision.

Step 6: Accept (fail to reject) the null hypothesis.

Step 7: At the 1% level of significance, there is insufficient evidence to reject the null hypothesis. That is, the mean difference in temperature between April and January is not significantly different than zero.

Step 8: The standard deviation was unknown and estimated to be 11.0 and the sample size was rather small, $n = 5 < 30$, we assumed Student's t-distribution with $\nu = 5 - 1 = 4$ degrees of freedom.

SECTION I: MATCHING TERMINOLOGY

A. $\chi^2 = \frac{(n-1)s^2}{\sigma^2} = \sum_{i=1}^{n}\left(\frac{x_i-\bar{x}}{\sigma}\right)^2$

B. $\chi^2 = \sum_{i=1}^{m}\frac{(O_i-E_i)^2}{E_i}, \nu = m-1$

C. $\chi^2 = \sum_{i=1}^{r}\sum_{j=1}^{c}\frac{(O_{ij}-E_{ij})^2}{E_{ij}}, \nu = (r-1)(c-1)$

D. Chi-square distribution

E. Goodness-of-fit

F. Simpson's Paradox

G. Test of Independence

1. _____ In a comparison of two categories, a relationship that holds among several groups can change or even reverse when combining the groups.
2. _____ A test using relative errors comparing a frequency table to the expected counts determined using a given probability distribution; the null hypothesis is that the given probability distribution fits the data's distribution.
3. _____ A test using relative errors comparing factors in a contingency table to determine if the factors are dependent; the null hypothesis is that the factors are independent.
4. _____ The probability distribution generated by summing normal z-scores-squared; that is, given $z \sim N(0,1)$, the probability distribution associated with
$$\sum_{i=1}^{v} z_i^2.$$
5. _____ The test statistics associated with hypothesis testing for variance
6. _____ The test statistics associated with hypothesis testing for goodness-of-fit
7. _____ The test statistics associated with hypothesis testing for independence

SECTION II: FILL IN THE BLANK

1. If a random variable X has a normal distribution with mean μ and standard deviation σ, then $Z^2 = \left(\frac{X-\mu}{\sigma}\right)^2$ follows a __________ distribution with _________ degree(s) of freedom.
2. If a random variable Z has a standard normal distribution with mean μ and standard deviation σ, then $U = \sum_{i=1}^{v} z_i^2$ follows a ____________ distribution with ________ degree(s) of freedom.

SECTION III: MULTIPLE-CHOICE QUESTIONS

1. Which one is appropriate to test if a die is balanced?
   (a) One sample z-test for mean
   (b) Two-sample proportion z-test
   (c) Chi-square test of independence
   (d) Chi-square test of goodness of fit
2. Which one is appropriate to test highest degree earned depends on gender?
   (a) One sample z-test for mean
   (b) Two-sample proportion z-test
   (c) Chi-square test of independence
   (d) Chi-square test of goodness of fit
3. Which one is NOT true for a chi-square distribution?
   (a) Skewed to the left
   (b) As the degree of freedom increases, the mean increases
   (c) Unimodal
   (d) Asymmetric

SECTION IV: WORKED PROBLEMS:

1. Based on the information in the chart below, $\hat{p}_1 = 0.621$, $\hat{p}_2 = 0.424$ and $\overline{p} = 0.544$; furthermore, when performing hypothesis testing for difference of proportion, the test statistic is $z = 2.96$ yielding a *p-value* of 0.00152. Do you believe that this is enough information to conclude that there is a bias against female students; that is, are male students accepted more often than female students; should females protest or sue on the bases of discrimination?

   CONTINEGNECY TABLES: In a university, the data regarding the acceptance of males and female of qualified students is collected and summarized as follows:

	Male	Female	
Accepted	90	39	129
Not Accepted	55	53	108
	145	92	237

2. Before speaking with a lawyer, you ask for a more detailed summary of the acceptance records for the qualified males and female students by college; the following expanded summary is given. Based on the information given below, would you proceed with legal action? Explain.

Engineering

	Male	Female	
Accepted	75	15	90
Not Accepted	25	5	30
	100	20	120

English

	Male	Female	
Accepted	15	24	39
Not Accepted	30	48	78
	45	72	117

3. Consider the batting average for two players: Player 1 and Player 2 where batting average is defined to be the ratio of the number of runs compared to number of outs. For both years Player 1 has the better batting averages, determine who has the better batting average overall. Explain.

	Year 1		Year 2	
	Player 1	**Player 2**	**Player 1**	**Player 2**
Runs	480	1050	750	405
Outs	6	15	15	9
	80	70	50	45
Better Batting Average	Player 1		Player 1	

INDEPENDENCE: Use $\chi^2 = \sum \frac{(O-E)^2}{E}$ with $\nu = (r-1)(c-1)$

4. Determine if in the clinical trials a success recovery is **independent** of the drug prescribed; that is, the null hypothesis is the events are independent.

O-Observer	Success	Failure	
Drug A	7	18	25
Drug B	12	33	45
Placebo	47	53	100
	66	104	170

	Success	Failure	
Drug A			25
Drug B	17.5		45
Placebo		61.2	100
	66	104	170

	Success	Failure	
Drug A	0.754		
Drug B		1.087	
Placebo	1.722		

5. Determine if a person's years of experience in given field are **independent** of the position they hold; that is, the null hypothesis is the events are independent.

***O*-Observer**	CEO	Pres.	V.P	
<5 years	8	18	51	77
5 to 10 year	12	19	59	90
>10 years	27	26	50	103
	47	63	160	270

***E*-Expected**	CEO	Pres.	V.P	
<5 years		17.97		77
5 to 10 year	15.67		53.33	90
>10 years		24.03		103
	47	63	160	270

χ^2	CEO	Pres.	V.P	
<5 years	2.179	0.000		
5 to 10 year		0.190	0.602	
>10 years	4.589		1.996	

GOODNESS-OF-FIT: Use $\chi^2 = \sum \frac{(O-E)^2}{E}$ with $\nu = m - 1$

6. The **M&M/Mars** Company claims that the proportions of M&Ms in bags of mini-packs are as follows in Table 1; that is, the null hypothesis is that the desired distribution "fits" the data. Test the **goodness-of-fit** of the distribution at the 0.05 level of significance.

Color	**Expected Percent**	**Expected Frequency** E	**Observed Frequency** O	**Observed Relative Frequency**	$\frac{(O-E)^2}{E}$
Red	13%	96.2	105	14.19%	0.80
Orange	20%	148	112	15.14%	
Yellow	14%		108	14.59%	0.19
Green	16%	118.4	159	21.49%	13.92
Blue	24%	177.6	155	20.95%	
Brown	13%		101	13.65%	0.24
TOTAL	100%		740	100%	26.79

Table 1: Desired proportions and actual proportions

7. At the 1% level of significance, determine if the following distribution follows the Poisson probability distribution given there are 100 pieces of information. Recall: $P(x) = \frac{\lambda^x e^{-\lambda}}{x!}$, where $\lambda = \mu = 5$.

Table 2: Summary Chart

X	Observed $O\%$	Expected $E\%$	Chi-square χ^2
0	2%		
1	6%		
2	4%		
3	13%		
4	11%		
5	14%		
6	22%		
7 or More	28%		
TOTAL	100%		

Perform the appropriate hypothesis testing, give a confidence interval for both variance and standard deviation and address the question of consistency.

8. The fan blades on commercial jet engines must be replaced when wear on these parts indicates too much variability to pass inspection. A large engine contains thousands of fan blades, and safety regulation requires that variability measurements on the population of all blades not exceed 0.18 mm^2. An engine inspector took a random sample of 61 fans blades from an engine with a sample variance 0.27 mm^2. Using a 0.01 level of significance, is the inspector justified in claiming that all the engine fan blades must be replaced?

Explain the apparent inconsistency in the significance statement and the confidence statement; does this change your decision? Explain.

9. The electronic connection in a commuter must be re-soldered when wear on these parts indicates too much variability in the current as it passes through the circuits; in a large commuter contains thousands of electronic connections, and safety regulation requires that variability measurements on the population of all electronic connections not exceed 0.12 ampere. An inspector took a random sample of 31 electronic connections with a sample variance 0.18 ampere. Using a 0.01 level of significance, is the inspector justified in claiming that all the electronic connection should be re-soldered?

KEY CHAPTER 10

SECTION I:

1. F
2. E
3. G
4. D
5. A
6. B
7. C

SECTION II:

1. chi-square, 1
2. chi-square, ν

SECTION III:

1. d
2. c
3. a

SECTION IV:

1. I do not recommend drawing a conclusion on summarized. Every time we crunch numbers, information is lost. This might have been on oversight, or intentionally done in an attempt to persuade; people can have hidden agendas.
2. With this additional information, it is clear that there is no bias. The Engineering department accepts exactly 75% of both males and females; and the English department accepts exactly one-third of both males and females. Within the individual colleges, an equal proportion of the qualified students are accepted. This is an example of Simpson's Paradox.
3. This is an example of Simpson's Paradox since when considered collectively, Player 1 has (480+750) = 1230 runs compared to (6+15) = 21 outs for a batting average of 59 whereas Player 2 has (1050+405) = 1455 runs compared to (15+9) = 24 outs for a batting average of 61. The relationship has reversed; this is not exactly paradoxical, but unexpected. However, it should be noted that there is very little difference in the overall batting averages and one could argue that they are not significantly different. For that matter, is there a significant difference between the yearly batting averages?

Overall

	Player 1	**Player 2**
Runs	1230	1455
Outs	21	24
	59	61
Better Batting Average		Player 2

4. **HT: Independence**

	Success	Failure	
Drug A	**9.7**	**15.3**	25
Drug B	17.5	**27.5**	45
Placebo	**38.8**	61.2	100
	66	104	170

	Success	Failure	
Drug A	0.754	**0.479**	
Drug B	**1.713**	1.087	
Placebo	1.722	**1.093**	
			6.848

Step 1: The null hypothesis is that success or failure of the treatment is independent of the drug prescribed.

Step 2: $\alpha = 0.01$

Step 3: $\chi^2 = 6.848$ (see chart) and with $\nu = (3-1)(2-1) = 2$, $\chi^2_{\nu,\alpha} = 9.21$

Step 4: Graphically illustrate the critical regions (acceptance and rejection regions) and the *p-value*.

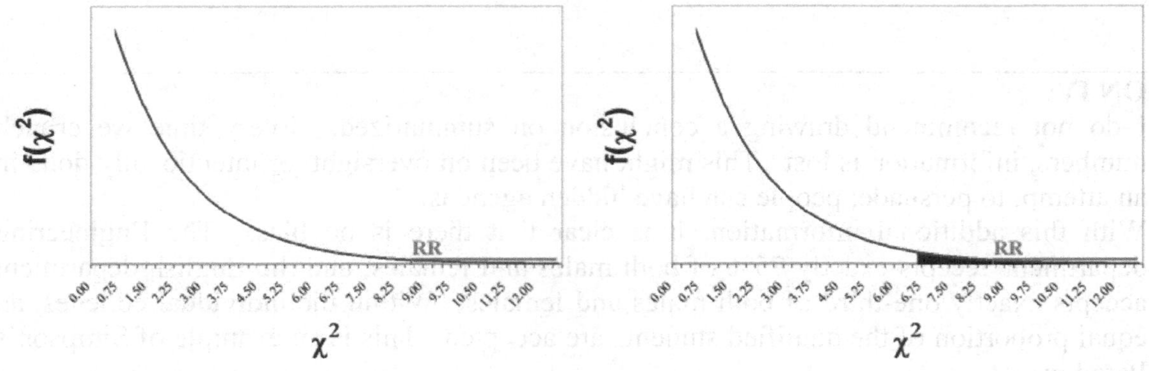

Step 5: *p-value* = 0.0326 using Excel and between 0.025 and 0.050 using chart.

Step 6: Fail to reject the null hypothesis.

Step 7: At the 0.01 level of significance, there is insufficient evidence to reject the null hypothesis; that is, the success of the treatment appears to be independent of the drug prescribed.

Step 8: Since there are at least a count of five in each cell (category), there is sufficient information to assume the chi-squared probability distribution with $\nu = (3-1)(2-1) = 2$ degrees of freedom.

5. **HT: Independence**

	CEO	Pres.	V.P	
<5 years	**13.40**	17.97	**45.63**	57
5 to 10 year	15.67	**21.00**	53.33	90
>10 years	**17.93**	24.03	**61.04**	179
	47	89	190	

	CEO	Pres.	V.P	
<5 years	2.179	0.000	**0.632**	
5 to 10 year	**0.858**	0.190	0.602	
>10 years	4.589	**0.161**	1.996	
				11.2066

Step 1: The null hypothesis is that the position a person holds is independent of the years of experience they have.

Step 2: $\alpha = 0.05$

Step 3: $\chi^2 = 11.21$ (see chart) and with $\nu = (3-1)(3-1) = 4$, $\chi^2_{\nu,\alpha} = 9.49$

Step 4: Graphically illustrate the critical regions (acceptance and rejection regions) and the *p-value*.

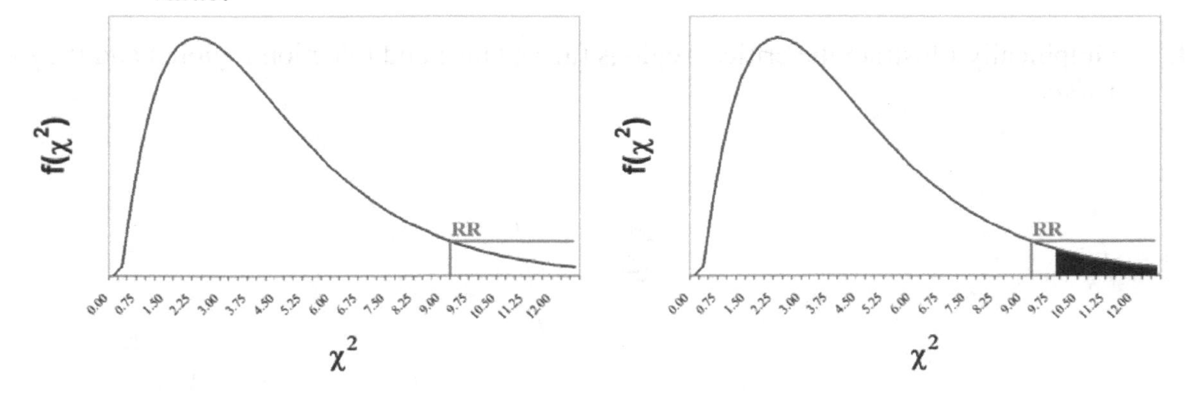

Step 5: *p-value* = 0.0326 using Excel and between 0.025 and 0.050 using chart.

Step 6: Reject the null hypothesis.

Step 7: At the 0.05 level of significance, there is sufficient evidence to reject the null hypothesis; that is, the position a person holds is dependent on the years of experience they have.

Step 8: Since there are at least a count of five in each cell (category), there is sufficient information to assume the chi-squared probability distribution with $\nu = (3-1)(3-1) = 4$ degrees of freedom.

6. **HT: Independence**

NOTE: The percent distribution for Plain M&Ms have recently been updated – these were the number according the website in 2006.

Color	Expected Percent	Expected Frequency E	Observed Frequency O	Observed Relative Frequency	$\frac{(O-E)^2}{E}$
Red	13%	96.2	105	14.19%	0.80
Orange	20%	148	112	15.14%	8.76
Yellow	14%	103.6	108	14.59%	0.19
Green	16%	118.4	159	21.49%	13.92
Blue	24%	177.6	155	20.95%	2.88
Brown	13%	96.2	101	13.65%	0.24
TOTAL	100%		740	100%	26.79

Step 1: The null hypothesis is that the distribution given by M&M Mars is a good-fit for the data.

Step 2: $\alpha = 0.05$

Step 3: $\chi^2 = 26.79$ (see chart) and with $\nu = 6-1=5$, $\chi^2_{\nu,\alpha} = 11.07$

Step 4: Graphically illustrate the critical regions (acceptance and rejection regions) and the *p-value*.

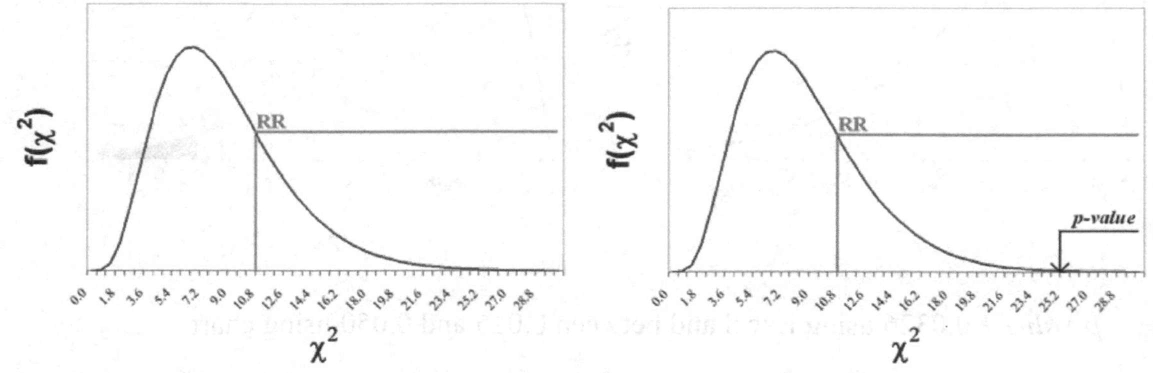

Step 5: *p-value* = 0. using Excel and between 0. and 0. using chart.

Step 6: Reject the null hypothesis.

Step 7: At the 0.05 level of significance, there is sufficient evidence to reject the null hypothesis; that is, the distribution given by M&M Mars is a not a good-fit for the data.

Step 8: Since there are at least a count of five in each cell (category), there is sufficient information to assume the chi-squared probability distribution with $\nu = 6-1=5$ degrees of freedom.

7. **GOODNESS-OF-FIT:** At the 1% level of significance, determine if the following distribution follows the Poisson probability distribution.

Table 2: Summary Chart

X	Observed $O\%$	Expected $E\%$	Chi-square χ^2
0	2%	$\frac{5^0 e^{-5}}{0!} \approx 0.7\%$	$\frac{(2-0.7)^2}{0.7} = 2.61$
1	6%	$\frac{5^1 e^{-5}}{1!} \approx 3.4\%$	$\frac{(6-3.4)^2}{3.4} = 2.05$
2	4%	$\frac{5^2 e^{-5}}{2!} \approx 8.4\%$	$\frac{(4-8,4)^2}{8.4} = 2.32$
3	13%	$\frac{5^3 e^{-5}}{3!} \approx 14.0\%$	$\frac{(13-14)^2}{14} = 0.08$
4	11%	$\frac{5^4 e^{-5}}{4!} \approx 17.5\%$	$\frac{(11-17.5)^2}{17.5} = 2.44$
5	14%	$\frac{5^5 e^{-5}}{5!} \approx 17.5\%$	$\frac{(14-17.5)^2}{7.5} = 0.72$
6	22%	$\frac{5^6 e^{-5}}{6!} \approx 14.6\%$	$\frac{(22-14.6)^2}{14.6} = 3.72$
7 or More	28%	$100\% - \begin{pmatrix} 0.7+3.4+8.4+14.0 \\ +17.5+17.5+14.6 \end{pmatrix}\% = 23.8\%$	$\frac{(28-23.8)^2}{23.8} = 0.75$
TOTAL	100%	100%	$\chi^2 = 14.69$

Step 1: The null hypothesis is that the defined probability distribution "fits" the Poisson probability distribution with a mean of five.

Step 2: $\alpha = 0.01$

Step 3: $\chi^2 = 14.69$ (see chart) and with $\nu = 7-1 = 6$, $\chi^2_{\nu,\alpha} = 16.81$

Chi-squared (given degree of freedom and level of significance)

AREA TO THE RIGHT

df	0.995	0.990	0.975	0.950	0.900	0.100	0.050	0.025	0.010	0.005
1	0.000	0.000	0.001	0.004	0.016	2.706	3.841	5.024	6.635	7.879
2	0.010	0.020	0.051	0.103	0.211	4.605	5.991	7.378	9.210	10.597
⋮	⋮	⋮	⋮	⋮	⋮	⋮	⋮	⋮	⋮	⋮
5	0.412	0.554	0.831	1.145	1.610	9.236	11.070	12.833	15.086	16.750
6	0.676	0.872	1.237	1.635	2.204	10.645	12.592	14.449	16.812	18.548
7	0.989	1.239	1.690	2.167	2.833	12.017	14.067	16.013	18.475	20.278

Step 4: Graphically illustrate the critical regions (acceptance and rejection regions) and the *p-value*.

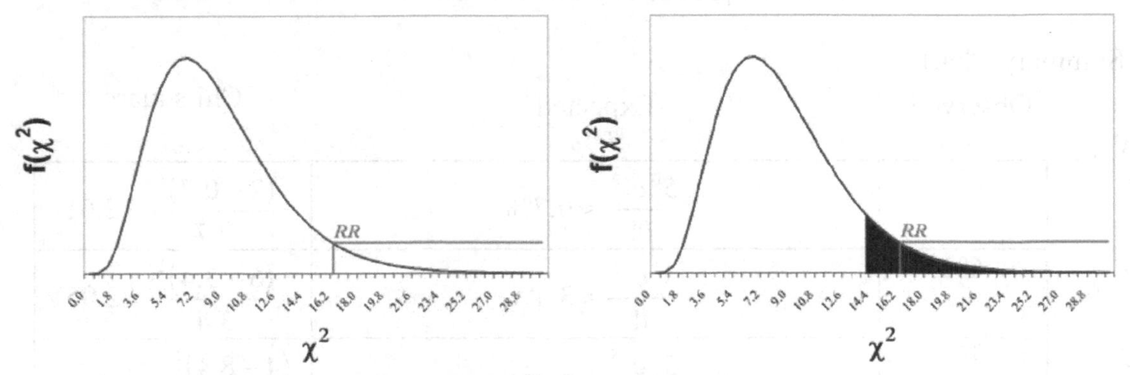

Step 5: *p-value* = 0.0228 using Excel and between 0.010 and 0.025 using chart.

Chi-squared (given degree of freedom and level of significance)

AREA TO THE RIGHT

df	0.995	0.990	0.975	0.950	0.900	0.100	0.050	0.025	0.010	0.005
1	0.000	0.000	0.001	0.004	0.016	2.706	3.841	5.024	6.635	7.879
2	0.010	0.020	0.051	0.103	0.211	4.605	5.991	7.378	9.210	10.597
⋮	⋮	⋮	⋮	⋮	⋮	⋮	⋮	⋮	⋮	⋮
5	0.412	0.554	0.831	1.145	1.610	9.236	11.070	12.833	15.086	16.750
6	0.676	0.872	1.237	1.635	2.204	10.645	12.592	14.449	16.812	18.548
7	0.989	1.239	1.690	2.167	2.833	12.017	14.067	16.013	18.475	20.278

Step 6: Fail to reject the null hypothesis.

Step 7: Here we do know knew if the assumptions are satisfied, if the total frequency is 1000, this will be significantly more information in that 1% of 1000 is 10, which satisfies the minimum count; however, if the sample size is 100, then 1% of 100 is 1, which is less than the minimum count of five recommended. However, we can not use expected frequencies versus observed frequencies; if the frequencies where given instead of the relative frequency our decision will be based on the assumption that there is enough information; hence, inferential statistics should be scrutinized.

Step 8: Since there are at least a count of five in each cell (category), there is sufficient information to assume the chi-squared probability distribution with $\nu = 6 - 1 = 5$ degrees of freedom.

8. **Variance**

CI:

Step 1: $\alpha = 0.01 \qquad \Rightarrow c = 1 - 0.01 = 0.99$

Step 2: As there is enough information to assume chi-squared distribution with $\nu = 61 - 1 = 60$ degrees of freedom.

Step 3: $\nu = 61 - 1 = 60$ $\chi_L^2 = 35.53$, $\chi_U^2 = 91.95$, $x_L = \dfrac{(61-1)\times 0.27}{91.95} = 0.179$,

$x_U = \dfrac{(61-1)\times 0.27}{35.53} = 0.456$; hence, the interval estimate $0.176 < \sigma^2 < 0.456$,

$0.420 < \sigma < 0.675$

Step 4: Interpret the meaning and usefulness of your result in the form of a confidence statement. I am 99% confident that the standard deviation of the fan blades is between 0.42 and 0.675.

Step 5: There is sufficient information to assume the chi-squared probability distribution with $\nu = 61 - 1 = 60$ degrees of freedom.

HT:

Step 1: The null hypothesis is that the variance is no more than 0.18.

Short hand: $H_0 : \sigma^2 = 0.18$

The alternative hypothesis is the variance is greater than the maximum allowed variance.

Short hand: $H_1 : \sigma^2 > 0.18$

Step 2: $\alpha = 0.01$

Step 3: $\chi^2 = \dfrac{(61-1)\times 0.27}{0.18} = 90$, $\nu = 61 - 1 = 60$, $\chi^2_{\nu,\alpha} = 88.38$

Step 4: Graphically illustrate the critical regions (acceptance and rejection regions) and the *p-value*.

Step 5: *p-value* = 0.0073 using Excel and the *p-value* < 0.01 according to the chart; there is significant information to reject the null hypothesis, that is,

Step 6: Reject the null hypothesis.

Step 7: At the 0.01 level of significant we reject that the variance of the fan is within specification – all fan blades need to be replaced.

Step 8: There is sufficient information to assume the chi-squared probability distribution with $\nu = 61 - 1 = 60$ degrees of freedom.

The apparent inconsistency is because the significance statement is a one-tail test and the confidence statement, based on the confidence interval, is two-tail. I would not let the affect my decision to replace the fan blades; this is a matter of public safety and not the time to split hairs. Furthermore, if you round to the second decimal place, then $0.18 < \sigma^2 < 0.46$ and this is consistent with the previous decision.

9. **Variance**

CI:

Step 1: $\alpha = 0.01 \qquad \Rightarrow c = 1 - 0.01 = 0.99$

Step 2: As there is enough information to assume chi-squared distribution with $\nu = 31 - 1 = 30$ degrees of freedom.

Step 3: $\nu = 31 - 1 = 30$, $\chi_L^2 = 13.79$, $\chi_U^2 = 53.67$, $x_L = \dfrac{(31-1)\times 0.18}{53.67} = 0.101$,

$x_U = \dfrac{(31-1)\times 0.18}{13.79} = 0.392$; hence, the interval estimate for the variance is $0.101 < \sigma^2 < 0.392$ and for the standard deviation, $0.317 < \sigma < 0.626$.

Step 4: I am 99% confident that the variance of the computer components is between 0.101 and 0.392.

Step 5: There is sufficient information to assume the chi-squared probability distribution with $\nu = 31 - 1 = 30$ degrees of freedom.

HT:

Step 1: The null hypothesis is that the variance is no more than 0.12.

Short hand: $H_0 : \sigma^2 = 0.12$

The alternative hypothesis is the variance is greater than the maximum allowed variance.

Short hand: $H_1 : \sigma^2 > 0.12$

Step 2: $\alpha = 0.01$

Step 3: $\chi^2 = \dfrac{(31-1)\times 0.18}{0.12} = 45$, $\nu = 31 - 1 = 30$, $\chi_{\nu,\alpha}^2 = 50.89$

Step 4: Graphically illustrate the critical regions (acceptance and rejection regions) and the *p-value*.

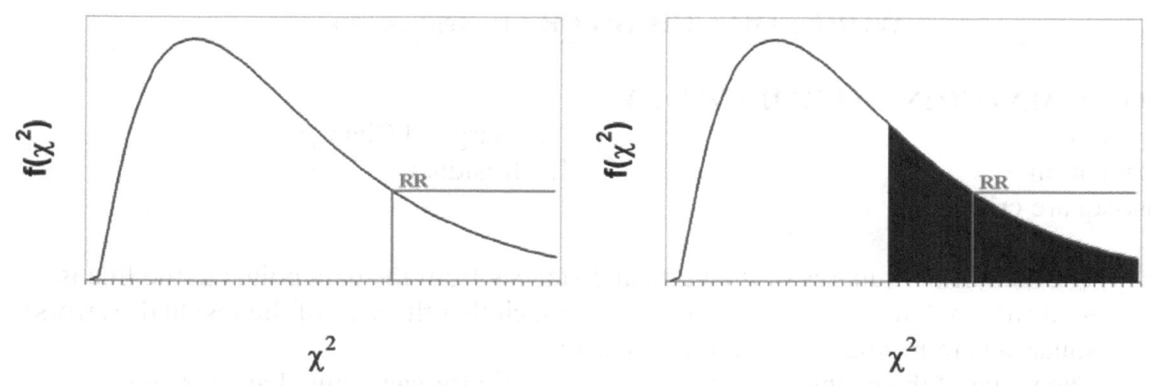

Step 5: *p-value* = 0.0386 using Excel and the *p-value* is between 0.025 and 0.050 according to the chart; there is significant information to reject the null hypothesis, that is,

Step 6: Fail to reject the null hypothesis.

Step 7: At the 0.01 level of significant we Fail to reject that the variance in the electronic components is outside specifications.

Step 8: There is sufficient information to assume the chi-squared probability distribution with $\nu = 31 - 1 = 30$ degrees of freedom.

SECTION I: MATCHING TERMINOLOGY

A. Extrapolation
B. Interpolation
C. Least-square criterion
D. Marginal Change
E. Residual

1. _____ The sum of the squares of the vertical distances from the data points to the line is made as small as possible; that is, the line such that the sum of the residuals (errors) squared is minimized – least-squares error.
2. _____ The value of the change in the response variable for each unit change in the explanatory variable.
3. _____ The **errors** or difference between the estimated response $\hat{y}_i$ and the actual measured response y_i collectively
4. _____ Estimating the $\boldsymbol{y}$ value for an $\boldsymbol{x}$ value between the observed $\boldsymbol{x}$ values in the data.
5. _____ Estimating the $\boldsymbol{y}$ value for an $\boldsymbol{x}$ value outside the domain generated by observed $\boldsymbol{x}$ value in the data

SECTION II: FILL IN THE BLANK

1. Correlation does not imply causation; hence, a high correlation may be due to causality or due to a ____________ ____________ from a ____________ ____________.
2. In terms of the number of data points n, what is the degrees of freedom for the statistic r which estimates the true correlation coefficient ρ in a **simple linear regression** and explain the loss of freedom. $\nu =$ ________________
3. In terms of the number of data points n, what is the degrees of freedom for the statistic r which estimates the true correlation coefficient ρ in a multiple linear regression with p explanatory variables. $\nu =$ ________________
4. Give the formula for computing the **standard error** of estimation S_e in simple linear regression and the minimum requirement for the number of data points n.

$$S_e = \_\_\_\_\_\_\_\_\_\_\_\_\_\_\_\_$$

SECTION III: MULTIPLE-CHOICE QUESTIONS

1. Suppose that the regression line for three data points (0,1), (2, 5), and (3, 9) is $\hat{y} = 0.71 + 2.57x$. Which one is an interpolation?
   (a) $\hat{y} = 0.71 + 2.57(-0.5)$ (b) $\hat{y} = 0.71 + 2.57(2.5)$
   (c) $\hat{y} = 0.71 + 2.57(3.8)$ (d) $\hat{y} = 0.71 + 2.57(4)$
2. Suppose that the regression line for three data points (0,1), (2, 5), and (3, 9) is $\hat{y} = 0.71 + 2.57x$. Which one is an extrapolation?
   (a) $\hat{y} = 0.71 + 2.57(-0.5)$ (b) $\hat{y} = 0.71 + 2.57(2.5)$
   (c) $\hat{y} = 0.71 + 2.57(3.8)$ (d) $\hat{y} = 0.71 + 2.57(4)$
3. Which correlation coefficient of the followings shows the weakest linear relationship between two variables?
   (a) $r = -1$ (b) $r = 0$ (c) $r = 0.5$ (d) $r = 1$

SECTION IV: WORKED PROBLEMS:

1. Simple Linear Regression

Dependent variable is: Y
No Selector
R squared = 12.9%   R squared (adjusted) = 11.1%
s = 152.6 with 50 - 2 = 48 degrees of freedom

Source	Sum of Squares	df	Mean Square	F-ratio
Regression	166218	1	166218	7.14
Residual	1.11748e6	48	23280.7	

Variable	Coefficient	s.e. of Coeff	t-ratio	prob
Constant	232.933	41.18	5.66	≤ 0.0001
X	8.41686	3.15	2.67	0.0103

Figure 1: Regression Analysis $y = \beta_0 + \beta_1 x + \varepsilon$

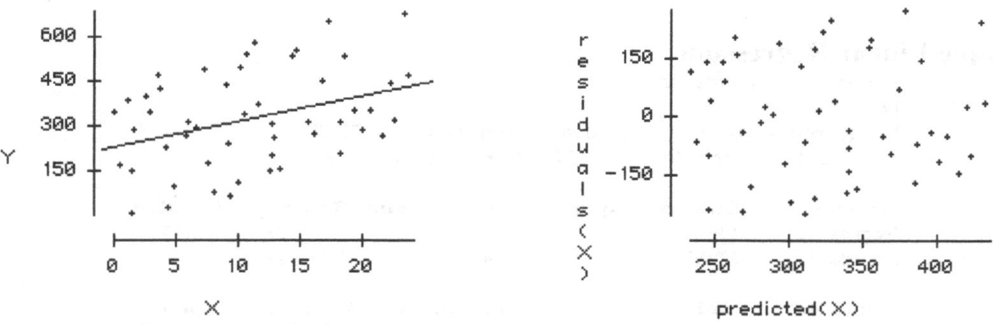

Figure 2: Scatter plot including regression line   **Figure 3**: Scatter plot of residuals

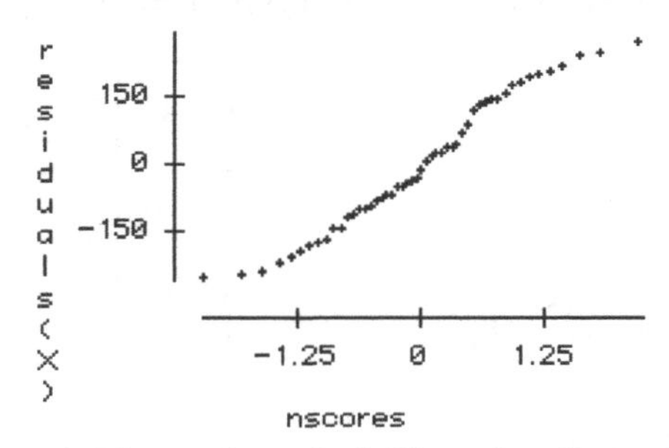

Figure 4: Normal probability plot for residuals

a. State the correlation coefficient r. Note: $R^2 = r^2$ and is given by Figure 1.
b. Does the correlation coefficient indicate a low (weak), moderate, high (strong) correlation?
c. Is this correlation positive or negative?
d. Write a complete sentence that describes the coefficient of determination in terms of the percent of the variation in the response variable, y, is explained by the least-squares regression model and the explanatory variables?
e. State the regression model $\hat{y} = b_0 + b_1 x$ defined in Figure 1; interpret the chart.
f. Give the 95% confidence interval for β_1 and interpret.
g. Use the above model to estimate the response given the $x = 10$.

h. Is the estimate (prediction), $\hat{y}$, given in previous question, an interpolation or an extrapolation?

i. Use the above model to estimate the response given the $x = 40$.

j. Is the estimate (prediction), $\hat{y}$, given in previous question, an interpolation or an extrapolation?

k. In testing the null hypothesis, $H_0 : \beta_1 = 0$, see Figure 1; state the *p*-value and at the 0.05 level of significance determine whether the explanatory variable x significantly contributes to the response variable y.

l. In the statistical model, $y = \beta_0 + \beta_1 x + \varepsilon$, where $\beta's$ are the weights that drive the estimates of the response variable and ε is the random error. State the assumption with respect to ε and how Figures 3 and 4 illustrate this point. Explain.

2. **Simple Linear Regression**

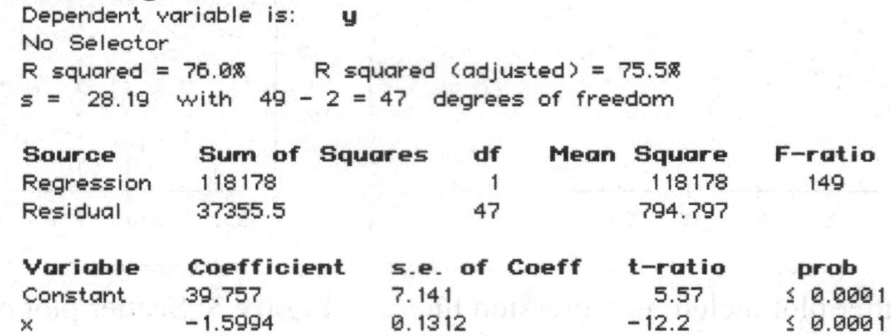

Dependent variable is: y
No Selector
R squared = 76.0%   R squared (adjusted) = 75.5%
s = 28.19 with 49 - 2 = 47 degrees of freedom

Source	Sum of Squares	df	Mean Square	F-ratio
Regression	118178	1	118178	149
Residual	37355.5	47	794.797	

Variable	Coefficient	s.e. of Coeff	t-ratio	prob
Constant	39.757	7.141	5.57	≤ 0.0001
x	-1.5994	0.1312	-12.2	≤ 0.0001

Figure 5: Regression Analysis $y = \beta_0 + \beta_1 x + \varepsilon$

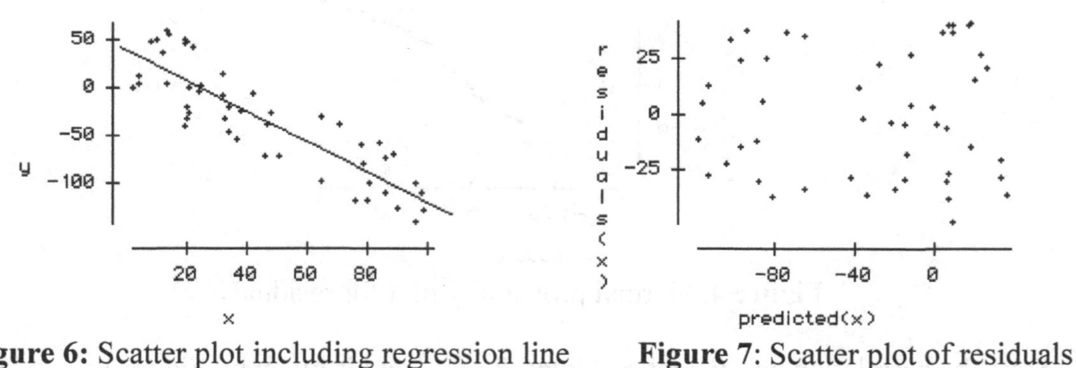

Figure 6: Scatter plot including regression line

Figure 7: Scatter plot of residuals

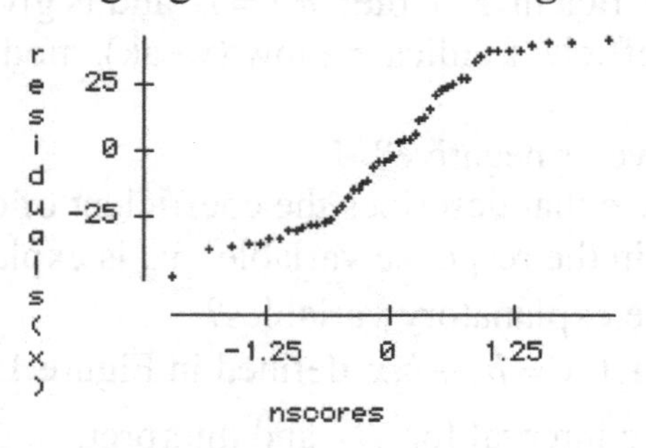

Figure 8: Normal probability plot for residuals

a. State the correlation coefficient r. Note: $R^2 = r^2$ and is given by Figure 5.
b. Does the correlation coefficient indicate a low (weak), moderate, high (strong) correlation?
c. Is this correlation positive or negative?
d. Write a complete sentence that describes the coefficient of determination in terms of the percent of the variation in the response variable, y, is explained by the least-squares regression model and the explanatory variables?
e. State the regression model $\hat{y} = b_0 + b_1 x$ defined in Figure 5; interpret the chart.
f. Use the above model to estimate the response given that $x = 125$.
g. Is the estimate (prediction), $\hat{y}$, given in previous question, an interpolation or an extrapolation?
h. Use the above model to estimate the response given that $x = 40$.
i. Is the estimate (prediction), $\hat{y}$, given in previous question, an interpolation or an extrapolation?
j. In testing the null hypothesis $H_0 : \beta_1 = 0$, see Figure 5; state the p-value and at the 0.05 level of significance determine whether the explanatory variable x significantly contributes to the response variable y.

3. Given the statistical model $\hat{y} = 9x + 47$, where the response variable is the expected exam score and x is the number of hours studied a week. Using a complete sentence, state and interpret the **marginal change**. In this simple linear regression, does the intercept have meaning and if so, **interpret** the y-intercept

5. Given $r = \dfrac{n\sum xy - (\sum x)(\sum y)}{\sqrt{n\sum x^2 - (\sum x)^2}\sqrt{n\sum y^2 - (\sum y)^2}}$, $b = \dfrac{n\sum xy - (\sum x)(\sum y)}{n\sum x^2 - (\sum x)^2}$, and $a = \bar{y} - b\bar{x}$; using the table below, find the **Correlation Coefficient** and the **Least-Squares Regression Line,** $\hat{y} = a + bx$.

Count	x	y	xy	x^2	y^2
1	1	4	4	1	16
2	1	1	1	1	1
3	2	7	14	4	49
4	3	9	27	9	81
5	5	5	25	25	25
	12	26	71	40	172

6. Given $r=\frac{n\sum xy-\left(\sum x\right)\left(\sum y\right)}{\sqrt{n\sum x^2-\left(\sum x\right)^2}\sqrt{n\sum y^2-\left(\sum y\right)^2}}$, $b=\frac{n\sum xy-\left(\sum x\right)\left(\sum y\right)}{n\sum x^2-\left(\sum x\right)^2}$, and $a=\bar{y}-b\bar{x}$; using the table below, find the **correlation coefficient** and the **least squares regression line,** $\hat{y}=a+bx$.

Count	x	y	xy	x^2	y^2
1	5	7	35	25	49
2	6	10	60	36	100
3	7	6	42	49	36
4	8	6	48	64	36
5	9	5	45	81	25
6	10	13	130	100	169
7	11	13	143	121	169
8	12	13	156	144	169
9	13	10	130	169	100
10	14	13	182	196	169
11	15	16	240	225	256
12	16	13	208	256	169
13	17	21	357	289	441
14	18	15	270	324	225
15	19	14	266	361	196
16	20	8	160	400	64
17	21	17	357	441	289
18	22	12	264	484	144
19	23	25	575	529	625
20	24	25	600	576	625
	290	262	4268	4870	4056

7. Given $r = \dfrac{n\sum xy - (\sum x)(\sum y)}{\sqrt{n\sum x^2 - (\sum x)^2}\sqrt{n\sum y^2 - (\sum y)^2}}$, $b = \dfrac{n\sum xy - (\sum x)(\sum y)}{n\sum x^2 - (\sum x)^2}$, and $a = \bar{y} - b\bar{x}$; using the table below, find the **correlation coefficient** and the **least squares regression line**, $\hat{y} = a + bx$.

Count	x	y	xy	x^2	y^2
1	0	5	0	0	25
2	0	6	0	0	36
3	0	1	0	0	1
4	0	1	0	0	1
5	1	4	4	1	16
6	1	6	6	1	36
7	1	0	0	1	0
8	1	-1	-1	1	1
9	1	4	4	1	16
10	1	1	1	1	1
11	2	2	4	4	4
12	2	-1	-2	4	1
13	2	-1	-2	4	1
14	2	3	6	4	9
15	2	7	14	4	49
16	3	-1	-3	9	1
17	3	4	12	9	16
18	4	4	16	16	16
19	4	-1	-4	16	1
20	4	1	4	16	1
	34	44	59	92	232

8. Given $r = \frac{1}{n-1}\sum\left(\frac{x_i - \bar{x}}{s_x}\right)\left(\frac{y_i - \bar{y}}{s_y}\right)$ and using the table below, find the **correlation coefficient**; discuss the **strength** and **direction**.

Count	x	y	$x-\bar{x}$	$y-\bar{y}$	$(x-\bar{x})^2$	$(y-\bar{y})^2$	z_{x_i}	z_{y_i}	$z_{x_i}z_{y_i}$
1	1	4.0	-3.8	-7.4	14.063	55.502	-1.457	-1.444	2.103
2	1.5	5.4	-3.3	-6.0	10.563	36.271	-1.263	-1.167	1.474
3	2.5	6.8	-2.3	-4.7	5.063	21.801	-0.874	-0.905	0.791
4	3.5	8.9	-1.3	-2.6	1.563	6.701	-0.486	-0.502	0.244
5	4.5	11.4	-0.3	-0.1	0.063	0.004	-0.097	-0.012	0.001
6	5.5	13.8	0.8	2.3	0.563	5.246	0.291	0.444	0.129
7	6.5	12.1	1.8	0.6	3.063	0.386	0.680	0.120	0.081
8	6.5	15.6	1.8	4.2	3.063	17.233	0.680	0.805	0.546
9	7.5	17.3	2.8	5.8	7.563	33.733	1.068	1.126	1.202
10	8.5	19.4	3.8	7.9	14.063	62.758	1.457	1.535	2.236
SUMS	48	114.68			59.625	239.635			8.811
MEAN	4.8	11.5			6.625	26.6			
STD DEV	2.6	5.16			2.574	5.160			

9. **Multiple Linear Regression**

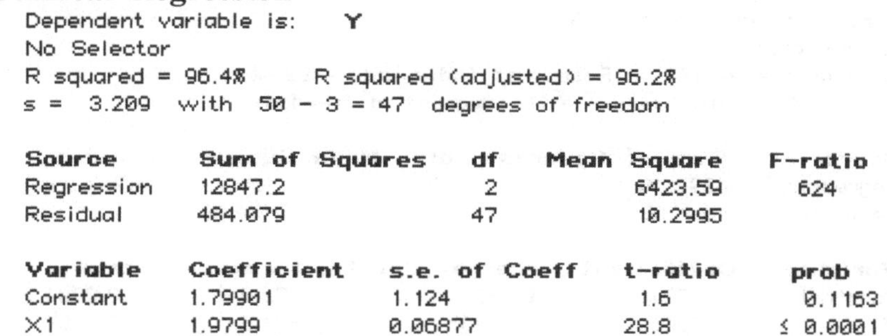

Dependent variable is: Y
No Selector
R squared = 96.4%   R squared (adjusted) = 96.2%
s = 3.209 with 50 - 3 = 47 degrees of freedom

Source	Sum of Squares	df	Mean Square	F-ratio
Regression	12847.2	2	6423.59	624
Residual	484.079	47	10.2995	

Variable	Coefficient	s.e. of Coeff	t-ratio	prob
Constant	1.79901	1.124	1.6	0.1163
X1	1.9799	0.06877	28.8	≤ 0.0001
X2	-369.458e-6	0.003305	-0.112	0.9115

Figure 9: Regression Analysis $y = \beta_0 + \beta_1 x_1 + \beta_2 x_2 + \varepsilon$

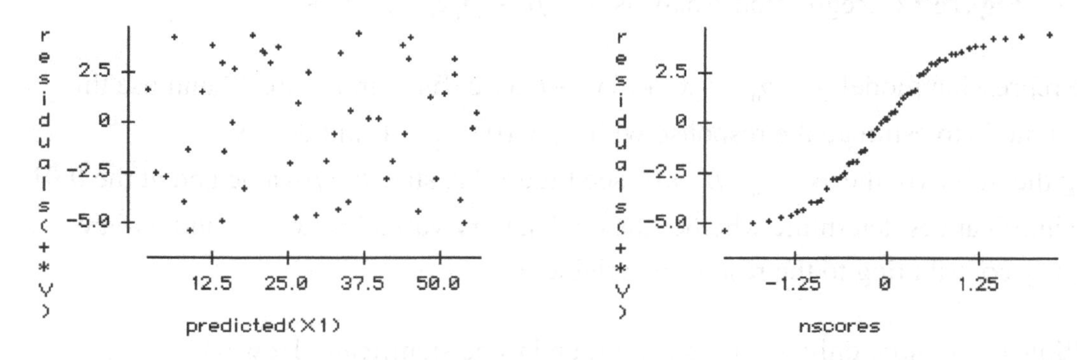

Figure 10: Scatter plot of residuals **Figure 11**: Normal probability plot for residuals

a. Write a complete sentence which describes the coefficient of determination in terms of the percent of the variation in the response variable, y, is explained by the least-squares regression model and the two explanatory variables x_1 and x_2?

b. State the regression model $\hat{y} = b_0 + b_1 x_1 + b_2 x_2$ defined in Figure 9.

c. In testing the null hypothesis, $H_0 : \beta_i = 0$, see Figure 9, state the *p*-value and at the 0.01 level of significances determine whether the explanatory variables, x_1 and x_2, are significantly contributing to the response variable y.

d. In the statistical model, $y = \beta_0 + \beta_1 x_1 + \beta_2 x_2 + \varepsilon$, where $\beta's$ are the weights that drive the estimates of the response variable and ε is the random error. Determine if the assumption regarding ε are satisfied and how Figures 10 and 11 illustrate this point. Explain.

10. **Multiple Linear Regression**

Dependent variable is: Y
No Selector
R squared = 99.1% R squared (adjusted) = 99.0%
s = 1.244 with 30 - 4 = 26 degrees of freedom

Source	Sum of Squares	df	Mean Square	F-ratio
Regression	4397.16	3	1465.72	947
Residual	40.2565	26	1.54833	

Variable	Coefficient	s.e. of Coeff	t-ratio	prob
Constant	51.6721	0.7087	72.9	≤ 0.0001
X1	-1.28464	0.05433	-23.6	≤ 0.0001
X2	-0.0243816	0.02448	-0.996	0.3284
X3	0.192724	0.00469	41.1	≤ 0.0001

Figure 12: Regression Analysis $y = \beta_0 + \beta_1 x_1 + \beta_2 x_2 + \varepsilon$

e. State the regression model $\hat{y} = b_0 + b_1 x_1 + b_2 x_2 + b_3 x_3$ defined in Figure 12 and use this developed mode to estimate the response with $x_1 = 10$, $x_2 = 4$ and $x_3 = 9$.

f. In testing the null hypothesis, $H_0 : \beta_i = 0$, see Figure 12, state the *p*-value and at the 0.01 level of significances determine whether the explanatory variables, x_1, x_2 and x_3, are significantly contributing to the response variable y.

11. In a multiple regression, only x_1 and x_2 are found to be significant. However, insignificance can be an indication confounding variables. Given the correlation matrix below, does there appear to be confounding variables.

Matrix	x_2	x_3	y
x_1	0.17	-0.70	-0.6
x_2		-0.10	0.89
x_3			0.91

12. In a multiple regression, only x_1 and x_3 are found to be significant. However, insignificance can be an indication confounding variables. Given the correlation matrix below, does there appear to be confounding variables.

Matrix	x_2	x_3	y
x_1	0.17	-0.2	-0.6
x_2		0.01	-0.1
x_3			0.89

13. In the previous exercise, rank the variables by their individual contribution; that is, according to coefficient of determination.

KEY CHAPTER 11

SECTION I:

1. C
2. D
3. E
4. B
5. A

SECTION II:

1. common response, lurking variable
2. $n - 2$
3. $n - (p + 1)$
4. $S_e = \sqrt{\frac{\Sigma(\hat{y}_i - y_i)^2}{n-2}}$

SECTION III:

1. b
2. d
3. b

SECTION IV:

1. **Simple Linear Regression**
   a. $r = \sqrt{0.129} = 0.359$
   b. Weak to moderate **OR** weak
   c. Positive
   d. An estimated 12.9% of the variation in the response variable, y, is explained by the least-squares regression model and the explanatory variables.
   e. $\hat{y} = 232.933 + 8.41686x$
   f. Under the assumption that the data is normally distribution and a standard normal distribution suffices, $8.41686 \pm 1.96(3.15)$ ➔ (2.24286, 14.59086). OR, still under the assumption that the data is normally distributed, the empirical rule states that 95% of the data lies within 2 deviations of the mean; that is, $8.41686 \pm 2(3.15)$ ➔ (2.11686, 14.71686). However, while $n = 50 > 30$, σ is unknown, hence with 48 degree of freedom (on chart use 45 degrees of freedom, we have $t_c = 2.014$ and therefore the CI is

      $8.41686 \pm 2.014(3.15)$ ➔ **(2.07276, 14.76096).**

      Regardless, since zero is not contained in either the interval, we can infer that this coefficient is not zero and therefore the explanatory variable is a contributing variable; that is, a statistically significant variable.
   g. $\hat{y} = 232.933 + 8.41686(10) = 317.1016$
   h. Since, by looking at the scatter plot, 10 is in the domain of the data the estimation in the previous question is an interpolation.
   i. $\hat{y} = 232.933 + 8.41686(40) = 569.6074$
   j. Since, by looking at the scatter plot, 40 is not in the domain of the data the estimation in the previous question is an extrapolation.

k. The *p-value* $= 0.0103 < 0.05$ and therefore we reject the null hypothesis; that is, $\beta_1 \neq 0$ and hence the explanatory variable is a significantly contributing explanatory variable.
l. Figure 3 shows that the residual are random; that is, there is no obvious pattern in the residual plot. Moreover, Figure 4, the normal probability plot indicates that normally distributed residuals and a center that is approximately at zero. For a good model, the assumptions are that the residuals are random with standard normal distribution; that is, at least, the random error on average is zero, $E(\varepsilon) = 0$.

2. **Simple Linear Regression**
a. $r = -\sqrt{0.760} = -0.872$
b. Moderate to strong **OR** moderate
c. Negative
d. An estimated 76.0% of the variation in the response variable, y, is explained by the least-squares regression model and the explanatory variables.
e. $\hat{y} = 39.757 - 1.5994x$
f. $\hat{y} = 39.757 - 1.5994(125) = -160.168$
g. Since, by looking at the scatter plot, 125 is not in the domain of the data the estimation in the previous question is an extrapolation.
h. $\hat{y} = 39.757 - 1.5994(40) = -24.219$
i. Since, by looking at the scatter plot, 40 is in the domain of the data the estimation in the previous question is an interpolation.
j. The *p-value* $< 0.001 < 0.05$ and therefore we reject the null hypothesis; that is, $\beta_1 \neq 0$ and hence the explanatory variable is a significantly contributing explanatory variable.

3. The marginal change is m=9, that is, for each additional hour studied per week, one can expect an additional 9 points on the exam score. (1pt) The intercept does have meaning in that if one does not study (x=0) then they can expect an exam score of 47 points.

4. $$r = \frac{5\times 71 - 12\times 26}{\sqrt{5\times 40 - 12^2}\sqrt{5\times 172 - 26^2}} = 0.4236$$
$$b = \frac{5\times 71 - 12\times 26}{5\times 40 - 12^2} = 0.77,\ a = \frac{26}{5} - 0.77\times\frac{12}{5} = 3.36,\ \hat{y} = 3.36 + 0.77x$$

5. $$r = \frac{20\times 4268 - 290\times 262}{\sqrt{20\times 4870 - 290^2}\sqrt{20\times 4056 - 262^2}} = 0.7282,\ b = \frac{20\times 4268 - 290\times 262}{20\times 4870 - 290^2} = 0.7053$$
$$,\ a = \frac{262}{20} - 0.7053\times\frac{290}{20} = 2.874,\ \hat{y} = 2.874 + 0.7053x$$

6. $$r = \frac{20\times 59 - 34\times 44}{\sqrt{20\times 92 - 34^2}\sqrt{20\times 232 - 44^2}} = -0.2324,\ b = \frac{20\times 59 - 34\times 44}{20\times 92 - 34^2} = -0.46199,$$
$$a = \frac{44}{20} - (-0.46199)\times\frac{34}{20} = 2.98538,\ \hat{y} = 2.98538 - 0.46199x$$

7. The necessary interpretation is that $z_x = \frac{x-\bar{x}}{s_x}$ and $z_y = \frac{y-\bar{y}}{s_y}$; hence

$$r = \frac{1}{n-1}\sum\left(\frac{x-\bar{x}}{s_x}\right)\left(\frac{y-\bar{y}}{s_y}\right) = \frac{1}{n-1}\sum z_x z_y \text{ and therefore } r = \frac{1}{10-1}\times 8.811 = 0.979,$$

Strong positively correlation

8. **Multiple Linear Regression**

a. An estimated 96.4% of the variation in the response variable, y, is explained by the least-squares regression model and the two explanatory variables x_1 and x_2.

b. $\hat{y} = 1.79901 + 1.9799x_1 - 3.69458\times 10^{-4}x_2$

c. For the first explanatory variable, x_1, the *p-value* $< 0.001 < 0.01$ and therefore we reject the null hypothesis; that is, $\beta_1 \neq 0$ and hence this explanatory variable is a significantly contributing explanatory variable. However, for the second explanatory variable, x_2, the *p-value* =0.9115 >> 0.01 and therefore we fail to reject the null hypothesis; that is, $\beta_1 \approx 0$ and hence this explanatory variable is not a significantly contributing explanatory variable and therefore by the law of parsimony can be removed from the model

d. Not all of the assumptions are stratified; while the residuals do appear to be random in Figure 10, the normality of the residuals fails, illustrated in Figure 11 by the fact that the normal plot is not a straight line. Therefore, while our model explains a great deal of the variance, more information could improve this model.

9. **Multiple Linear Regression**

a. $\hat{y} = 51.67 - 1.28x_1 - 0.02x_2 + 0.19x_3$, $\hat{y} = 40.5$

b. *p_1-value* $\leq$0.0001 Significant, *p_2-value*=0.3284 Insignificant
p_3-value $\leq$0.0001 Significant

10. Yes, as x_3 is highly correlated to the response y and less so with respect to the other explanatory variables, and yet is not included in the multiple regression model, it is highly likely that x_3 is confounded with x_1.

11. No, there is no significant correlation between x_2 and the other three variables; namely, x_1, x_2 and y.

12. The most explanatory variable is x_3, explaining 79% of the variation in the subject response, the second contributing variable is x_1 which only explains 40% of the variation in the subject response; however the third variable, x_2, (which does not significantly contribute to the subject response) only explains 1% of the variation in the subject response and is not strongly correlated to any other variable.

Using Technology

Using Technology in Statistics

Introducation to EXCEL 2007

At first glance, this spreadsheet might be overwhelming; however, with a little working knowledge; this software will be extremely useful in organizing and analyzing data. If you open Excel to be in the full window, you will see the window below.

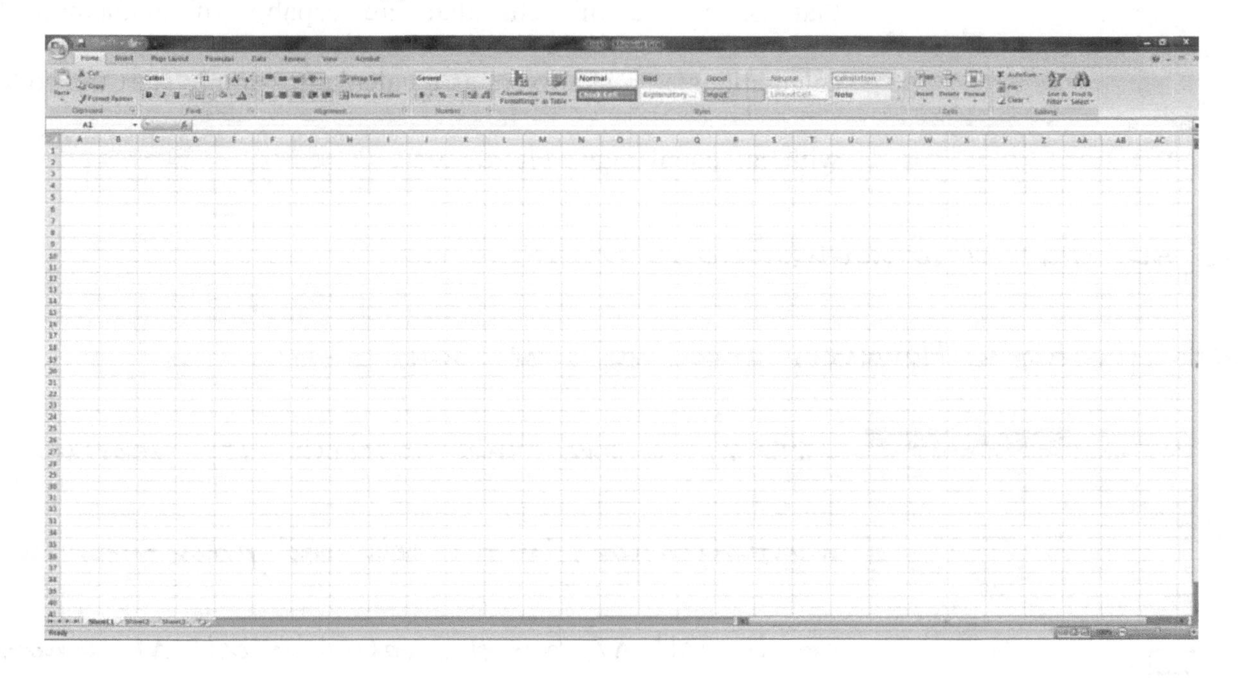

You can use each cell to type text in. *Text means words or strings of characters that is not a statement to be computed.* ***NOTE***: *It is like battleship that is the word* Bob *is typed in cell* **A1**.

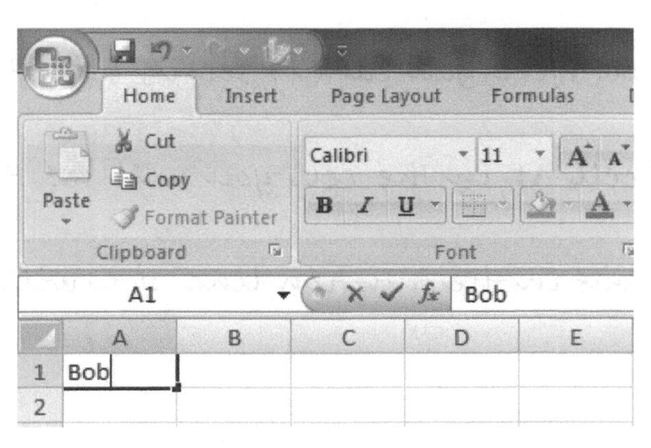

NOTE: The word typed, Bob, *appears both in the cell* **A1** *as well as next to the function key, fx, which can be used to view all functions preprogrammed in Excel.*

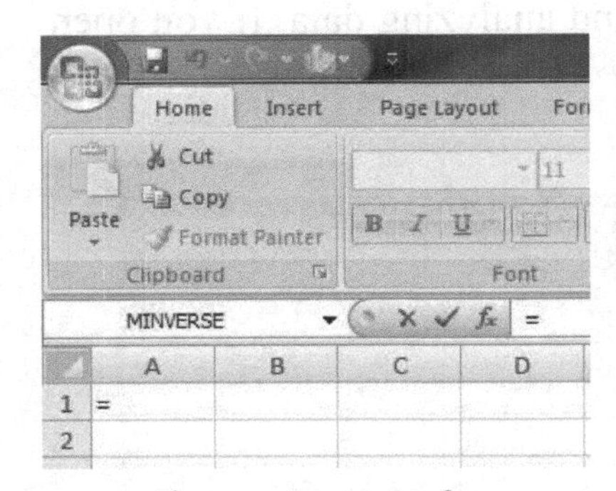

However, a more useful application of Excel is as spreadsheet, that is, a grid of cells that are capable of mathematical calculations. To use Excel as a calculator, simply start the code with an equal sign. *Here we see the start of a mathematical equation in both locations. However, once we code, say*

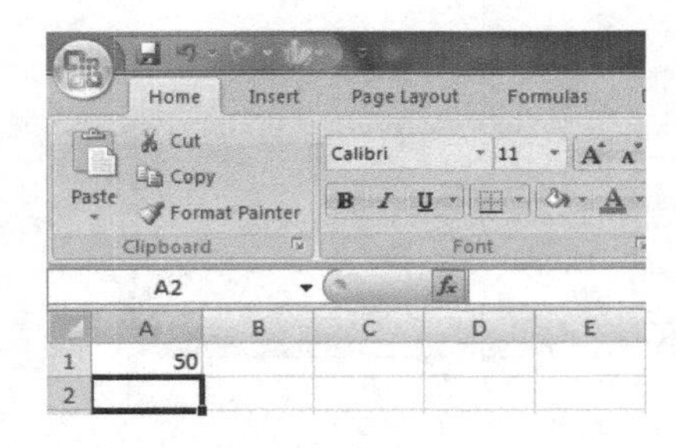

$= 25 * 2$, *where the asterisk (**) *represents multiplication, in the cell and press enter, we are in cell* **A2**, *but the value in cell* **A1** *is now* **50**. *Here you cannot see it, but if you return to cell* **A1**, *in the cell you will see the evaluation, but in the function line, you will see the code.*

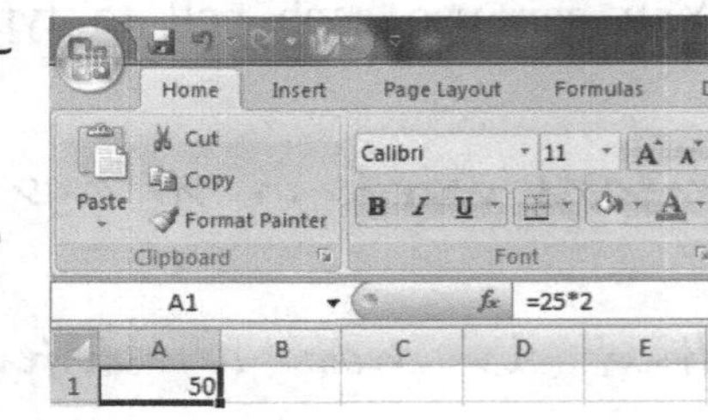

A3	=A1*A2			
	A	B	C	D	E
1	50				
2	17				
3	850				
4					

You can also play with previously computed numbers; for example, if you have one value in cell **A1** and other value in cell **A2**, then in cell **A3**, we can create an equation such as $= \boldsymbol{A1} * \boldsymbol{A2}$.

What is nice about Excel is, once this cell is coded, if we change either cell **A1** or **A2**, the information in cell **A3** is automatically recalculated.

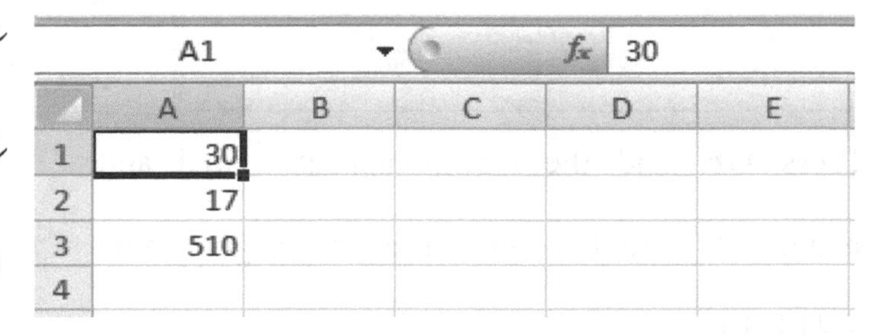

Here, when we changed the value in the cell **A1** to 30 and press Enter, the value in **A3** changes to **510**.

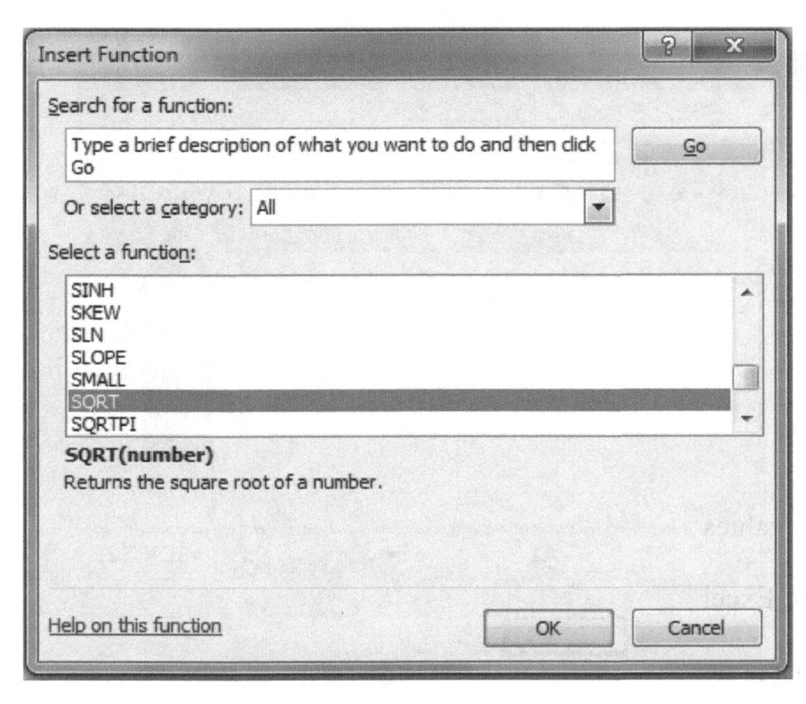

To further illustrate the power of Excel, we can use the function key, *fx*, which will bring up the following wizard. You can type a brief description of what you are looking for, view all categories (as shown) or select a specific category.

First, **select a function**, then the

wizard will illustrate how to use the function; for example here, the **SQRT(<value>)** function, where the <value> is a **number**, returns the square root of a number; namely, the square root of the given <value>.

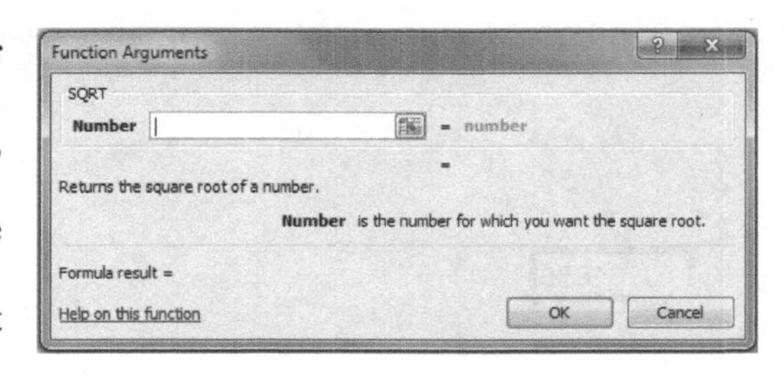

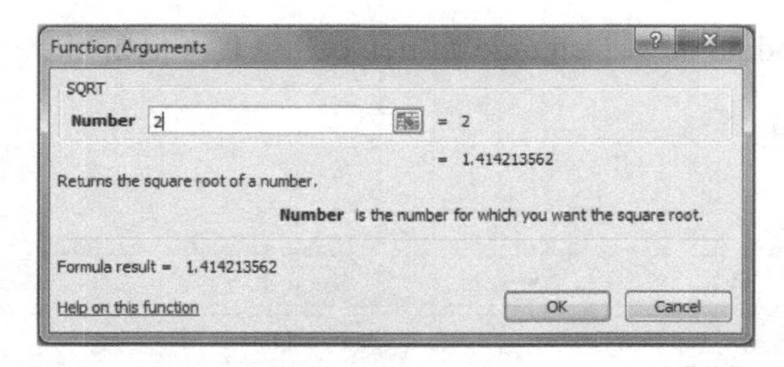

Once you select this function by clicking **OK**, the wizard will ask for the **number** for which you want the square root. Once you type in a number, Excel will display the information in the wizard. Press **OK** and the results appear coded and evaluated. Here, the square root of 2 is give to be 1.414214.

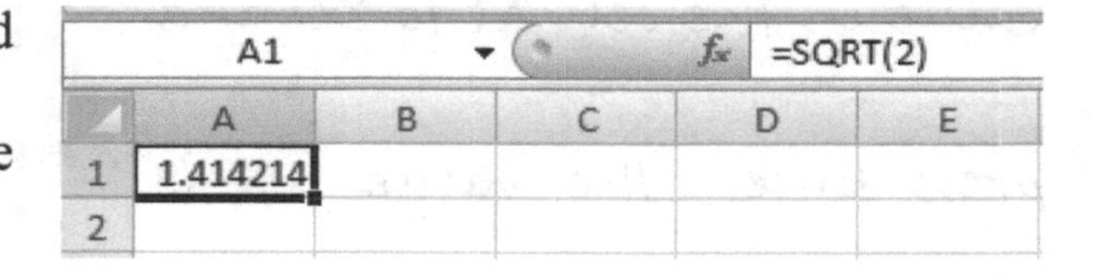

By using the **Number** option, we can increase or decrease the number of visible digits.

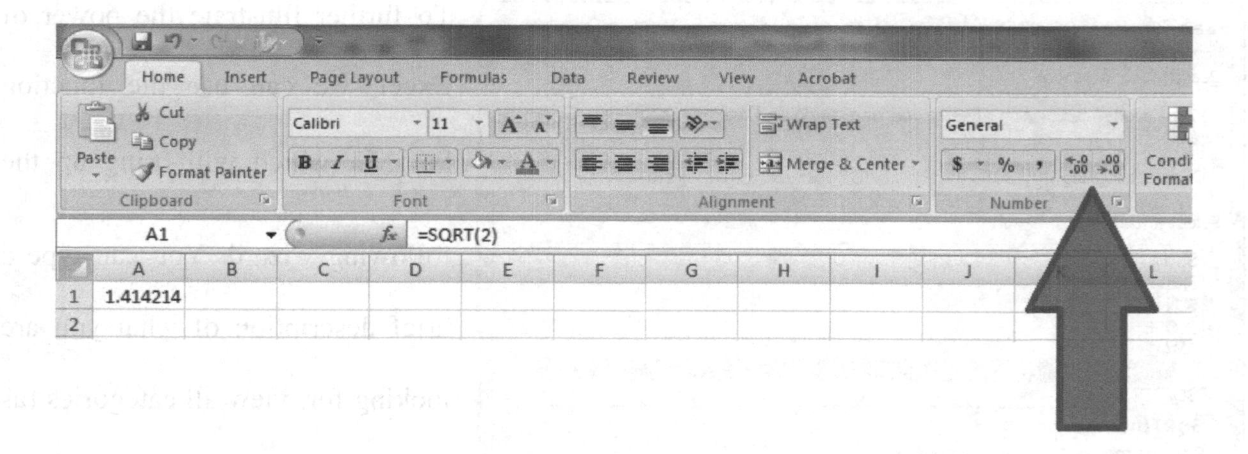

However, Excel keeps these values accurate to twelve decimals. That is, Excel will give the square root of two accurate

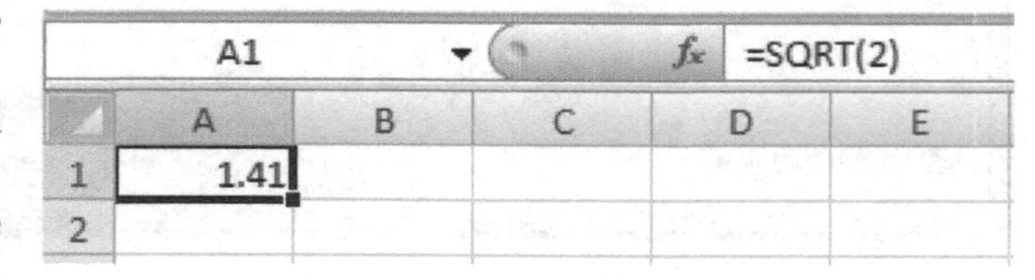

to **1.4142135623731**. To have Excel round this to exactly two decimals, we can use the code **=ROUND(**<value>,<number>**)**, where the <value> is rounded to the given <number> of decimals places.

A1	f_x	=ROUND(SQRT(2),2)		
	A	B	C	D	E
1	1.410000				
2					

EXCEL — BASIC COMMANDS FOR ARITHMETIC

- Note: to have Excel read the command as mathematical; you must start with an equal sign: **=<command code>**
  - ADDITION + (plus sign)
  - DIVISION / (backslash)
  - EXPONENTIAL e^x **=EXP(**<value *x*>**)**
  - MULTIPLICATION * (asterisk)
  - POWER ^ (carrot key)
  - ROUND **=ROUND(**<value>,<number>**),** where the <value> is rounded to the given <number> of decimals
  - SUBTRACTION - (minus sign)

For more advanced analysis under **Data**, there is an **Add-on** that performs **Data Analysis**. This will be useful in descriptive and inferential statistics. If this option is not plugged-in, go to the last option in the upper menu where one of the options is **More Commands**...

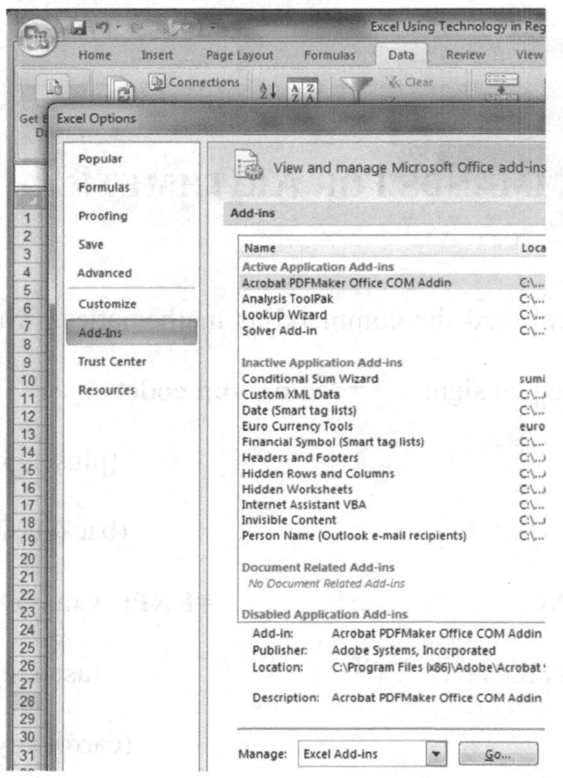

Customize the Quick Access Toolbar, Under **Add-ins**, **Solver Add-in** and then **Go...** which will take you to the **Add-ins**, check **Analysis ToolPak** and **OK**.

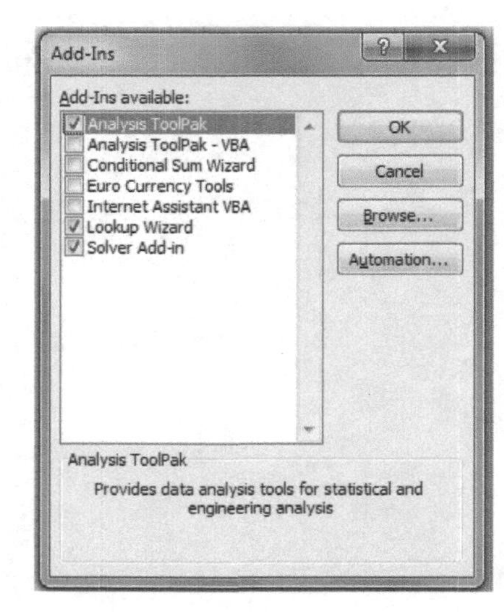

Then you will see **Data Analysis** in the **Analysis** submenu under the main menu **Data**.

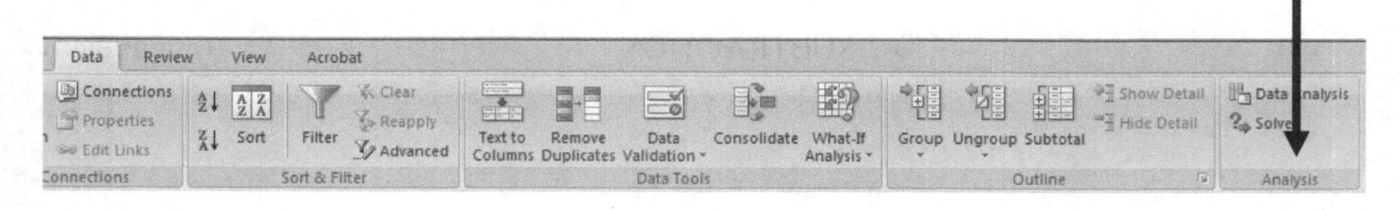

For more advanced analysis of grammar, go to the last option in the upper menu where one of the options is **More Commands**...

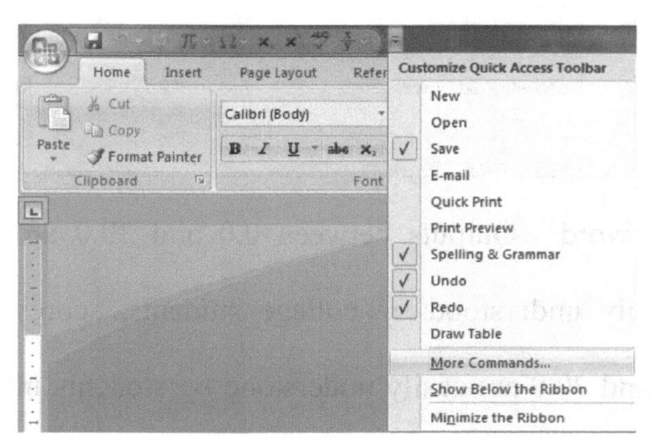

This menu will open to **Customize**; however, we want to edit the **Proofing**. Under **When correcting spelling and grammar in Word**, select all including **Show readability statistics**, then select **OK**.

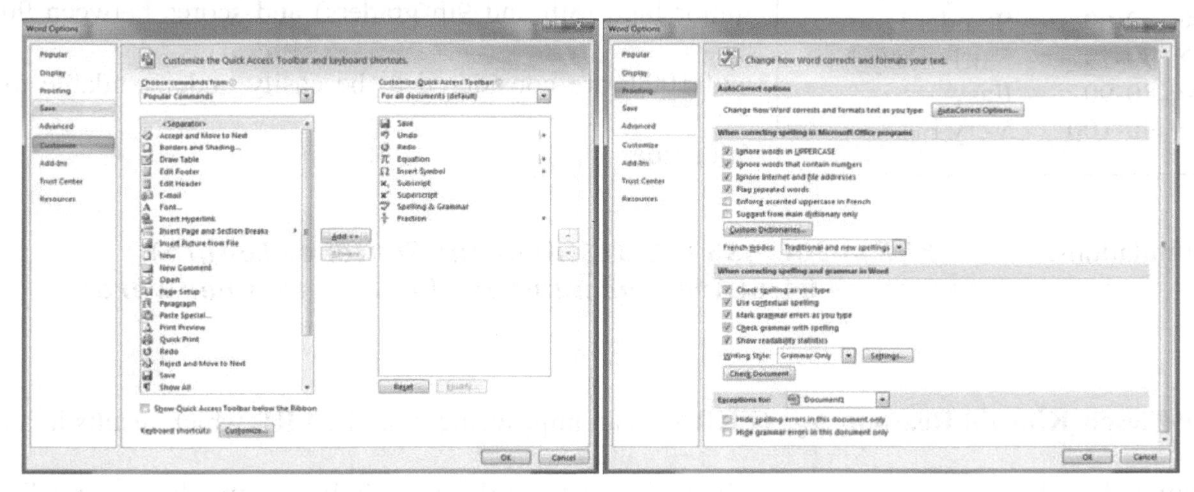

This option allows students to grade themselves using statistical measures of their write-up, this summary includes basic summary statistics: **Counts** (**Words**, **Characters**, **Paragraphs** and **Sentences**), **Averages** (**Sentences per Paragraph**, **Words per Sentence** and **Characters per Word**) and **Readability** (**Passive Sentences**, **Flesch Reading Ease** and **Flesch-Kincaid Grade Level**). The first test set of statistics will be covered in detail throughout the text (mainly in chapter 3), however, the readability statistics are not as common. A passive sentence has three elements, (1) a form of the word be (is, are, was, were, been or be), (2) a verb and (3) past form. Passive sentences are not bad when used correctly. The **Flesch Reading Ease** (**FRE**) is a mathematical manipulation of the average sentence length and the average number characters per word. Outputs between 0.0 and 30.0 are considered easily understood by college students, scores between 60.0 and 70.0 are easily understood by students in junior high (8th and 9th graders) and scores between 90.0 and 100.0 are considered to be easily understandable to a 5th grader.

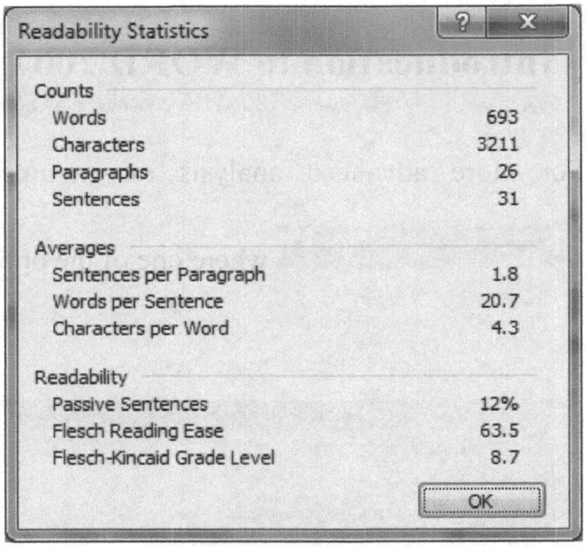

Readability Statistics

Counts	
Words	693
Characters	3211
Paragraphs	26
Sentences	31
Averages	
Sentences per Paragraph	1.8
Words per Sentence	20.7
Characters per Word	4.3
Readability	
Passive Sentences	12%
Flesch Reading Ease	63.5
Flesch-Kincaid Grade Level	8.7

OK

RULE OF THUMB: FRE

- ⇨ 0-29 Very Confusing
- ⇨ 30-49 Difficult
- ⇨ 50-59 Fairly Difficult
- ⇨ 60-69 Standard
- ⇨ 70-79 Fairly Easy
- ⇨ 80-90 Easy
- ⇨ 90-100 Very Easy

Formulations:

$$FRE = 206.835 - 1.015(Average\ Sentence\ Length) \\ -84.6(Average\ number\ of\ characters\ per\ word)$$

The **Flesch-Kincaid Reading Age** (**FKRA**) is an improvement on the **FRE** which results in an estimated grade-level; that is, the 8.7 shown in the example above indicates an 8th grade reading level.

Formulations:

$$FKRA = 0.39(Average\ Sentence\ Length) \\ + 11.8(Average\ number\ of\ characters\ per\ word) - 15.59$$

Data Mining using the WWW

There are countless numbers of data sets available through the World Wide Web and the Internet. If you know the topics you are interested in finding data for, then using your favorite search engine (Google, Bing, Yahoo, etc.) you can begin your search. For example, if we wanted to research hurricanes we could search the keywords "data" and "hurricane"; it is strongly recommended that you add the word "data" or "statistics" to ensure that you start with the raw information and not with many articles already written about the subject matter.

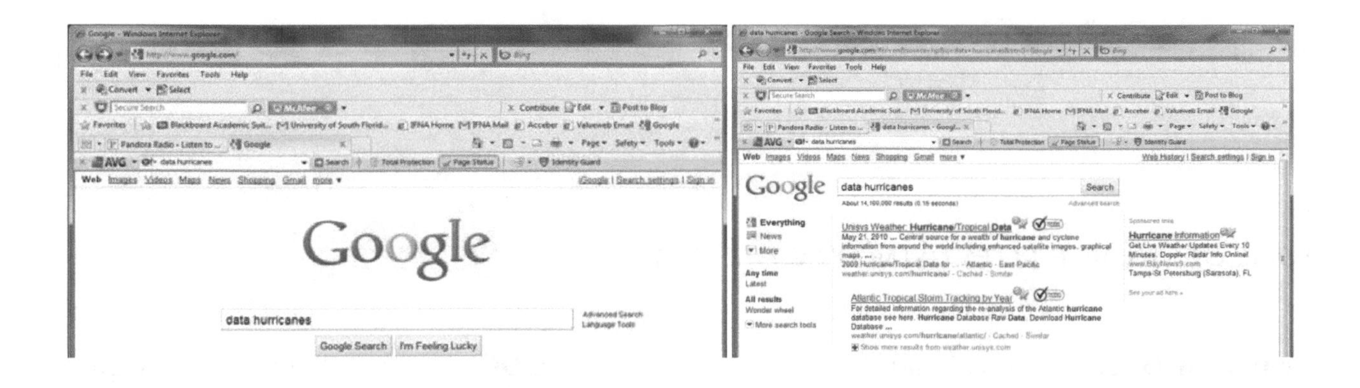

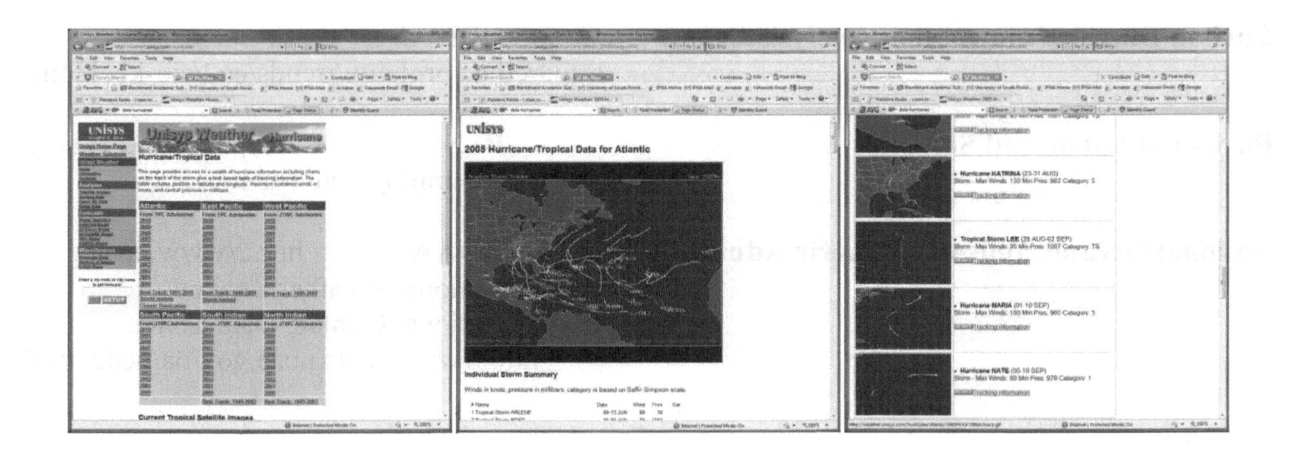

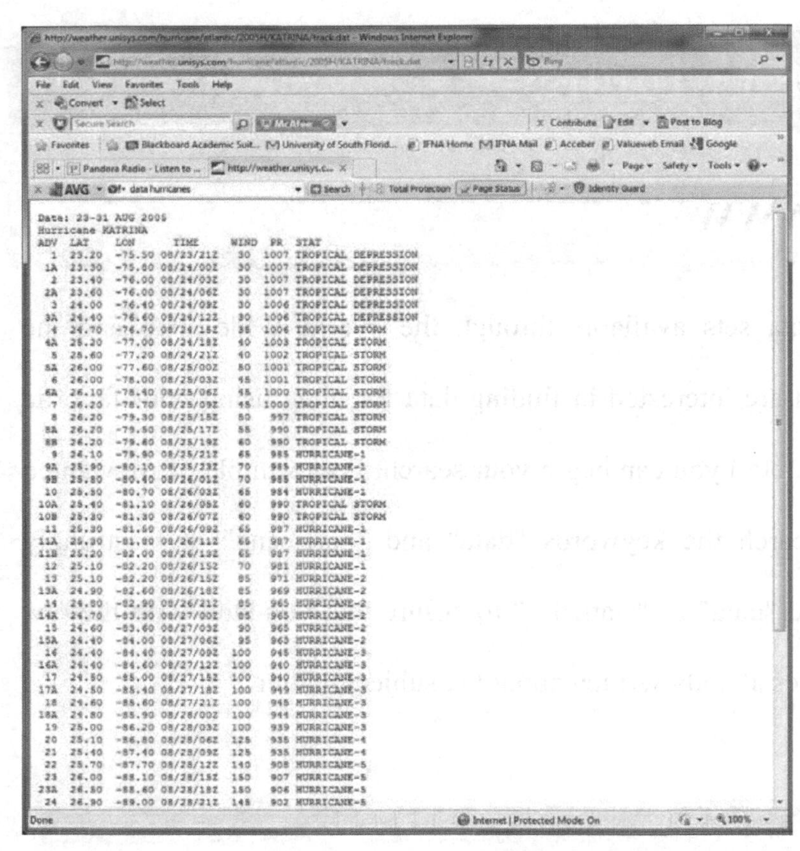

Date: 23-31 AUG 2005
Hurricane KATRINA

ADV	LAT	LON	TIME	WIND	PR	STAT
1	23.20	-75.50	08/23/21Z	30	1007	TROPICAL DEPRESSION
1A	23.30	-75.80	08/24/00Z	30	1007	TROPICAL DEPRESSION
2	23.40	-76.00	08/24/03Z	30	1007	TROPICAL DEPRESSION
2A	23.60	-76.00	08/24/06Z	30	1007	TROPICAL DEPRESSION
3	24.00	-76.40	08/24/09Z	30	1006	TROPICAL DEPRESSION
3A	24.40	-76.60	08/24/12Z	30	1006	TROPICAL DEPRESSION
4	24.70	-76.70	08/24/15Z	35	1006	TROPICAL STORM
4A	25.20	-77.00	08/24/18Z	40	1003	TROPICAL STORM
5	25.60	-77.20	08/24/21Z	40	1002	TROPICAL STORM
5A	26.00	-77.60	08/25/00Z	50	1001	TROPICAL STORM
6	26.00	-78.00	08/25/03Z	45	1001	TROPICAL STORM
6A	26.10	-78.40	08/25/06Z	45	1000	TROPICAL STORM
7	26.20	-78.70	08/25/09Z	45	1000	TROPICAL STORM
8	26.20	-79.30	08/25/15Z	50	997	TROPICAL STORM
8A	26.20	-79.50	08/25/17Z	55	990	TROPICAL STORM
8B	26.20	-79.60	08/25/19Z	60	990	TROPICAL STORM
9	26.10	-79.90	08/25/21Z	65	985	HURRICANE-1
9A	25.90	-80.10	08/25/23Z	70	985	HURRICANE-1
9B	25.80	-80.40	08/26/01Z	70	985	HURRICANE-1
10	25.50	-80.70	08/26/03Z	65	984	HURRICANE-1
10A	25.40	-81.10	08/26/05Z	60	990	TROPICAL STORM
10B	25.30	-81.30	08/26/07Z	60	990	TROPICAL STORM
11	25.30	-81.50	08/26/09Z	65	987	HURRICANE-1
11A	25.30	-81.80	08/26/11Z	65	987	HURRICANE-1
11B	25.20	-82.00	08/26/13Z	65	987	HURRICANE-1
12	25.10	-82.20	08/26/15Z	70	981	HURRICANE-1
13	25.10	-82.20	08/26/15Z	85	971	HURRICANE-2
13A	24.90	-82.60	08/26/18Z	85	969	HURRICANE-2
14	24.80	-82.90	08/26/21Z	85	965	HURRICANE-2
14A	24.70	-83.30	08/27/00Z	85	965	HURRICANE-2
15	24.60	-83.60	08/27/03Z	90	965	HURRICANE-2
15A	24.40	-84.00	08/27/06Z	95	963	HURRICANE-2
16	24.40	-84.40	08/27/09Z	100	945	HURRICANE-3
16A	24.40	-84.60	08/27/12Z	100	940	HURRICANE-3
17	24.50	-85.00	08/27/15Z	100	940	HURRICANE-3
17A	24.50	-85.40	08/27/18Z	100	949	HURRICANE-3
18	24.60	-85.60	08/27/21Z	100	945	HURRICANE-3
18A	24.80	-85.90	08/28/00Z	100	944	HURRICANE-3
19	25.00	-86.20	08/28/03Z	100	939	HURRICANE-3
20	25.10	-86.80	08/28/06Z	125	935	HURRICANE-4
21	25.40	-87.40	08/28/09Z	125	935	HURRICANE-4
22	25.70	-87.70	08/28/12Z	140	908	HURRICANE-5
23	26.00	-88.10	08/28/15Z	150	907	HURRICANE-5
23A	26.50	-88.60	08/28/18Z	150	906	HURRICANE-5
24	26.90	-89.00	08/28/21Z	145	902	HURRICANE-5

Then this information can be gleaned, copied and pasted into such software as **Excel** where further analysis can be performed. Here, the file is given in a text file; some are given in an **Excel** file and the rest in various data organizing software such as **Geographical Information Systems (GIS)**.

SOME OF THE WEB SITES USINED IN THE TEXT:

Center for Disease Control and Prevention — **CDC** http://www.cdc.gov/
Infant Mortality

Carbon Dioxide Information Analysis Center — **CDIAC**
http://cdiac.ornl.gov/trends/co2/sio-keel.html

Bureau of Labor and Statistics — **BLS** http://www.bls.gov/
Unemployment Rate

National Oceanic and Atmospheric Administration — **NOAA** http://www.noaa.gov/
National Weather Service
National Climate Data Center
http://www.ncdc.noaa.gov/oa/ncdc.html

An Official Web Site of the **United States Government** http://www.data.gov

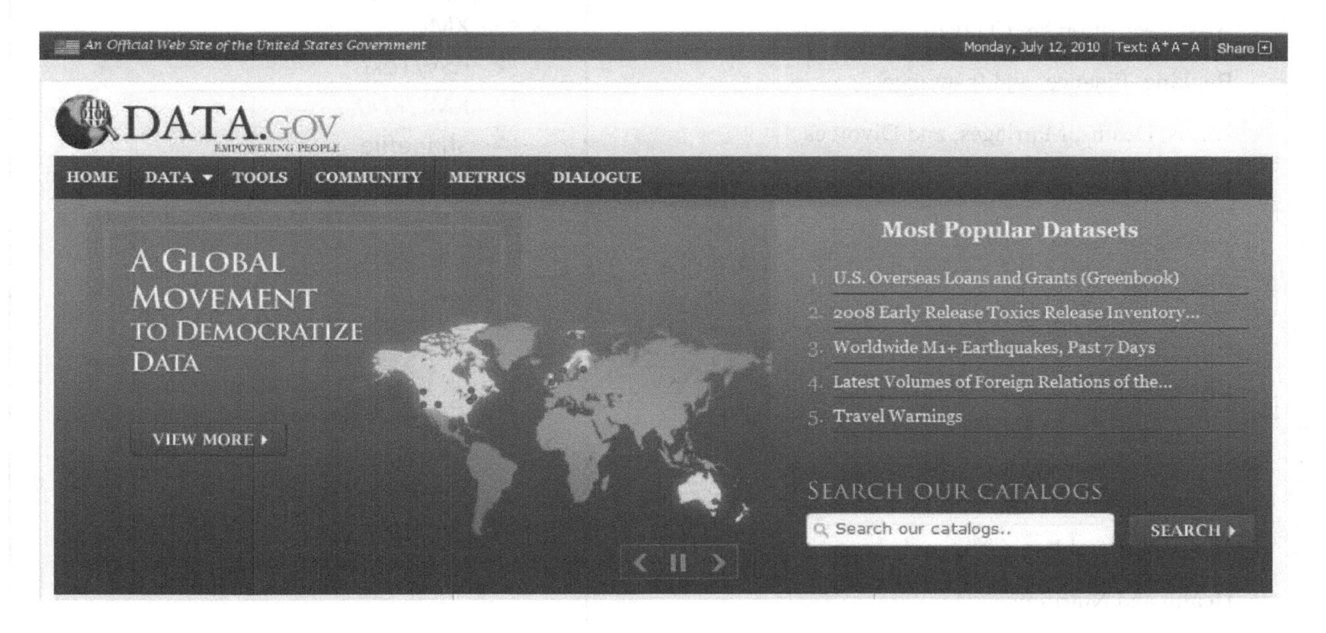

Under **Data ∀"Raw" Data Catalog**

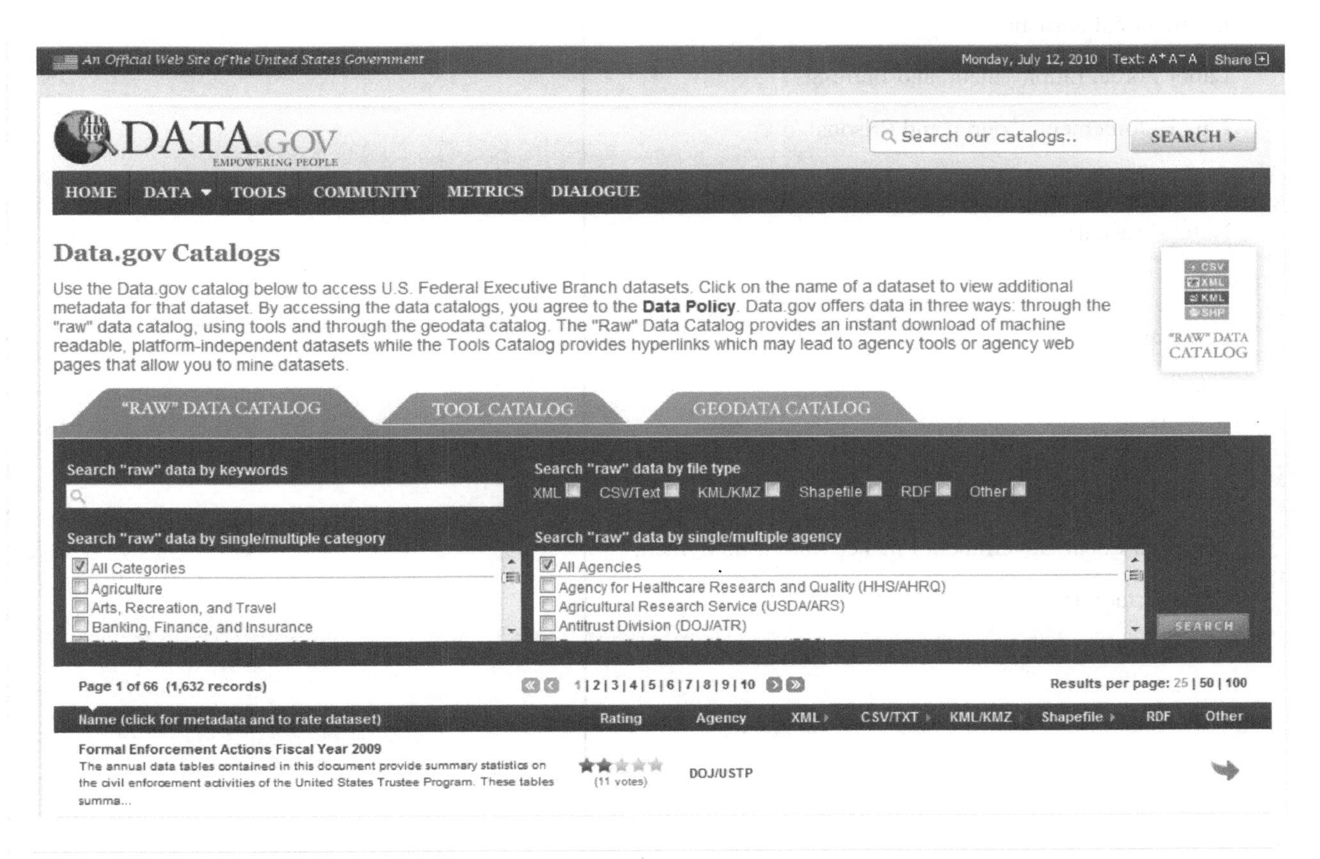

- [x] All Categories
- [ ] Agriculture
- [ ] Arts, Recreation, and Travel
- [ ] Banking, Finance, and Insurance
- [ ] Births, Deaths, Marriages, and Divorces
- [ ] Business Enterprise
- [ ] Construction and Housing
- [ ] Education
- [ ] Elections
- [ ] Energy and Utilities
- [ ] Federal Government Finances and Employment
- [ ] Foreign Commerce and Aid
- [ ] Geography and Environment
- [ ] Health and Nutrition
- [ ] Income, Expenditures, Poverty, and Wealth
- [ ] Information and Communications
- [ ] International Statistics
- [ ] Labor Force, Employment, and Earnings
- [ ] Law Enforcement, Courts, and Prisons
- [ ] National Security and Veterans Affairs
- [ ] Natural Resources
- [ ] Other
- [ ] Population
- [ ] Prices
- [ ] Science and Technology
- [ ] Social Insurance and Human Services
- [ ] State and Local Government Finances and Employment
- [ ] Transportation
- [ ] Wholesale and Retail Trade

The categories listed to the left are all the available categories, which are available in a multitude of formats.

⇨ XML
⇨ CSV/Text
⇨ KML/KMX
⇨ Shapefile
⇨ RDF
⇨ Other

Search "raw" data by single/multiple agency

- All Agencies
- Agency for Healthcare Research and Quality (HHS/AHRQ)
- Agricultural Research Service (USDA/ARS)
- Antitrust Division (DOJ/ATR)
- Broadcasting Board of Governors (BBG)
- Bureau of Economic Analysis (DOC/BEA)
- Bureau of Indian Education (DOI/BIE)
- Bureau of Industry and Security (DOC/BIS)
- Bureau of Justice Statistics (DOJ/BJS)
- Bureau of Land Management (DOI/BLM)
- Bureau of Ocean Energy Management, Regulation and Enforcement (DOI/BOE)
- Bureau of the Public Debt (TREAS/BPD)
- Bureau of Transportation Statistics (DOT/BTS)
- Centers for Disease Control and Prevention (HHS/CDC)
- Centers for Medicare and Medicaid Services (HHS/CMS)
- Civil Division (DOJ/CIV)
- Commodity Futures Trading Commission (CFTC)
- Corporation for National and Community Service (CNS)
- Council on Environmental Quality (EOP/CEQ)
- Defense Technical Information Center (DOD/DTIC)
- Department of Agriculture (USDA)
- Department of Commerce (DOC)
- Department of Defense (DOD)
- Department of Education (ED)
- Department of Energy (DOE)
- Department of Health and Human Services (HHS)
- Department of Homeland Security (DHS)
- Department of Housing and Urban Development (HUD)
- Department of Justice (DOJ)
- Department of Labor (DOL)
- Department of State (STATE)
- Department of the Interior (DOI)
- Department of the Treasury (TREAS)
- Department of Transportation (DOT)
- Department of Veterans Affairs (VA)
- Economic Research Service (USDA/ERS)
- Election Assistance Commission (EAC)
- Employee Benefits Security Administration (DOL/EBSA)
- Employment and Training Administration (DOL/ETA)
- Energy Information Administration (DOE/EIA)
- Environmental Protection Agency (EPA)
- Executive Office of the President (EOP)

- ☐ Export-Import Bank of the US (EXIM)
- ☐ Farm Service Agency (USDA/FSA)
- ☐ Federal Aviation Administration (DOT/FAA)
- ☐ Federal Bureau of Investigation (DOJ/FBI)
- ☐ Federal Communications Commission (FCC)
- ☐ Federal Deposit Insurance Corporation (FDIC)
- ☐ Federal Election Commission (FEC)
- ☐ Federal Emergency Management Agency (DHS/FEMA)
- ☐ Federal Motor Carrier Safety Administration (DOT/FMCSA)
- ☐ Federal Railroad Administration (DOT/FRA)
- ☐ Federal Reserve Board (FRB)
- ☐ Federal Student Aid (ED/FSA)
- ☐ Federal Transit Administration (DOT/FTA)
- ☐ Food and Nutrition Service (USDA/FNS)
- ☐ Food Safety and Inspection Service (USDA/FSIS)
- ☐ Foreign Agricultural Service (USDA/FAS)
- ☐ General Services Administration (GSA)
- ☐ Institute of Museum and Library Services (IMLS)
- ☐ International Trade Administration (DOC/ITA)
- ☐ Internal Revenue Service (TREAS/IRS)
- ☐ Merit Systems Protection Board (MSPB)
- ☐ Millennium Challenge Corporation (MCC)
- ☐ Mine Safety and Health Administration (DOL/MSHA)
- ☐ National Aeronautics and Space Administration (NASA)
- ☐ National Agricultural Statistics Service (USDA/NASS)
- ☐ National Archives and Records Administration (NARA)
- ☐ National Cancer Institute (HHS/NCI)
- ☐ National Capital Planning Commission (NCPC)
- ☐ National Center for Education Statistics (ED/NCES)
- ☐ National Center for Health Statistics (HHS/NCHS)
- ☐ National Endowment for the Arts (NEA)
- ☐ National Endowment for the Humanities (NEH)
- ☐ National Highway Traffic Safety Administration (DOT/NHTSA)
- ☐ National Institute of Standards and Technology (DOC/NIST)
- ☐ National Institutes of Health (HHS/NIH)
- ☐ National Labor Relations Board (NLRB)
- ☐ National Library of Medicine (HHS/NLM)
- ☐ National Oceanic and Atmospheric Administration (DOC/NOAA)
- ☐ National Park Service (DOI/NPS)
- ☐ National Science Foundation (NSF)
- ☐ National Technical Information Service (DOC/NTIS)

- National Telecommunication and Information Administration (DOC/NTIA)
- National Transportation Safety Board (NTSB)
- Nuclear Regulatory Commission (NRC)
- Occupational Safety and Health Administration (DOL/OSHA)
- Occupational Safety and Health Review Commission (OSHRC)
- Office of Housing (HUD/OH)
- Office of Immigration Statistics (DHS/OIS)
- Office of Job Corps (DOL/OJC)
- Office of Management and Budget (EOP/OMB)
- Office of National Drug Control Policy (EOP/ONDCP)
- Office of Navajo and Hopi Indian Relocation (ONHIR)
- Office of Personnel Management (OPM)
- Office of Science and Technology Policy (EOP/OSTP)
- Office of the Assistant Secretary for Policy (DOL/OASP)
- Office of the Federal Register (NARA/OFR)
- Overseas Private Investment Corporation (OPIC)
- Pension Benefit Guaranty Corporation (PBGC)
- Railroad Retirement Board (RRB)
- Securities and Exchange Commission (SEC)
- Selective Service System (SSS)
- Small Business Administration (SBA)
- Social Security Administration (SSA)
- Tennessee Valley Authority (TVA)
- U.S. Citizenship and Immigration Services (DHS/USCIS)
- US Agency for International Development (USAID)
- US Attorney's Office (DOJ/USAO)
- US Bureau of Labor Statistics (DOL/BLS)
- US Bureau of Reclamation (DOI/USBR)
- US Census Bureau (DOC/CENSUS)
- US Consumer Product Safety Commission (CPSC)
- US Equal Employment Opportunity Commission (EEOC)
- US Fish and Wildlife Service (DOI/FWS)
- US Food and Drug Administration (HHS/FDA)
- US Forest Service (USDA/FS)
- US Geological Survey (DOI/USGS)
- US International Trade Commission (USITC)
- US Patent and Trademark Office (DOC/USPTO)
- US Trade Representative (EOP/USTR)
- US Trustee Program (DOJ/USTP)
- Veterans Benefits Administration (VA/VBA)
- Veterans Health Administration (VA/VHA)
- Wage and Hour Division (DOL/WHD)
- White House (EOP/White House)

Data using EXCEL

The data sets introduced in "**Chapter 0: Introduction to Real World Data**" are available in **Appendix A** as well in the accompanying Excel file "**Appendix A Data Sets EXCEL**".

There are a total of 31 data sets, the first of which includes the **age** and **tumor size** of cancer in **breast cancer** patients.

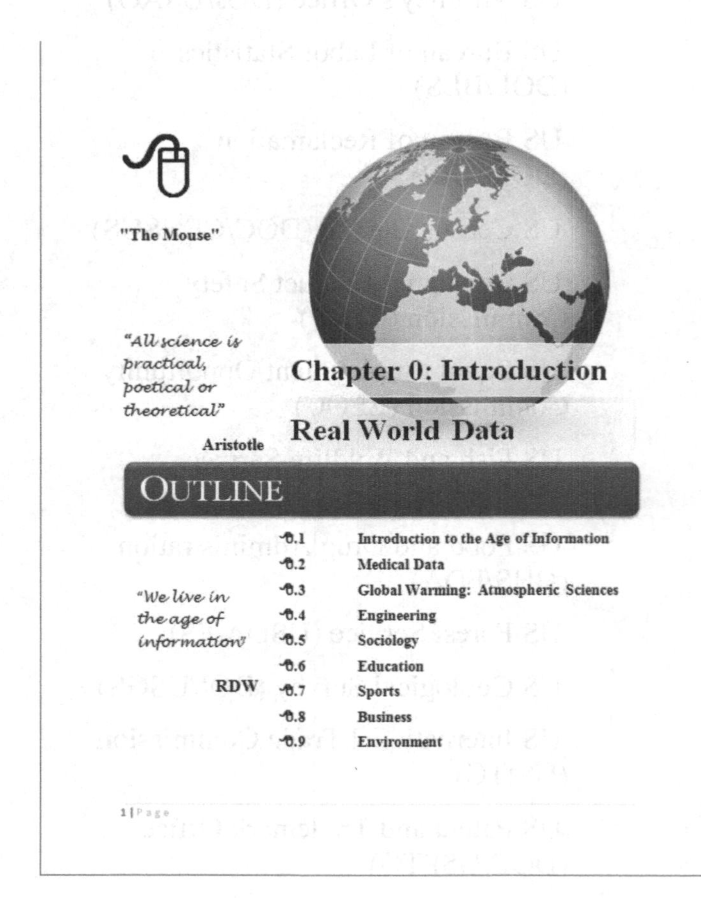

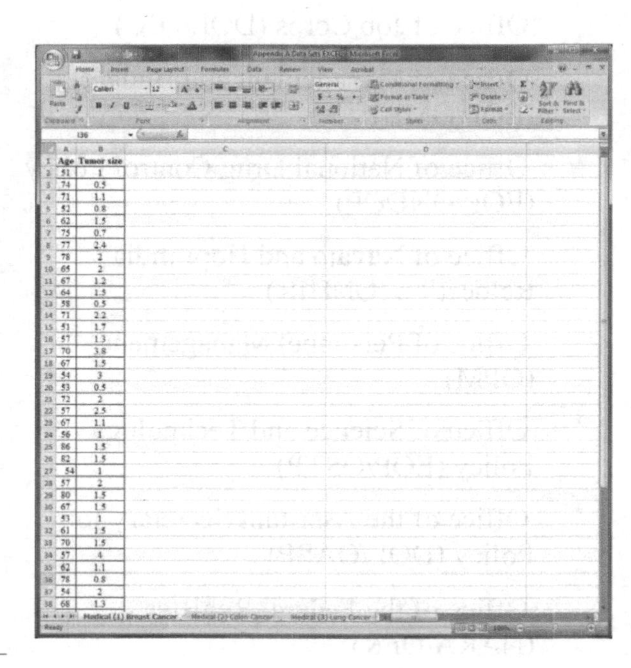

Age	Tumor size
51	1
74	0.5
71	1.1
52	0.8
62	1.5
75	0.7
77	2.4
78	2
65	2
67	1.2
64	1.5
58	0.5
71	2.2
51	1.7
57	1.3
70	3.8
67	1.5
54	3
53	0.5
72	2
57	2.5
67	1.1
56	1
86	1.5
82	1.5
54	1
57	2
80	1.5
67	1.5
53	1
61	1.5
70	1.5
57	4
62	1.1
78	0.8
54	2
68	1.3

Each data set is in its own worksheet, shown at the bottom of the screen. Below, we see that the first few data sets are in **Medical**: (1) **Breast Cancer**, (2) **Colon Cancer** and (3) **Lung Cancer**, etc.

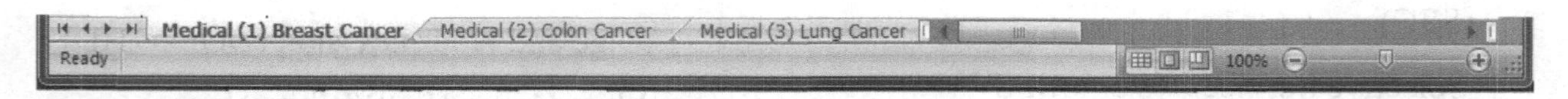

Terminology using EXCEL

You will need to use the accompanying **EXCEL** file "**Using Technology in Terminology**" or the list provided in this section. *Note: The 190 terms are given in an **EXCEL** file and are not presently in any specific order.*

FORMAT: Bold key words to be **emphasized**, **label figures** and **tables**, and **paginate**.

QUESTION 1 On the **Terminology List** (see Appendix) are 190 words, the many of which will are covered in the first three chapters (Part 1) as well as commonly used throughout the text and 80 words of which are flagged (⚐) and must be included. A minimum of **100 words** must be included in the first graded assignment, a dictionary. We encourage you to incorporate as much technology as possible. The nicer presentations will include more detailed **formatting** such as **Cover Page, Pagination**, and **front only**. **Alphabetize** and **enumerate** each word; entries should include the **term** (word) being defined and a **definition**. (Optional) Use the word, in statistical context, in a complete sentence.

In the 2007 Edition of Microsoft Word, under Insert, there is the option to include a Cover Page in the first column, to insert a Page Number

(Pagination) in the Header & Footer column and printing this document will allow for Front Only.

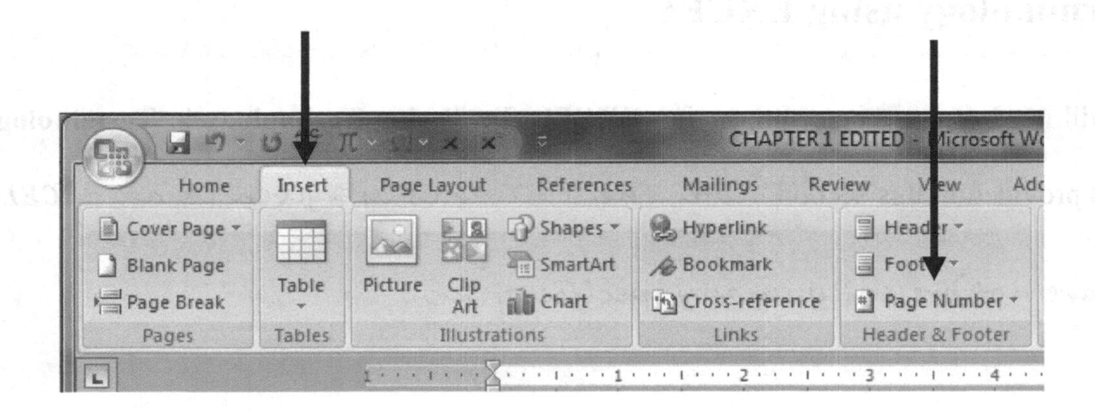

You can use **EXCEL** to sort these terms alphabetically – otherwise, you will have to organize this information manually. *In **EXCEL**, simply highlight the columns (using the last column – as this is the column to be sorted, the remaining are additional information that needs to be sorted with the words) and then under Data, sort A to Z.*

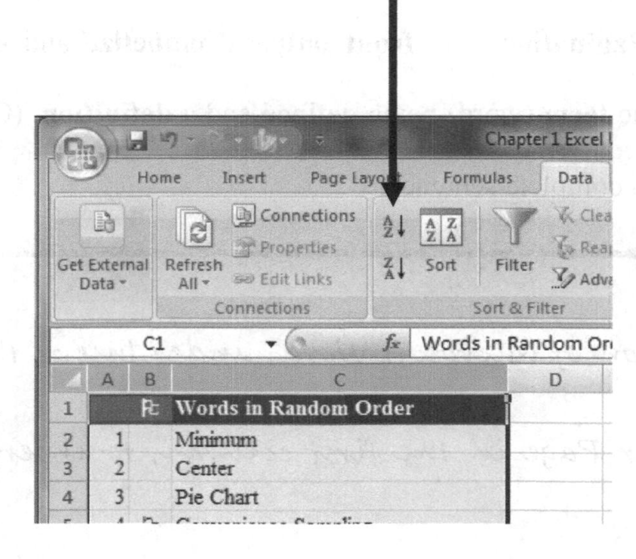

Terminology using WORD 2007

You can then simply start alphabetically and use the index of the book or search online, or, my suggestion is first going by chapter, including all words found in the first few chapters. When using a word processor such as **WORD**, moving between entries can be easily done.

Without the use of a computer, I suggest using index cards for the first draft, then alphabetize the index cards and create a final draft. All words requiring definitions can be found in the text and others defined in the accompanying **Lecture Notes**; all can be researched in the library or online.

Using Word, we can extract the information from the **EXCEL** file "**Dictionary Terms**", copy and paste into Word. It will appear in a table which we can first sort out all the flagged terms. Then after selecting the additional terms, we can sort the terms alphabetically.

Word can also sort the words even when enumerated using sort from A to Z.

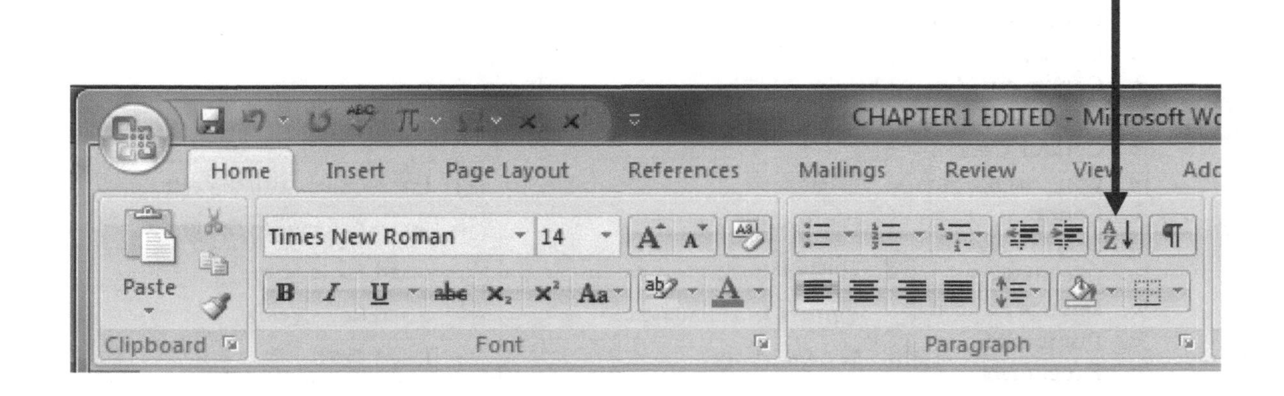

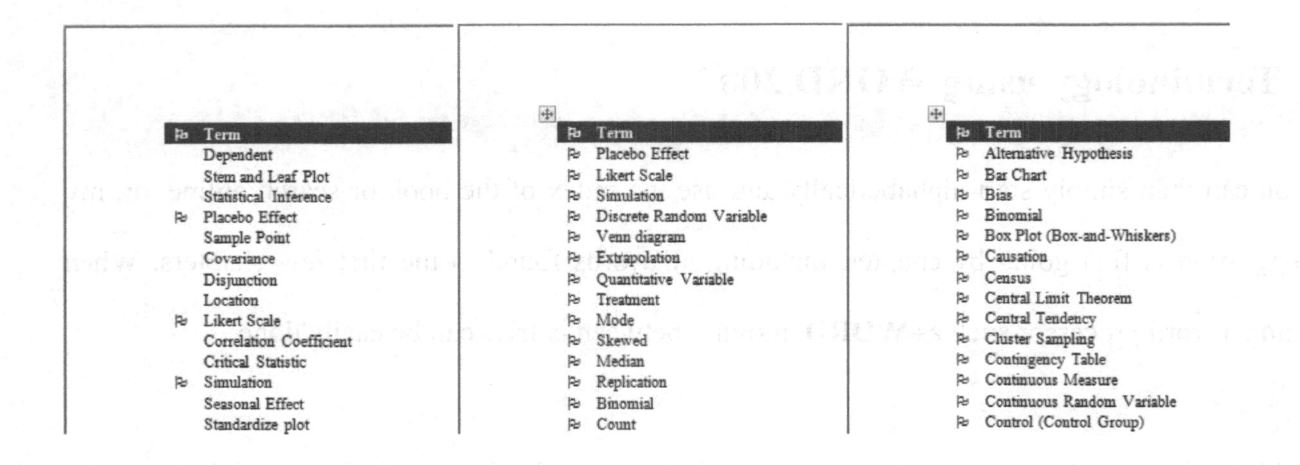

To add a column for the definition, over the second column, right click and under **Insert, Insert Columns to the Right**. Then in the new column, add the researched definitions.

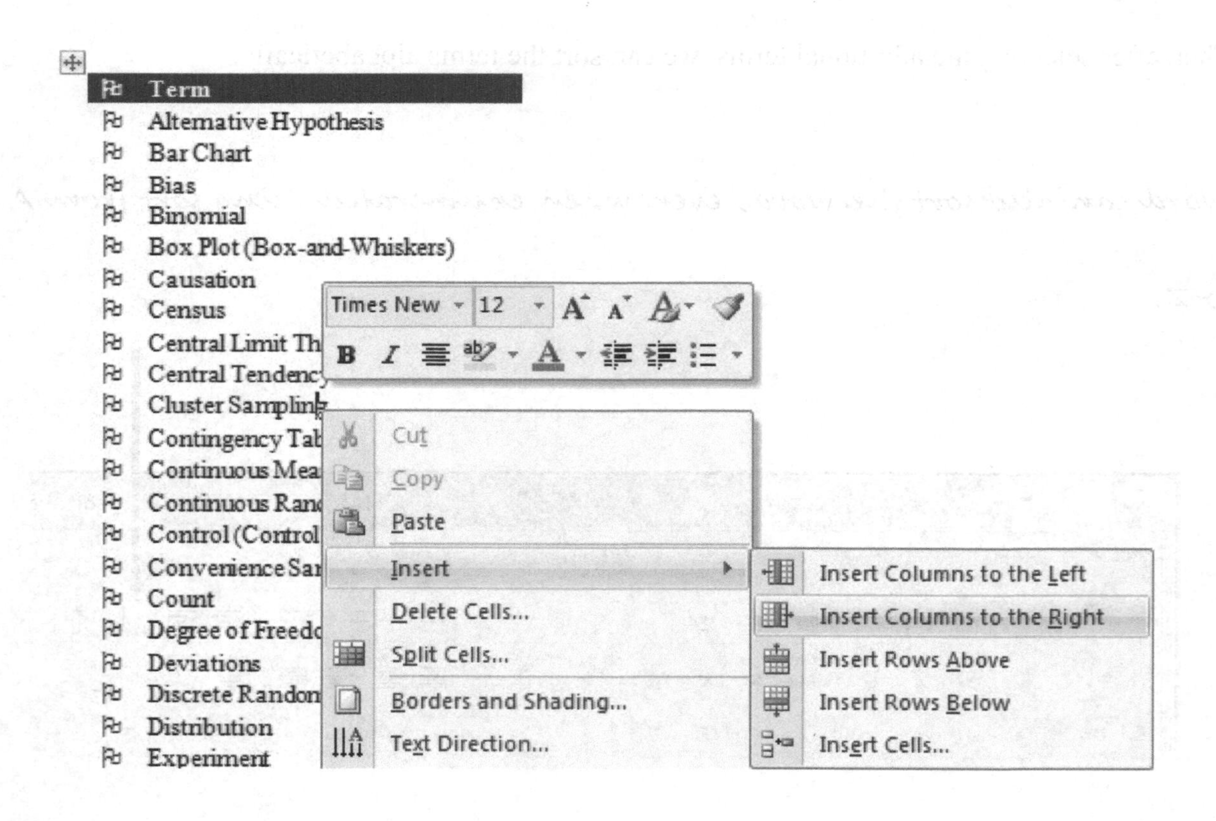

Terminology using the WWW

We have seen how the Internet can be used to find data. However, the internet is the epitome of the Age of Information in that we can find anything via the WWW. We can find articles on various topics using Google:

Searching the topics "alternative hypothesis", Google comes up with about 19,200,000 results, the first of which is **Wikipedia**, the free online encyclopedia

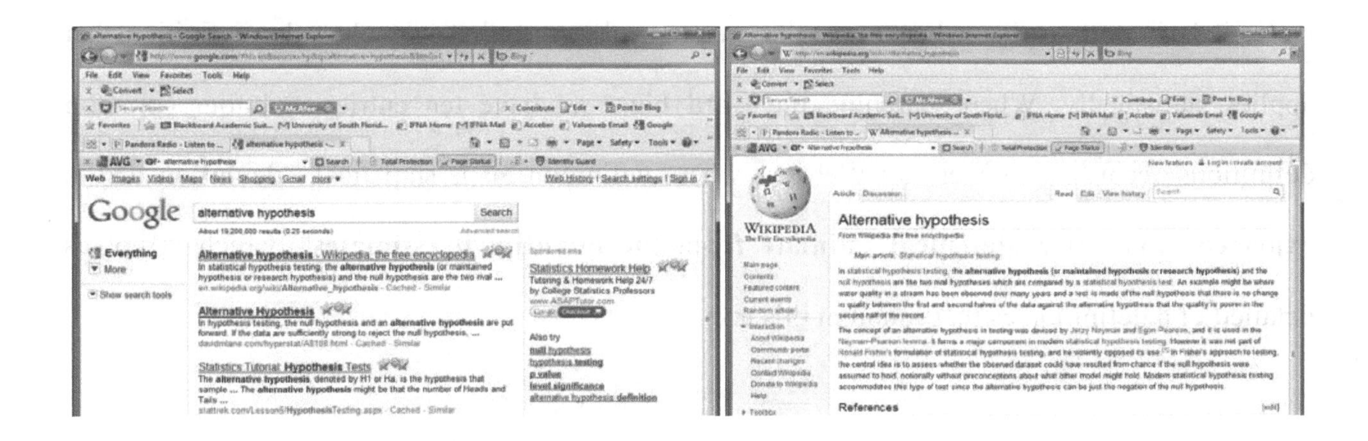

Alternatively, we can first search out a dictionary using Google, Bing, or other search engines.

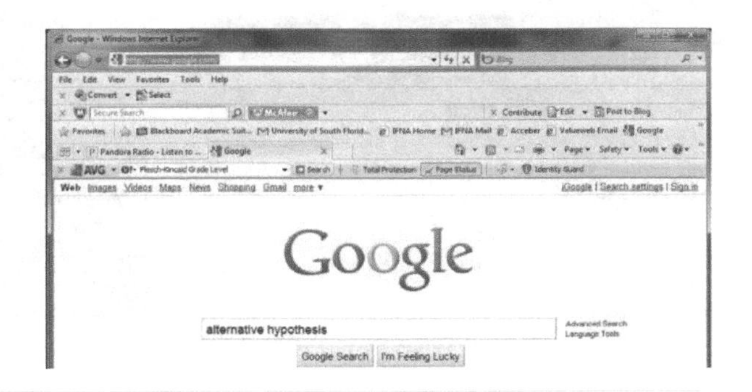

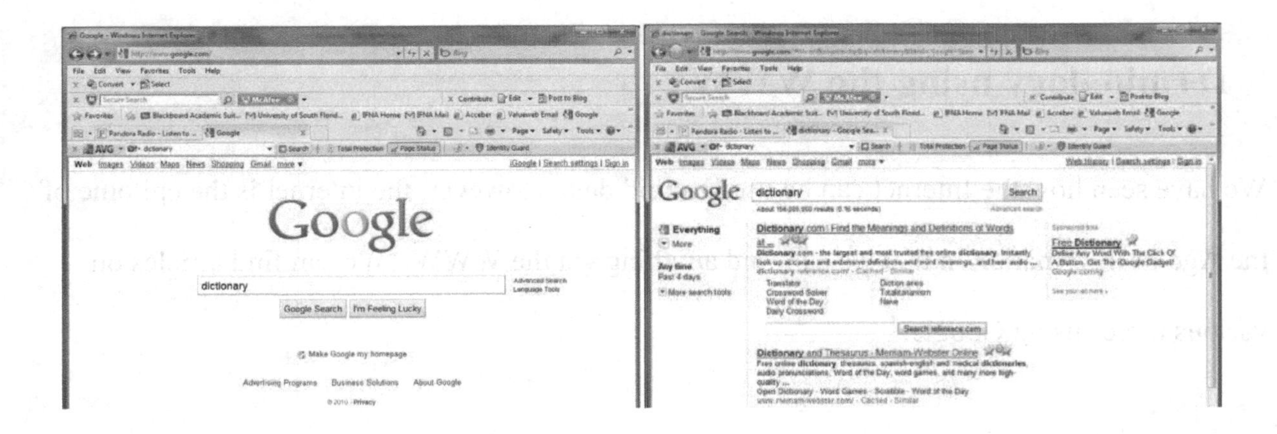

Dictionary.com is a common dictionary; however, Merriam-Webster and Google Dictionary are other online resources that can be used. Note in the search for "dictionary", about 157,000,000 results were found in 0.19 seconds.

Note: it is important that when researching statistical terms, that we select the definition that applies statistically. When searching the word **bias**, we have ten entries and four common definitions according to Merriam-Webster, where definition **3d** is statistical, "**deviation of the expected value of a statistical estimate from the quantity it estimates**", which is not as detailed of a definition as that found in this text.

⚐	Term	⚐	Term	⚐	Term
	Dependent		Double Blind		Experimental Design
	Stem and Leaf Plot		Independent Random Sample	⚐	Quartiles
	Statistical Inference	⚐	Median	⚐	Deviations
⚐	Placebo Effect		Trimmed Mean		Nominal Measure
	Sample Point		Statistical Adjustment		Percentiles
	Covariance		Sample Variance		Circle Graph (Pie Chart)
	Disjunction	⚐	Replication		Single Blind
	Location	⚐	Binomial	⚐	Spread
⚐	Likert Scale		Random Sampling Error	⚐	Type II Error
	Correlation Coefficient	⚐	Count	⚐	Response Variable
	Critical Statistic		Time Series Graph	⚐	Line Graph
⚐	Simulation		Population	⚐	Distribution
	Seasonal Effect		Sample Space		Anonymous (Anonymity)
	Standardize plot	⚐	Inferential Statistics		Dependent Random Sample
	Continuous Uniform	⚐	Rate	⚐	Statistic
	Point Estimate		Explanatory Variable		PP plot
	Uniform Distribution		Counting rules		Sample Data (Sample)
	Ranking		Placebo		Frequency Distribution
⚐	Discrete Random Variable	⚐	Bias		Standard Deviation
⚐	Venn diagram	⚐	Cluster Sampling		Sample Standard Deviation
	Confidential	⚐	Voluntary Sampling	⚐	Type I Error
	Randomization	⚐	Lurking Variable		Weighted Mean (Weighted Average)
	Sampling Distribution	⚐	Continuous Random Variable	⚐	Interval Measure
⚐	Extrapolation		Coefficient of Variation		Class Mark (Midpoint)
⚐	Quantitative Variable		Standard Score	⚐	Variability
	Correction for Continuity		QQ plot		Class Boundaries
⚐	Treatment		Tree Diagram	⚐	Simple Linear Regression
⚐	Mode		Incorrect arithmetic		Statistically Significant
	Percentage plot	⚐	Probability		Mutually exclusive events
	Discrete Distribution	⚐	Qualitative Variable	⚐	Simple Random Sample
	Confounded Variables	⚐	Sample Size		Standard Average
⚐	Skewed		Institutional review board	⚐	p-value

⚐	Term	⚐	Term	⚐	Term
	Conjunction	⚐	Contingency Table		Goodness-of-fit
⚐	Relative Frequency		Relative-frequency	⚐	Instrument
⚐	Pareto Chart		Block Design	⚐	Residuals
	Poisson: Expected Value	⚐	Measure		Moments
	Expected Value		Event	⚐	Shape
⚐	Parameter		Class Limits	⚐	Experiment
⚐	Census		Gaussian Probability Distribution		Inter-quartile Range
⚐	Maximum		Class Width		Independent
⚐	Control (Control Group)		Population Size	⚐	Odds
⚐	Ordinal Measure		Experimental Study		Conditional probability
	Normal Probability Distribution	⚐	Convenience Sampling	⚐	Mean
	Descriptive Statistics		Skewed Right	⚐	Ratio Measure
	Time Series Data		Cumulative Frequency		Frequency Polygon
⚐	Systematic Sampling		Variable		Sample Survey
	Hidden Bias		Binominal Distribution	⚐	Null Hypothesis
	Dot Plot		Sample Mean		Survey Error
	Variance		Regression		Correlation
⚐	Outliers		Degree of Confidence		Population Standard Deviation
	Probability Distribution	⚐	Alternative Hypothesis	⚐	Statistics
⚐	Degree of Freedom		Continuous Distribution		Reliability (Reliable Measure)
⚐	Stratified Sample		Ogive	⚐	Causation
	Non Adherers		Skewed Left		Robust
⚐	Margin of Error		Voluntary Response	⚐	Box Plot (Box-and-Whiskers)
⚐	Continuous Measure		Degree of Confidence	⚐	Individual
	Random Variable		Random Sample	⚐	Symmetric
⚐	Central Tendency		Expected Count (Independent Events)	⚐	Bar Chart
⚐	Interpolation	⚐	Minimum		Discrete Uniform
⚐	Informed Consent	⚐	Scatter Plot	⚐	Marginal Change
	Discrete Measure	⚐	Range	⚐	Histogram
⚐	Central Limit Theorem	⚐	Trend		Compound event
	Categorical Variable		Observational Study		
⚐	Valid Measure (Validity)		Hypothesis Testing		

Using Technology in Graphical Representations C2

Graphical Representations using EXCEL

Once you have gathered information on a topic of interest to you and summarized this information descriptively, then the data can be depicted graphically. Information may need to be reorganized and/or summarized to produce some of the graphic representations.

FORMAT: Bold key words to be **emphasized**, **label figures** and **tables**, and **paginate**.

*Using the data you found in **Using Technology in Descriptive Statistics**, create the following summary charts and the associated graphics.*

QUESTION 1 Using your data, draw a **bar chart** for the qualitative variable. Comment, is this a **balanced** design? If so, then re-analyze the information so that there are varying counts; draw **histograms** for the quantitative variables Comment, on the **symmetry** or **skewness** of the data; Discuss **outlines** and **gaps.** Draw **box plots** for the quantitative variables by category (that is, the qualitative variable) and include at least the **five-number summary**. If this is a **time series**, include line graph for at least the outlined response variable, by category if possible. Is there a **trend** or **seasonal effect**?

Bar Charts

The qualitative variable here is a balanced design as readings are made each year for each of the distinct categories: **winter wheat, spring wheat** and **Durum wheat**. Hence, this will not be an interesting bar chart as it does not yield any additional information. However, if we consider **Yield** for **All wheat** and the readings for **Yields** below average versus the mean **Yields** that are located above the average - average here meaning standard mean, we have the following summary table. Note: this table was taken directly from the Excel worksheet and **Pasted** in Word.

	Frequency
Below Average	19
Above Average	16

This summary information can be counted by Excel using the **COUNTIF** command, otherwise extract the data you need to summarize, **Sort** the data as shown in **Using Technology in Terminology, Chapter 1** - and then simply count those less than the mean, say **m**, then there are (**n-m**) that are greater than or equal to the mean. Once we have this summary information, we can compute the total count by summing the two counts using the command **SUM**. Finally, we can highlight these cells, go to **Insert** and under **Charts** select **Column** and the desired design.

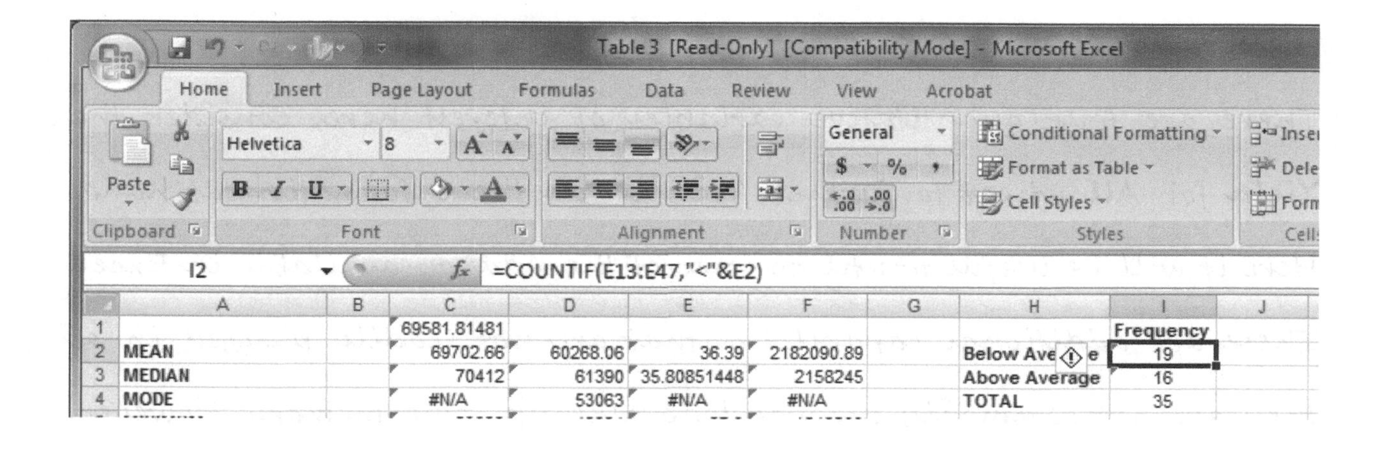

With a moderate amount of formatting: selecting a chart with labels on the axis, labeling these axis, we see that there are more readings (19) where the yield is below average and what might initially appear to be significantly fewer readings (16) below average. However, you must be careful not to skew the perspective, see Figure 1 below. If Excel starts the vertical axis with a number greater than 0, you must **Format Axis** – this is done by selecting the vertical axis, right clicking and selecting **Format Axis** and set the Minimum to a fixed 0.0.

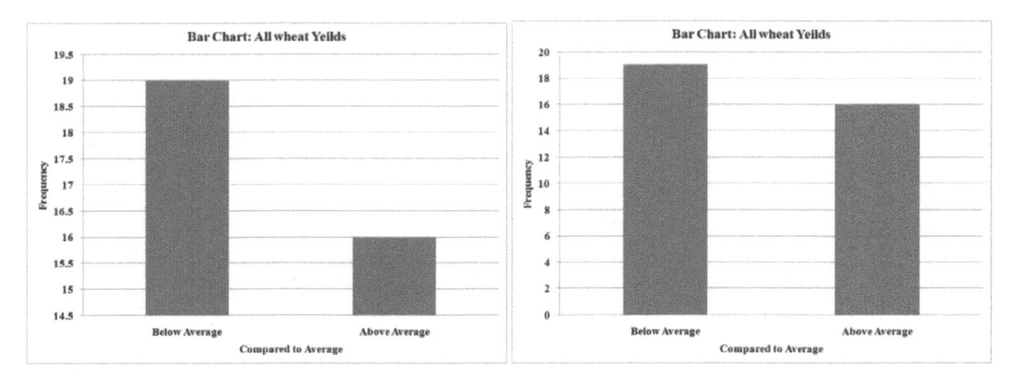

Figure 1: Skewed Perspective Correct View

Histograms

There are four quantitative variables of interest here, consider the **Yield for All wheat** to further focus in on the information at hand. Here it will be useful to utilize some of the Add-on available in Excel. These are additional capabilities that are not readily plugged in as they are not commonly used and do take up some memory. However, once this add-in is plugged into Excel, this will be very useful in basic statistical analysis.

Under **Data**, there is an **Add-on** that performs **Data Analysis**

If this option is not plugged-in, go to the last option in the upper menu where one of the options is **More Commands**...

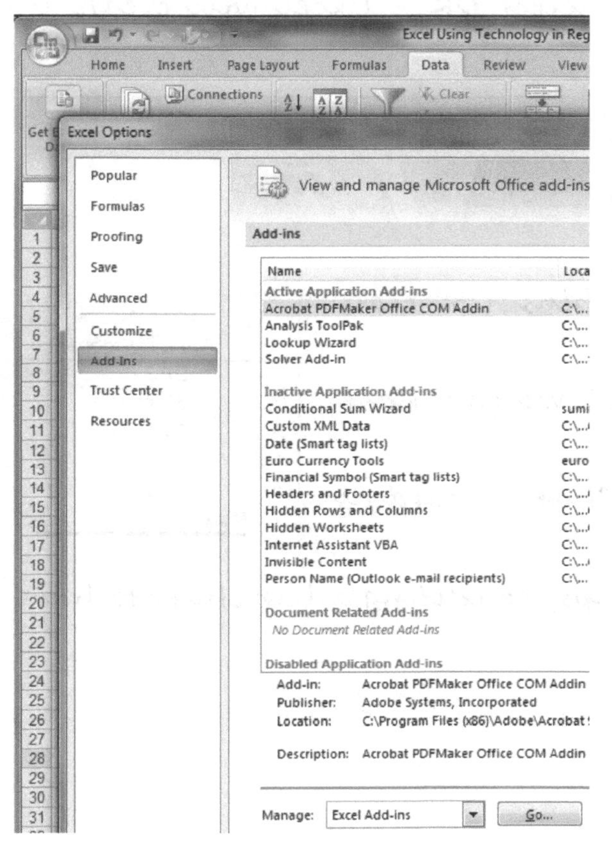

Customize the Quick Access Toolbar, Under **Add-ins**, **Solver Add-in** and then **Go...** which will take you to the **Add-ins**, check **Analysis ToolPak** and **OK**.

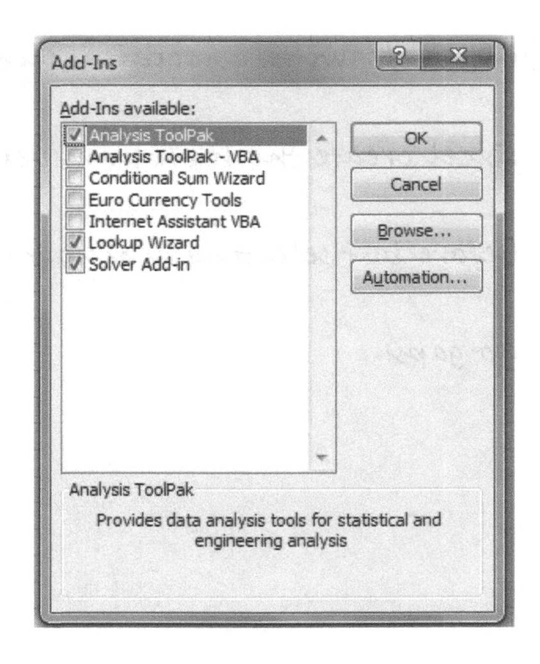

Back to the **Data Analysis and Graphics: Histograms...**

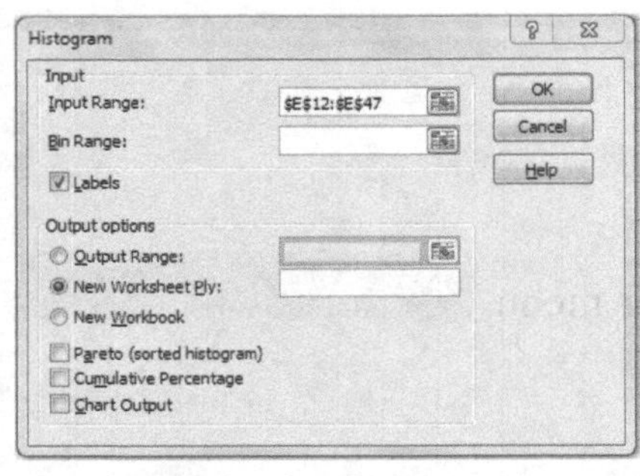

Under **Data Analysis**, select **Histogram** and **OK**. This will send you to a wizard where, if you have the input range and bins set up, enter this information – otherwise, enter the Input Range (and check of if there are labels) and then simply select **OK** – Excel will create its own bins and count.

Once the information is put into **bins** (or **class intervals** with associated **class marks**) we can have Excel create the histogram using the **Chart** wizard as before but selecting a histogram (no gaps) or editing a bar chart to have no gaps.

	A	B
1	*Bin*	*Frequency*
2	27.3	1
3	30.7	2
4	34.1	7
5	37.4	9
6	40.8	10
7	More	6

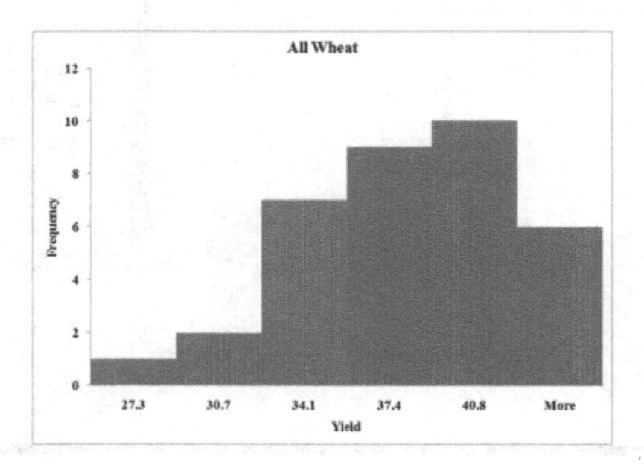

Figure 2: Histogram of yield for all wheat

Symmetric vs. Skew

This quantitative variable is not symmetric, as also indicated by the descriptive statistics in Chapter 2, the mean is less than the median. In the graphic representation above, the less frequent 27.3 (smaller yields) pull the mean down and to the left of the median – i.e. **skewed left**.

Gaps &Outliers

There are no gaps or apparent outliers – the gaps are obvious, but the outliers can more readily be detected using descriptive statistics such as the five-number summary – see Chapter 2 – in addition to the graphic based on these five numbers, the **Box-and-Whisker** plot.

To detect outliers, consider the summary information found in Using Technology in Descriptive Statistics, Chapter 2. That is, the **minimum**, **first quartile**, **median**, **third quartile** and the **maximum** for **Yield** (**all wheat**).

	A	B	E
1			
2	MEAN		36.39
3	MEDIAN		35.80851448
4	MODE		#N/A
5	MINIMUM		27.3
6	MAXIMUM		44.18822909
7	Q1		33.7
8	Q3		39.44431891
9	RANGE		16.88822909
10	VARIANCE		18.23206709
11	STANDARD DEVIATION		4.27
12	Year	Type	Yield
13	1971	All	33.9

K	L	M
Minimum	1	27.30
Q1	1	33.70
Median	1	35.81
Q3	1	39.44
Maximum	1	44.19

Now, Excel does not draw box-and-whisker plots directly, but plotting the five-number summary versus a constant, say 1, then a scatter plot can give the basis for the plot. Then dropping this image into **Paint**, we can add detail.

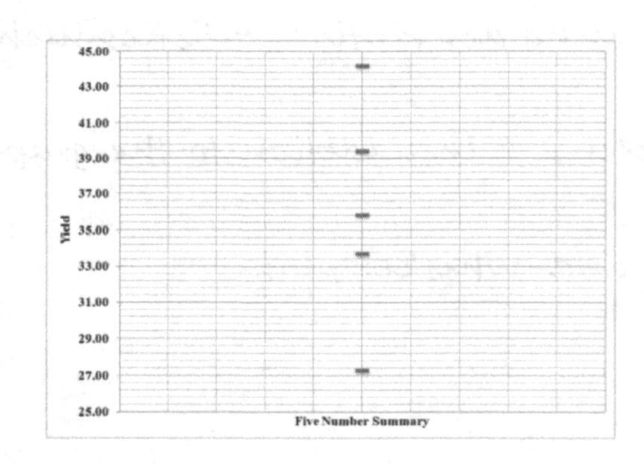

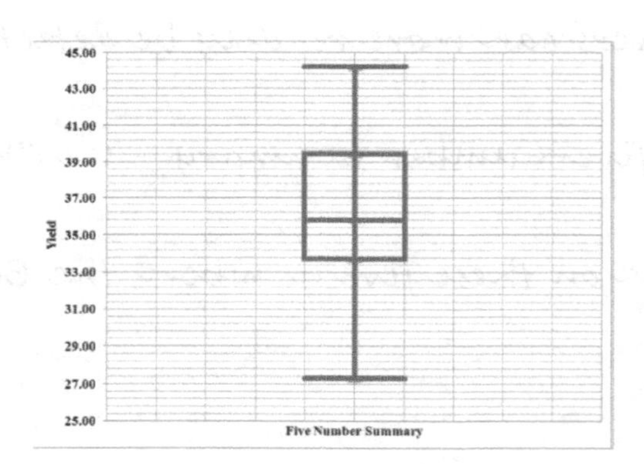

Figure 2: Box-and-whisker plot for yield (all wheat) - first without the box and whiskers, just the five-number summary and second, with the box and whiskers.

We can further define the interval outside of which the information is considered an outlier. As the data is not symmetric, it is better to define the outliers in terms of the quartiles and the interquartile range. That is, an outlier is any data point outside of

$$(Q_1 - 1.5IQR, Q_3 + 1.5IQR).$$

We have the quartiles, hence the interquartile range is

$$IQR = Q_3 - Q_1.$$

	K	L	M
1	Minimum	1	27.30
2	Q1	1	33.70
3	Median	1	35.81
4	Q3	1	39.44
5	Maximum	1	44.19
6			
7	IQR		5.74
8	Lower Limit		25.1
9	Upper Limit		48.1

Using Excel, given Q_3 is in cell **M4** and Q_1 is in cell **M2**, then **IQR** can be determined in **M7** using the code $= M4 - M2$. Then we can compute the lower limit, $= M2 - 1.5 * M7$ and the upper limit, $= M4 + 1.5 * M7$. In this example, there are no outliers – this is because the **minimum** 27.3 is greater than the **lower limit** of **25.1** and the **maximum 44.19** is less than the **upper limit** of **48.1**. Hence, there are no data values that fall outside the overall pattern of the graph.

Line Graphs & Time Series

As time is one of the available variables, we can consider the line graph of Yield over time. In Excel, highlight the explanatory variable (time) and the subject response (yield) and under **Insert** select either **Line Graph** or **Scatter Plot**. Note here, unlike in bar charts, the vertical axis can be adjusted to fit the data in the viewing window.

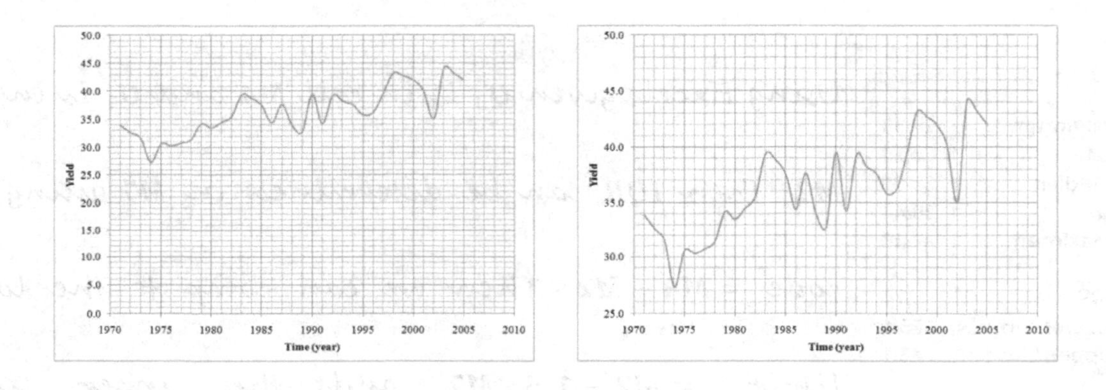

Figure 3: Time series graph for yield (all wheat) by year - first without the vertical scale starting at zero and second, graphed in a smaller window with better focus.

Here, there is not a **seasonal effect**, the **Yield** does not show a regular periodicity – there are ups and downs, but not on a regular time interval. However, there is an overall **trend**; though weak, there is a tendency to increase over time.

- Note: Conditioning can become very elaborate; for this reason, alternatives to coding in Excel have been given.
  - CONCATENTATION &
  - COUNTIF **=COUNTIF(**<data array>,<condition>**)**

Note: conditioning can become very elaborate; for this reason, alternatives to coding in Excel have been given. However, as illustrated in the snap shot above, one conditioning statement might be when a number is **less than** or **greater than a specified value**. For example, if the specified value is located in **E2**, then the code **"<"&E2** is the condition, is **less than the specified value in E2**. Here, the ampersand sign (**&**) acts as a connector, concatenating the two expressions.

  - SUM **=SUM(**<data array>**)**

Graphical Representations using EXCEL

Using the ***TI* – 83**, using the techniques outlined in Chapter 2 Using Technology in **Descriptive Statistics**, put the data values and the frequencies in two distinct lists, say ***L*1**, and ***L*2**. Then press **2nd STAT PLOT**. This screen will allow you to turn on various statistical plots including **scatter plots**, **histograms** and **box plots**.

QUESTION 2 Using your data, draw a **histogram** and a **box plot** for the following data:.

*For the example above, we have the following **histogram** and **box plot**.*

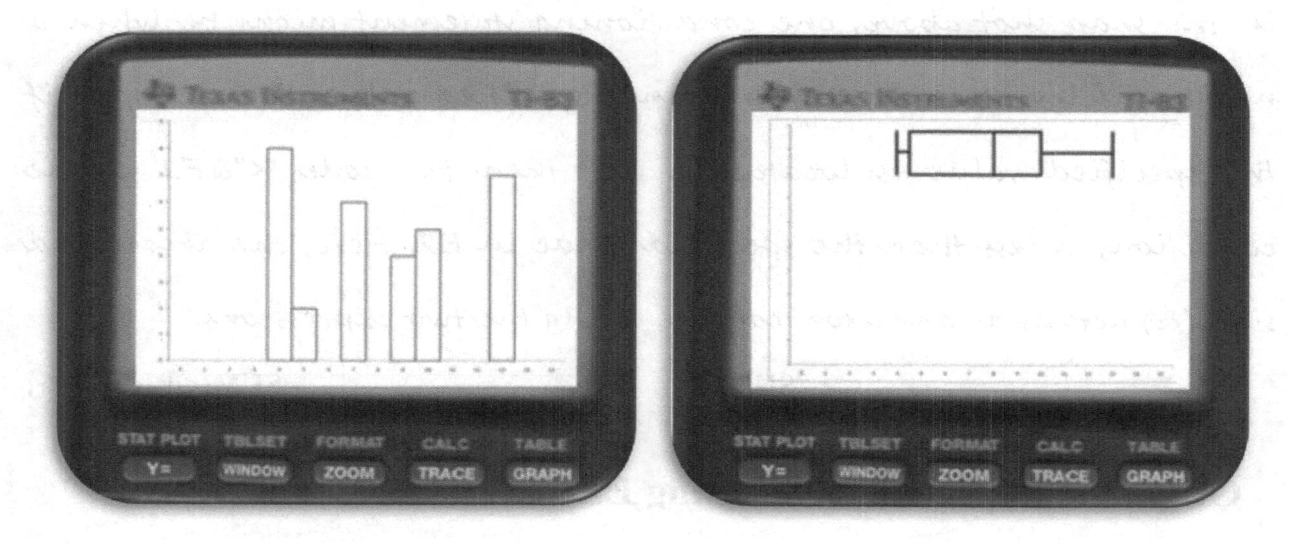

*The five-number summary can be more easily read from the summary statistics under $\boldsymbol{STAT} > CALC$ **1:**$1 - \boldsymbol{Var\ Stats}$, we see the minimum is $\mathbf{4}$, the first quartile is $\mathbf{4.5}$, the median is $\mathbf{8}$, the third quartile is $\mathbf{10}$ and the maximum is $\mathbf{13}$.*

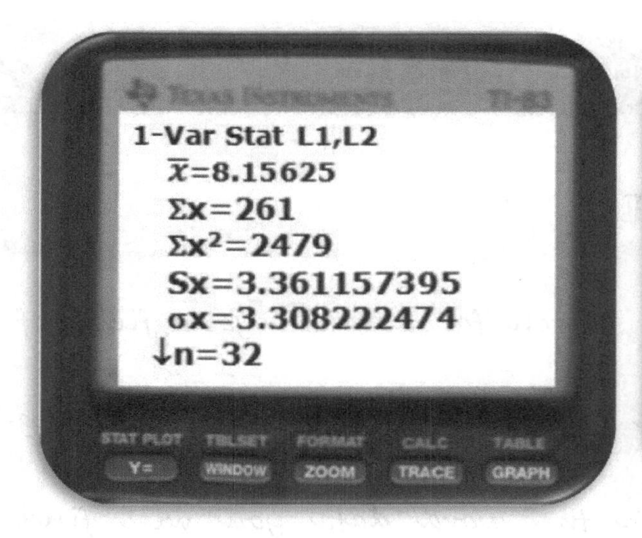

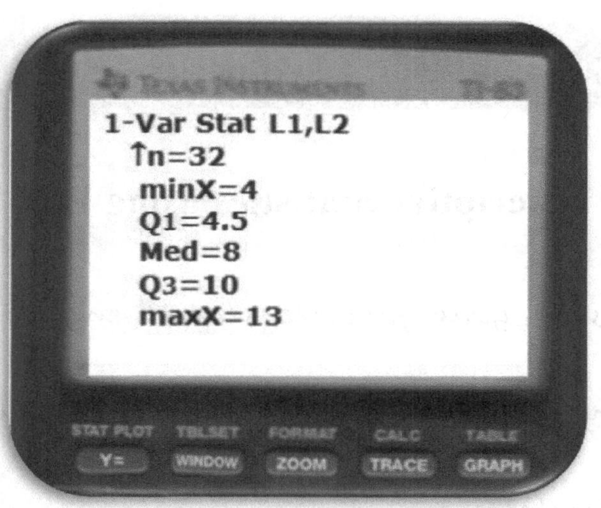

TI 83 — BASIC COMMANDS FOR GRAPHICS

- **STAT > EDIT**
  - To enter a list, use **EDIT** and simply type data values and press **ENTER**
    - **STAT PLOT (2nd Y=)** and turn on the desired plot and select style
      - scatter plots
      - frequency polygons
      - histogram
      - box plot I
      - box plot II
      - ogive graph
    - **GRAPH**

Using Technology in Descriptive Statistics C3

Descriptive Statistics using EXCEL

Using your favorite search engine, search for data in your field of interest and find information you can analyze. For example, using Google even if you simply search the word **data** you will find approximately 1.47 million results, one of which is the site Data.gov, which under Metrics you will find all Federal Agencies participating with Data.gov.

FORMAT: Bold key words to be **emphasized**, **label figures** and **tables**, and **paginate**.

QUESTION 1 You must first gather information on a topic of interest to you. This data must include at least one **qualitative variable** and two **quantitative variables** (a **response variable** and an **explanatory variable**.) Information may need to be reorganized and/or summarized.

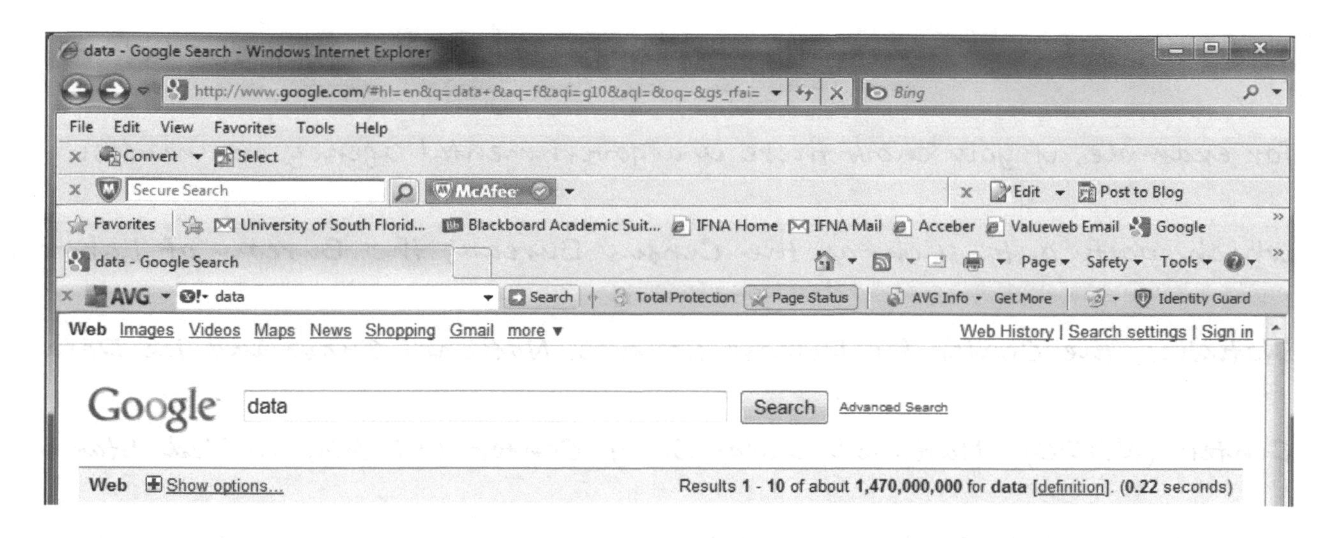

By adding additional keywords, you can find data that is more specific to your research as well as (hopefully) reduce the number of results. This assignment is intended to illustrate the difficulty of finding and cleaning data. However, there are a multitude of data sets outlined in the Data Discussion (Chapter 0) and provided in the Appendix.

QUESTION 2 State the **Data** source and description: website where data was gleaned, the variables of interest and sampling methods, etc.

The more detail you know about what you are looking for, the better - for example, if you know there is a governmental agency or university which posts data such as the **Census Bureau**, the **Bureau of Labor Statistics**, the **Center for Disease Control**, **National Snow and Ice Data Center** (NSIDC), **National Data Buoy Center** (NDBC), **United States Department of Agriculture** (USDA), among others. For example, starting with the **USDA** at **www.ers.usda.gov** browsing by subject, select **Crops**; then, there are briefings on several different crops, without loss of generality (for academic proposes), select Corn. From this link, we have a write-up about corn with links to **Feed Grains Database**. In this link, we have several data options, one of which is **Wheat Yearbook Data Tables** which includes the supply, demand, and price data related to wheat.

QUESTION 3 In your data set, identify the **variables;** characterizing them as **Qualitative** or **Quantitative**, **Discrete** or **Continuous**, and finally as the **Subject Response** or **Explanatory**. In your data set, identify the **level of measures** for each variable. For each quantitative variable, give **descriptive statistics** for each of the variables (if the statistic exists); that is, the **mean**, **median**, **mode**, **minimum**, **maximum**, **quartiles**, **range**, **variance** and **standard deviation**. For example, for qualitative data the mode may exist, but not the mean. Include the **coefficient of variance** and the **10% trimmed mean**. Discuss any possible **lurking variables**.

In the tables located in the search described above, there are 36 files containing data, the third of which contains the following information about ***all wheat*** *and for* ***Durum wheat****.*

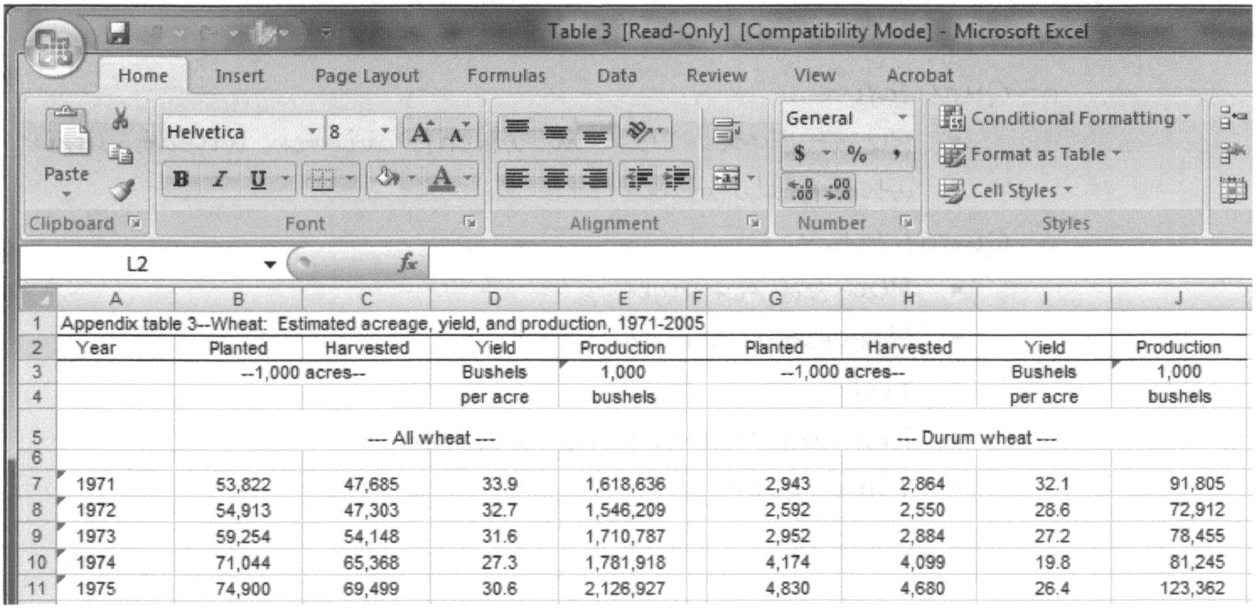

Table 3 [Read-Only] [Compatibility Mode] - Microsoft Excel

Appendix table 3--Wheat: Estimated acreage, yield, and production, 1971-2005

Year	Planted	Harvested	Yield	Production	Planted	Harvested	Yield	Production
	--1,000 acres--		Bushels per acre	1,000 bushels	--1,000 acres--		Bushels per acre	1,000 bushels
	--- All wheat ---				--- Durum wheat ---			
1971	53,822	47,685	33.9	1,618,636	2,943	2,864	32.1	91,805
1972	54,913	47,303	32.7	1,546,209	2,592	2,550	28.6	72,912
1973	59,254	54,148	31.6	1,710,787	2,952	2,884	27.2	78,455
1974	71,044	65,368	27.3	1,781,918	4,174	4,099	19.8	81,245
1975	74,900	69,499	30.6	2,126,927	4,830	4,680	26.4	123,362

In this example, there are six variables: estimated **acreage** (**planted** and **harvested** in 1000 acres), **yield** (bushels per acre), **production** (1000 bushels), **type** (Durum wheat, winter wheat, other spring wheat, all wheat) and **time** (1971-2005). The qualitative variable is **type** as this one of two categories (all or Durum wheat) and the other five variables: **acreage planted**, **acreage harvested**, **yield**, **production** and **time** are quantitative. Here, let Production be the subject response. Therefore, we want to better understand how plant type, acreage, yield and time relate or explain the amount of production.

- ⇨ Variables
  - Qualitative
    - Plant Type: Durum wheat, winter wheat, spring wheat, all wheat
  - Quantitative
    - Planted Acreage
    - Harvested Acreage
    - Yield
    - Production (Response Variable)
    - Time (year)

For the summary information, we can extract the information without superfluous row(s) and "clean" the data. **Cleaning** the data entails such things as removing blank rows, ensuring that all numerical information is being read as numerical – in Excel one way to determine this is where the numbers align – to the left, it is being read as a character string, to the right, a numerical value. Other edits may include aligning data into a single data array and possibly reorganizing and/or recoding the information.

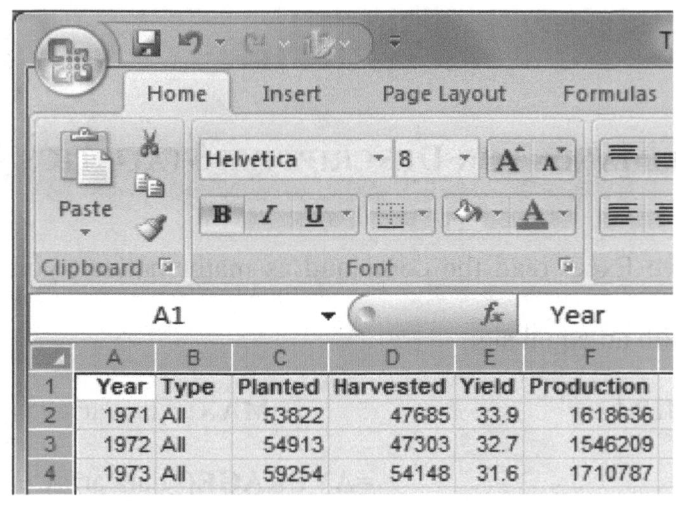

	A	B	C	D	E	F
1	Year	Type	Planted	Harvested	Yield	Production
2	1971	All	53822	47685	33.9	1618636
3	1972	All	54913	47303	32.7	1546209
4	1973	All	59254	54148	31.6	1710787

Then we can use Excel to compute the **mean**, **median**, **mode**, **minimum**, **maximum**, **quartiles**, **range**, **variance** and **standard deviation**. First, insert ten rows above the headers presently in the first row. Highlight the first nine rows, right click and select Insert.

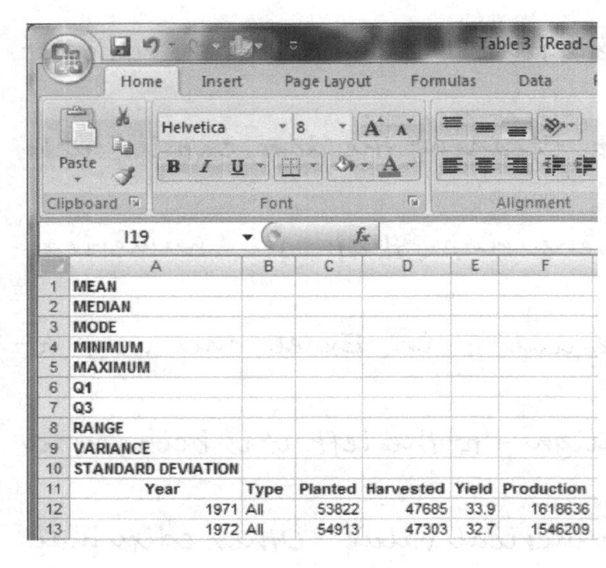

Then in the first column (or insert a starter column) label the information accordingly. There are Excel commands to compute each of these. Note however, we do not need this summary information for year or type and hence, we will begin coding in column C.

EXCEL — BASIC COMMANDS FOR DESCRIPTIVE STATISTICS

❖ Note: to have Excel read the command as mathematical; you must start with an equal sign.

- ➢ MAXIMUM **=MAX(**<data array>**)**
- ➢ MEAN **=AVERAGE(**<data array>**)**

Note: Excel can also compute a "trimmed" mean as well using the command **=TRIMMEAN(**<data array>, <percentage>**).**

- ➢ MEDIAN **=MEDIAN(**<data array>**)**
- ➢ MINIMUM **=MIN(**<data array>**)**

➢ MODE **=MODE(**<data array>**)**

Note: as the Mode may fail to exist, this descriptive statistic may appear as #N/A which means this measure is not applicable.

➢ QUARTILE(S) **=QUARTILE(**<data array>,<quartile>**)**

➢ RANGE **=MAX(**<data array>**)-MIN(**<data array>**)**

Or one can refer to the above **MIN** *and* **MAX** *by referring to the cells as one would in Battleship; if* ***C4*** *is the minimum and* ***C5*** *is the maximum, then the range is* $= \boldsymbol{C5} - \boldsymbol{C4}$.

➢ STD. DEVIATION **=STDEV(<data array>)**

Note here, the variance is the standard deviation squared, and therefore, had we computed the standard deviation first using Excel in cell ***C10****, then the variance is found using the code* ***=C10^2****. Hence, the caret key (^) is indicative of a power and therefore,* ***^2*** *indicates the power of two or a square.*

➢ VARIANCE **=STDEV(<data array>)^2**

Once you have this in one column, you can highlight the information and copy to the remaining columns; that is, highlight the cells $C1{:}C10$ and when you see **+** then drag the formulas to columns ***D***, ***E*** and ***F***.

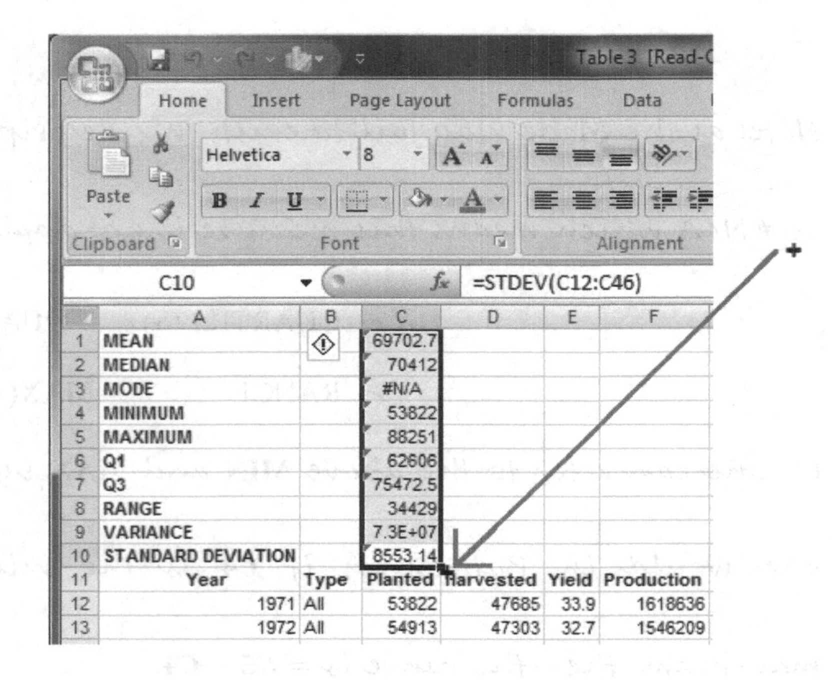

	A	B	C	D	E	F
1	MEAN		69702.7			
2	MEDIAN		70412			
3	MODE		#N/A			
4	MINIMUM		53822			
5	MAXIMUM		88251			
6	Q1		62606			
7	Q3		75472.5			
8	RANGE		34429			
9	VARIANCE		7.3E+07			
10	STANDARD DEVIATION		8553.14			
11	Year	Type	Planted	Harvested	Yield	Production
12	1971	All	53822	47685	33.9	1618636
13	1972	All	54913	47303	32.7	1546209

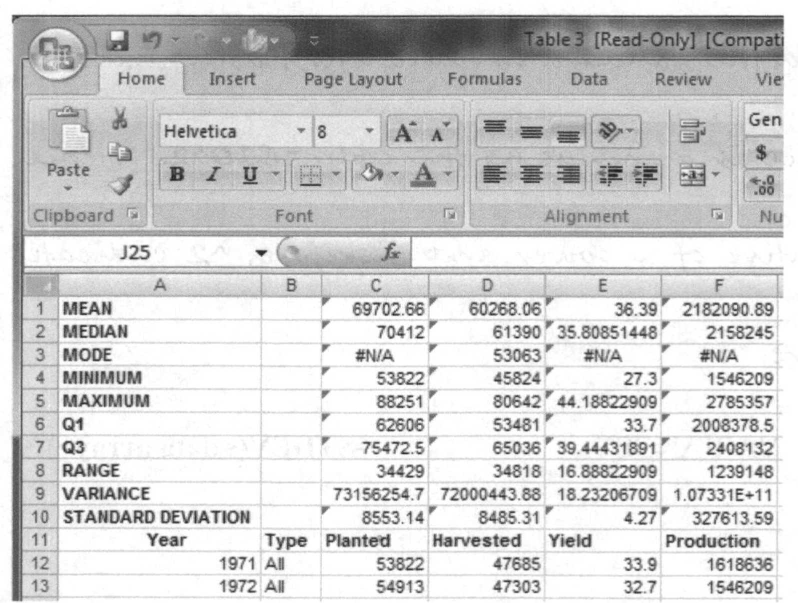

	A	B	C	D	E	F
1	MEAN		69702.66	60268.06	36.39	2182090.89
2	MEDIAN		70412	61390	35.80851448	2158245
3	MODE		#N/A	53063	#N/A	#N/A
4	MINIMUM		53822	45824	27.3	1546209
5	MAXIMUM		88251	80642	44.18822909	2785357
6	Q1		62606	53481	33.7	2008378.5
7	Q3		75472.5	65036	39.44431891	2408132
8	RANGE		34429	34818	16.88822909	1239148
9	VARIANCE		73156254.7	72000443.88	18.23206709	1.07331E+11
10	STANDARD DEVIATION		8553.14	8485.31	4.27	327613.59
11	Year	Type	Planted	Harvested	Yield	Production
12	1971	All	53822	47685	33.9	1618636
13	1972	All	54913	47303	32.7	1546209

In our example, this shows that (for all wheat), the mean number of planted acreage is 69,702.66 whereas the mean number of harvested acreage is 60,268.06 with a mean yield of 36.39 bushels per acre and the mean production of 2,182, 090.89 bushels. The median for both the planted and harvested acreage is greater than mean acreage, which is indicative of a skew in the data - this might be a response to time.

Descriptive Statistics using TI-83

To determine the same information using the $TI-83$, we must first input the data into a **List**. Starting by pressing the key marked **STAT**, shown right to being the process of enter the data.

Once we have this menu up, we need to edit the list of data. Select **Edit**.

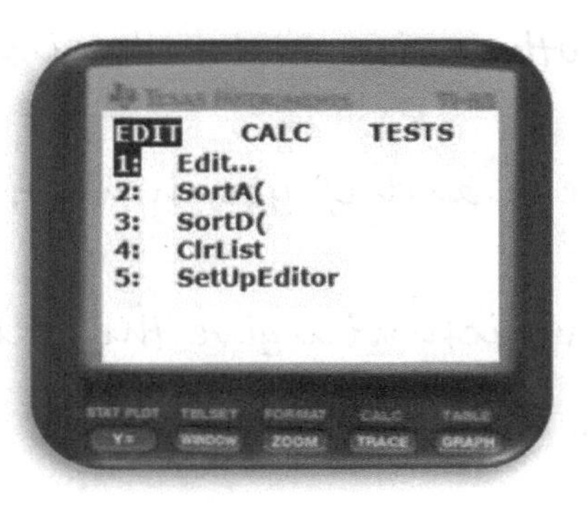

Then enter the data into any list, and if you have frequency data (and not listed data, then put the data values in one list and the frequencies in a second list. Then quit this menu: **2nd MODE (QUIT)**. Then re-enter the **STAT** menu as above. Then using the arrow keys, select the **CALC** menu.

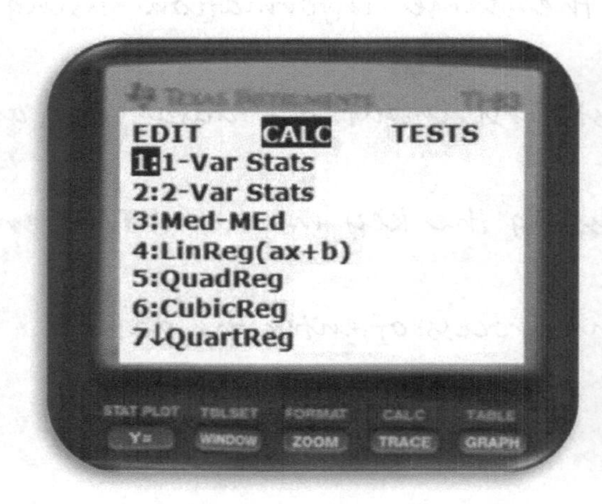

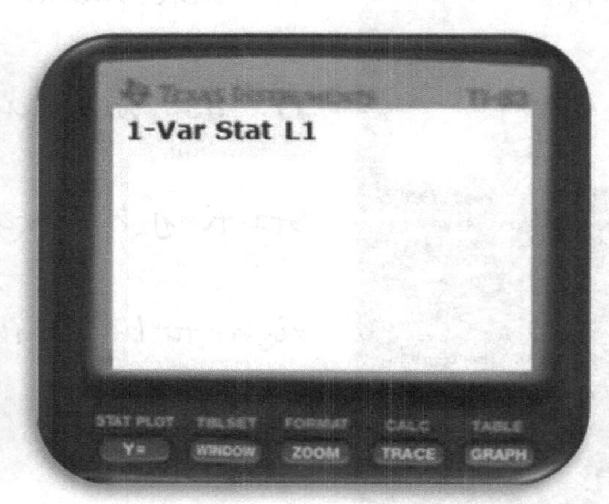

Select **1-Var Stat** and if the data is in list one, this will suffice; otherwise, enter the list where the data is located using **2nd > L1** or **L2**, etc. and if you have frequency data in **L1** and **L2**, use: **1-Var Stat L1, L2** which will give the following descriptive statistics.

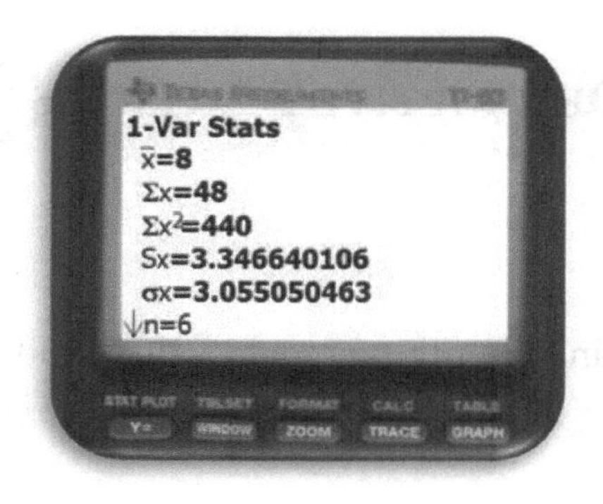

The **sample mean** is **8**, the sum of the data ($\sum x$) is **48** and the sum of the data-squared ($\sum x^2$) is equal to **440**. The **standard deviation** assuming this is a **sample** (s) is approximately **3.346** whereas under the assumption that this is population data, the **standard population deviation** (σ) is about **3.055**.

Using the down arrow (**blue keys**), we can view the remaining summary statistics: the **minimum** (**minX**) value is **4**, the **first quartile** **Q_1** is **5**, the **median** (**Med**) is **8**, the **third quartile** **Q_3** is **10**, the **maximum** (**maxX**) is **13**.

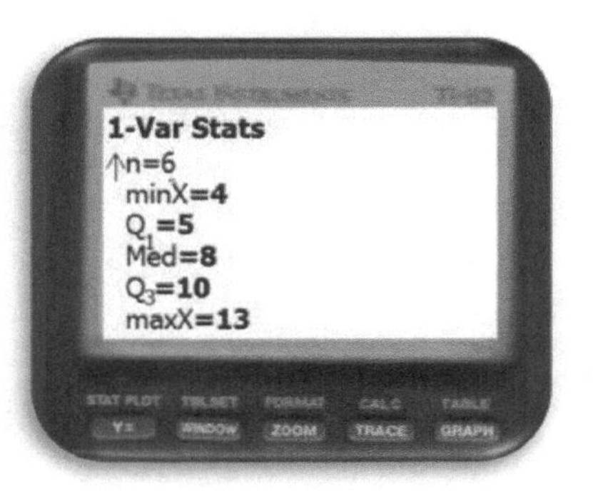

TI 83 — BASIC COMMANDS FOR DESCRIPTIVE STATISTICS

❖ **STAT > EDIT**

- To enter a list, use **EDIT** and simply type data values and press **ENTER**
- To clear list, using the arrow keys move up onto the list to be cleared and select **CLEAR** and **ENT ER**
- To sort data in list $L\#$ in ascending order, use $\mathbf{SortA}(L\#)$
- To sort data in list $L\#$ in descending order, use $\mathbf{SortD}(L\#)$

❖ **STAT > CALC**

- To compute summary information for data listed in $L\#$

  1-Var Stats $L\#$

- Frequency data with data in Li and frequencies in Lj

  1-Var Stats Li, Lj

Using Technology in Probability C4

Probabilities using EXCEL

You will need to used the accompanying **Excel** file "Excel Chapter 4 Using Technology in Probability" to generate the information needed for many of the following questions.

FORMAT: Bold key words to be **emphasized**, **label figures** and **tables**, and **paginate**.

Question 1: **Simulate** or toss a single fair (new) coin with a sample size of 10, 50 and 100 and give frequency tables; include step-by-step outline of **simulating** or **experimental** procedure. What is the **probability** of a head in your **simulation** or **experiment**? Comment on the percent heads and how the **law of large number** applies.

Above asks for the tossing of a fair coin; however, in the worksheet **Die Simulator**, there is the code necessary to simulate a fair die of sample

	A	B	C	D	E	F	G	H
1	Number of Roll	10		Roll	Simulation		Dice	Count
2				1	3		1	3
3				2	5		2	1
4				3	1		3	3
5				4	6		4	1
6				5	3		5	1
7				6	1		6	1
8				7	2			
9				8	4			
10				9	1			
11				10	3			
12								

size $n \leq 1000$. This simulator is a random generator and will re-generate. To stop the simulator from regenerating,

J	K	L	M	N	O	P	Q
Dice	Count		Dice	Count		Dice	Count
1	4		1	9		1	16
2	0		2	8		2	23
3	0		3	7		3	16
4	2		4	12		4	12
5	1		5	7		5	13
6	3		6	7		6	20

Copy the data and Paste Special, Value only.

Moreover, as this is a generator, it can simulate the three different sample sizes rather quickly. Just set the **Number of Rolls** equal to the various counts and the accompanying frequency table automatically counts each possible outcome. Hence, after using **Copy/Paste Special** three times, we have the summary information needed.

Here we see that when $n = 10$, this is not enough information when there are six possible outcomes – each outcome, on average, is expected to occur once or twice, however some do not occur at all. The relative frequencies range from **0%** to **40%** and not the expected **1/6 (16.7%)**; however, as stated by the **Law of Large Numbers**, as the sample size increases, the statistic approaches the parameter. That is, as the sample size increases, the estimated proportions approach the true proportions. When $n = 100$, the proportion of $1s$ is 16%. This is approximately the 16.7% expected on average, as well as the estimated proportions range from 12% to 23%. This is significantly less deviant than when n is small; even when $n = 50$, the relative frequencies range from 14% to 24%, significantly better than when $n = 10$.

HINT: You can use this **simulation** to simulate your coin by recoding the data; say, let evens represent heads and odds represent tails. This mapping matches the probability structure of a fair die to that of a fair coin. Note: this is not the only possible coding – this **simulation** will work as long as we have matching probability structures.

Simulation (this is how the accompanying Excel file is set up) – see the worksheet "Die Simulator" or "Alt Die Simulator".

Step 1 Set up Control (highlighted in yellow) as the counter (**A1:B1**)

Step 2 Set up Counter (**D1:D1001**) **D1="Count", D2=1, D3=D2+1, Copy/Paste D3 to D4:D1001**

Step 3 Create a random number between 0 and 1 (**RAND**), multiply by a large number greater than largest number to be simulated) and make this value an integer (**INT**), then use modular algebra (**MOD**) to generate a number in the set 0,1,2,3,4,5 and add 1 to create a number in the set 1, 2, 3, 4, 5 and 6.

Step 4 Once this data is simulated, then using **COUNTIF**, we can count the various outcomes within the simulation (**G1:H7**). For code using **COUNTIF**, see **H2:H7**.

NOTE: Alternatively, one can generate a random number between 0 and 1 and then partition this interval into six equal intervals, see "Alt Simulation" in the file "Chapter 4 Excel Using Technology in Probability" OR one can simply use a random number chart or can simply generate the data with a coin.

Question 2: Using the simulator given in the worksheet "**Three Coin Simulator**" which simulates tossing three "unfair" coins (a quarter, a dime and a nickel) with a sample size of 30, set the probabilities of heads to make the coins **unfair** – at present they are all set at 50%, that is, "fair" coins.

	A	B	C	D
1	P(H)=	50%	50%	50%
2	Count	Quarter	Dime	Nickle

In the **EXCEL** worksheet, QN represents the intersection of Q and N, or $Q \cap N$. Use the simulated information to draw the associated Venn diagram, include the number of tosses with no heads, that is, Q'D'N' or $Q' \cap D' \cap N'$. Answer the following questions including an illustration or **Venn Diagram.** Determine the following: **$n(Q' \cap D' \cap N')$, P(Q), P(D), P(N), $P(D \cap N)$, P(D only), $P(Q \cup D)$** and **Odds(Q).**

G	H	I
Number of Heads	Frequency	Estimated Proportion
n(Q)=	19	63%
n(D)=	14	47%
n(N)=	16	53%
n(QD)=	10	
n(QN)=	11	
n(DN)=	7	
n(QDN)=	5	

For the **Venn diagram**, Excel will not draw this for you directly. IT can draw the basic outline of the three circles as shown right; however, it does not readily allow for labeling of the intersection. However, if we drop this image into **Paint**, we can add the necessary detail using the simulated information. Start with the smallest piece they all have in common, namely the 5 times for which there was a head on all three coins. Then working our way out, we have **7-5=2** ways that the dime and nickel showed heads, but not the quarter, so forth and so on,

until we have completely filled in the regions within the circle and as there are 30 trials and only 26 total trials accounted for, there are 4 trials in which there are tails on all three coins, that is, no heads.

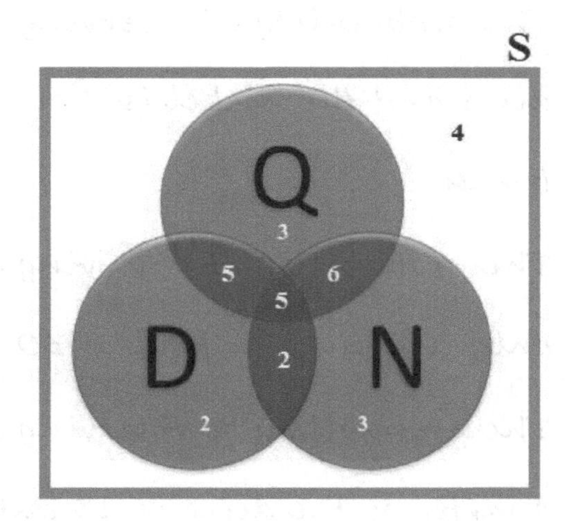

Hence, the answers follow directly:

$n(Q' \cap D' \cap N') = 4$ There are four trials such that there was not a head on the quarter (Q'), there was not a head on the dime (D') and there was not a head on the nickel (N').

$P(Q) = \frac{19}{30} = 0.63$	The probability of observing a head on the quarter is 19 out of a total of 30 trials or approximately 63%.
$P(D) = \frac{14}{30} = 0.47$	The probability of observing a head on the dime is 14 out of a total of 30 trials or approximately 47%.
$P(N) = \frac{16}{30} = 0.53$	The probability of observing a head on the nickel is 16 out of a total of 30 trials. or approximately 53%.
$P(D \cap N) = \frac{7}{30}$	The probability of observing a head on both the dime and the nickel is 7 out of a total of 30 trials.
$P(D\ only) = \frac{2}{30}$	The probability of observing a head on the dime only is 2 out of a total of 30 trials.
$P(Q \cup D) = \frac{23}{30}$	The probability of observing a head on the quarter or the dime is 23 out of a total of 30 trials.
$Odds(Q) = \frac{19}{11} = 19:11$	The odds of observing a head on the quarter is 19 out of a total of 30 trials or has the odds of 19 to 11.

Question 3: Product is ordered from three different companies: **A, B** and **C**. The proportions of defective product for each company are given next to each company. Using the generator in the worksheet "Tree diagram Values", change the number in the cell highlighted **yellow** and hit **ENTER**; then using the random values given, compute the following probabilities. Be sure to include a tree diagram illustrating the values given in the chart. State what is given and determine the following: **P(AD), P(BD), P(CD), P(D), P(D'), P(A|D), P(B|D)** and **P(C|D)**.

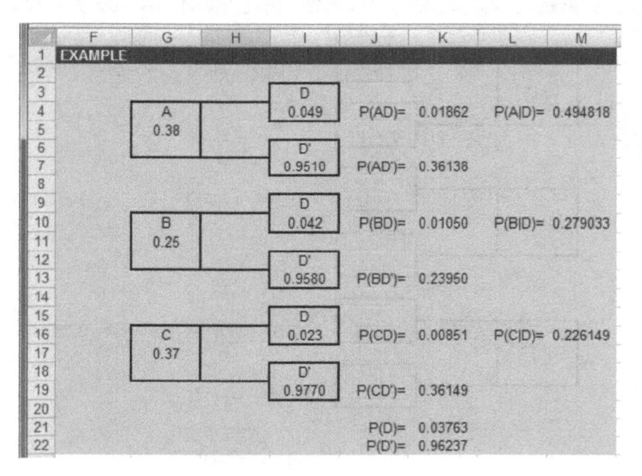

Highlighted in **blue**, the numbers used in the example problem are how each probability is computed. For example, the probability of being from company A and being defective, A∩D or AD, is given by the probability of A times the probability of defective given from company A. Hence, we have

$$P(AD)=P(A)\times P(D|A)=0.38\times 0.049=0.01862.$$

Using Excel, since P(A) is given in cell G5 and P(D|A) is given in cell 14, we can compute P(AD) in cell K4 as =G5*14, see coding in the worksheet. Similarly, all such probabilities can be computed using Excel, see K7, K10, K13, K16 and K19.

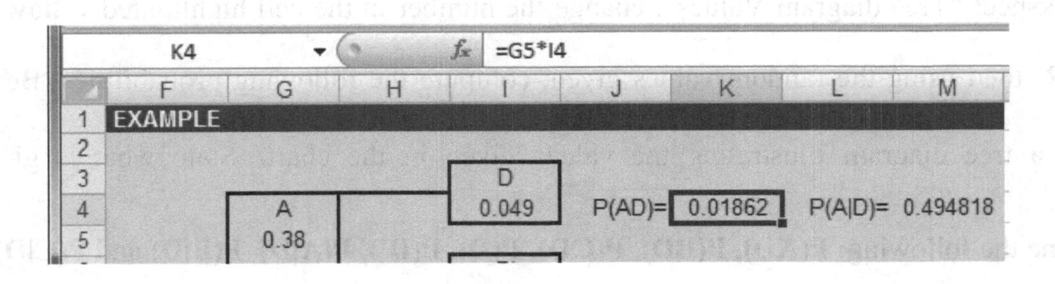

Once the probabilities of defective from either company A, company B or Company C, are known, we can combine these probabilities into the probability of being defective,

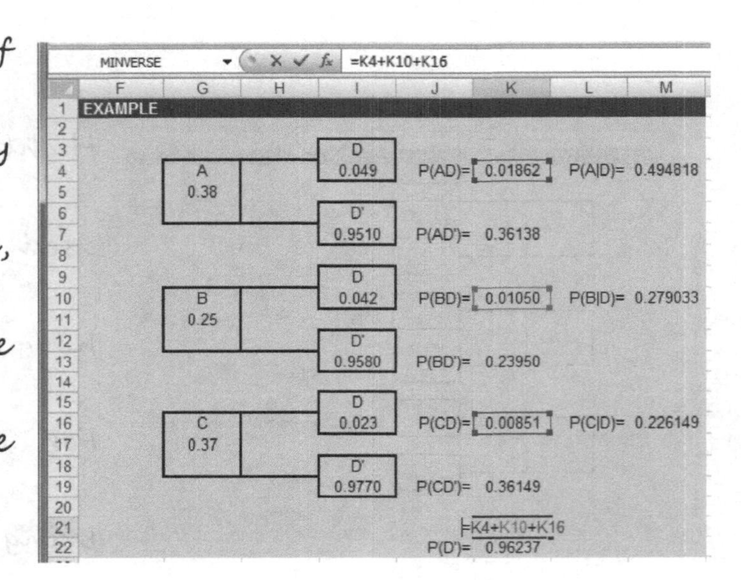

$$P(D) = P(AD \cup BD \cup CD)$$

$$= P(AD) + P(BD) + P(CD)$$

To compute this value using Excel, we have the individual probabilities in $K4$, $K10$ and $K16$; hence, the probability of defective can be computed in cell $K21$ using the code $= K4 + K10 + K21$.

We can also compute the probability of not being defective using $P(D') = 1 - P(D)$; in Excel, we have $P(D')$ computed in cell **K22** and since $P(D)$ is located in cell **K21**, we have the following coding, $= 1 - K21$. Hence we have the following:

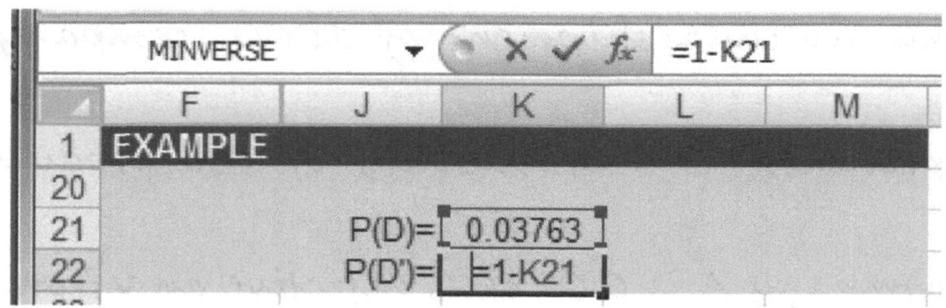

Given:

$P(A) = 0.38$	$P(B) = 0.25$	$P(C) = 0.37$
$P(D\|A) = 0.049$	$P(D\|B) = 0.042$	$P(D\|C) = 0.023$
$P(AD) = 0.01862$	$P(BD) = 0.01050$	$P(CD) = 0.00851$
$P(AD') = 0.36138$	$P(BD') = 0.23950$	$P(CD') = 0.36149$
$P(D) = 0.03763$	$P(D') = 0.96237$	$P(A\|D) = 0.4948$
$P(B\|D) = 0.2790$	$P(C\|D) = 0.2261$	

Interpretation:

That is, given that 38% of the product is ordered from company A, 25% of the product is ordered from company B, the remaining 37% is ordered from company C; furthermore, the probability of defective from company A, B and C, respectively, are 0.049, 0.042 and 0.023. This means in a shipment of 1000, company C has the fewest defective products. The probability of the product being defective and from company A is 0.01862, defective and from company B is 0.01050, and defective and from company C is (the least likely) 0.00851. Similar comments can be made regarding the probability of a product being from a given company and not being defective. The probability of being defective is 0.03763; that is, 3.763% of all products ordered are defective. Since the majority of the products are purchased from company A and company A has the highest proportion of defective products, the probability of being from company A given the product is defect is 49.48% (nearly half) whereas the probability a product is from company C given the product is defective is only 22.61%; the remaining 27.90% of defective products are from company B.

Question 4: Compute the number of **permutations** and **combinations** for selecting three out of four objects; that is, given $S = \{1,2,3,4\}$, how many way can we permute three out of four and how many ways can we combine three out of four. Illustrate all **permutations** and **combinations**.

To compute the number of Permutations in Excel, use the code **=PERMUT(**<n>,<r>**)** and to compute the number of Combinations, use the code **=COMBIN(**<n>,<r>**)**.

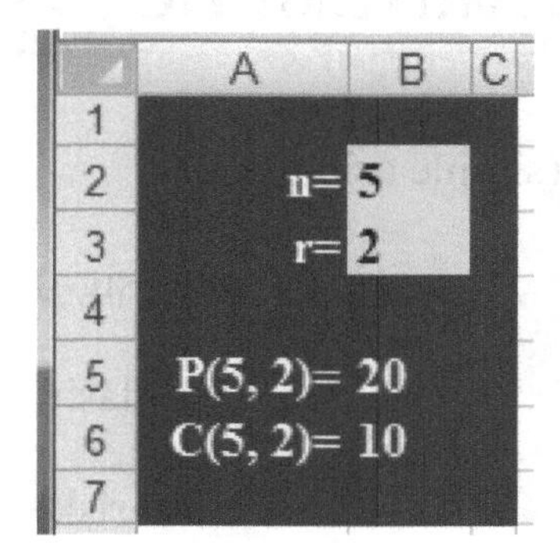

To illustrate all possible permutations and combinations, we can use lexicographical ordering. For example, consider the set $\boldsymbol{S} = \{\boldsymbol{A}, \boldsymbol{B}, \boldsymbol{C}, \boldsymbol{D}, \boldsymbol{E}\}$ and the number of ways to combine and permute two out of the five. Using Excel, we can see that there are 20 permutations and 10 combinations.

Permutations However, there are duplicate

AB AC AD AE combinations. The distinct **Combinations** are:

BA BC BD BE AB AC AD AE

CA CB CD CE BC BD BE

DA DB DC DE CD CE

EA EB EC ED DE

EXCEL	BASIC COMMANDS USED ARITHMETIC

- Note: these codes are at a lower level (simple arithmetic)
  - ADDITION + (plus sign)
  - SUBTRACTION - (en-dash)
  - MULTIPLICATION * (asterisk)
  - DIVISION / (backslash)
  - GROUPING SYMBOL ( ) (parentheses)

EXCEL — BASIC COMMANDS USED IN THIS SECTION

- Note: these codes are at a higher level and are used to simulate data.
  - COMBINATIONS **=COMBIN(**<n>,<r>)
  - FACTORIALS **=FACT(**<number>)
  - INTEGER **=INT(**<value>)

*Note: this integer function returns the greatest integer below the given value as known as the **Greatest Integer Function**.*

- MODULAR **=MOD(**<value>,<integer>)

Note: this modular function returns the remainder when the given value is divided by the specified integer.

- PERMUTATIONS **=PERMUT(**<n>,<r>)
- RANDOM NUMBER **=RAND()**

Note: the random number generated is between 0 and 1, not included with a uniform probability distribution.

Probabilities using TI-83

The TI – 83 calculator is capable of generating random digits that are ***uniformly distributed, factorials, permutations*** *and* ***combinations.***

Question 5: **Simulate** or toss a single fair ten sided dice with a sample size of 5, 10 and 15 and give frequency tables; included step-by-step outline of **simulating** or **experimental** procedure. What is the **probability** of a six in your **simulation** or **experiment**? Comment on the percent heads and how the **law of large number** applies.

Using the ***TI – 83****, under* ***MATH****) over to* ***PRB*** *and down to* ***5:randInt(****, then enter the minimum integer value, comma, ",", the maximum integer value, comma, ",", and the number of integers to be generated, followed by the closing parenthesis, ")".*

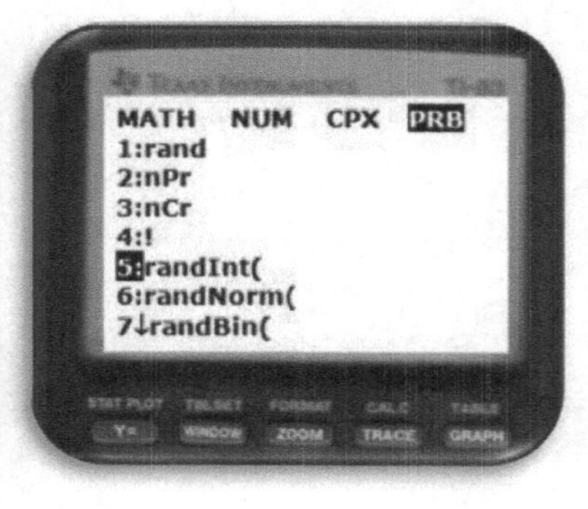

For example to simulate five tosses of a fair dice, we could use the code $\boldsymbol{randInt}(\mathbf{1}, \mathbf{6}, \mathbf{5})$.

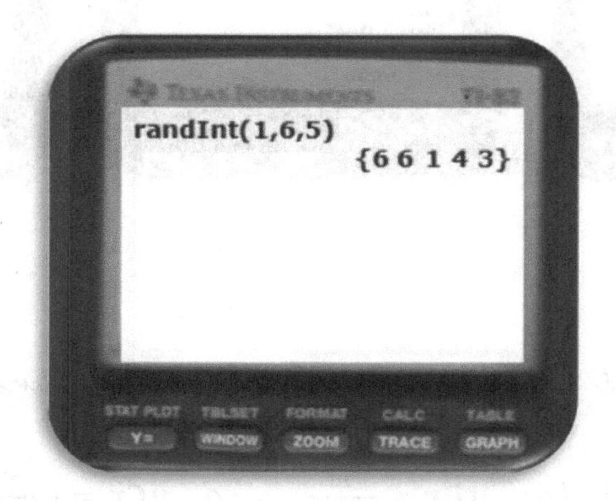

Question 6: Compute the number of **permutations** and **combinations** for each of problems below, where $\boldsymbol{n}$ is the number of distinct objects and $\boldsymbol{r}$ is the number of objects selected:

1. $\boldsymbol{n = 5, r = 4}$
2. $\boldsymbol{n = 5, r = 2}$
3. $\boldsymbol{n = 7, r = 4}$

Using the $\boldsymbol{TI - 83}$, under $\boldsymbol{MATH}$) over to $\boldsymbol{PRB}$ and down to **4:**! or we can use **2:** $\boldsymbol{nPr}$ or **3:** $\boldsymbol{nCr}$ then enter the minimum integer value, comma, ",", the maximum integer value, comma, ",", and the number of integers to be generated, followed by the closing parenthesis, ")".

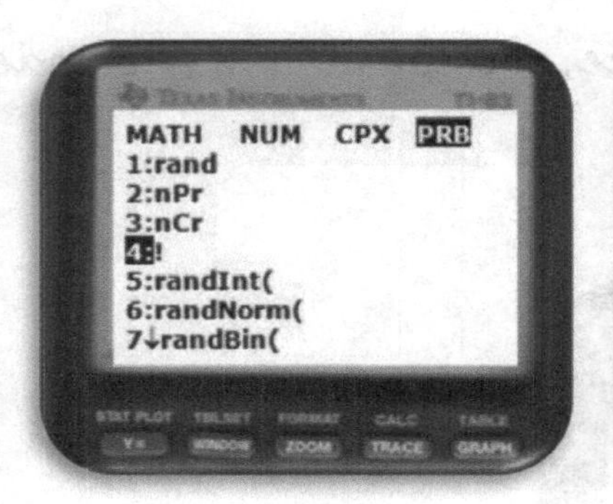

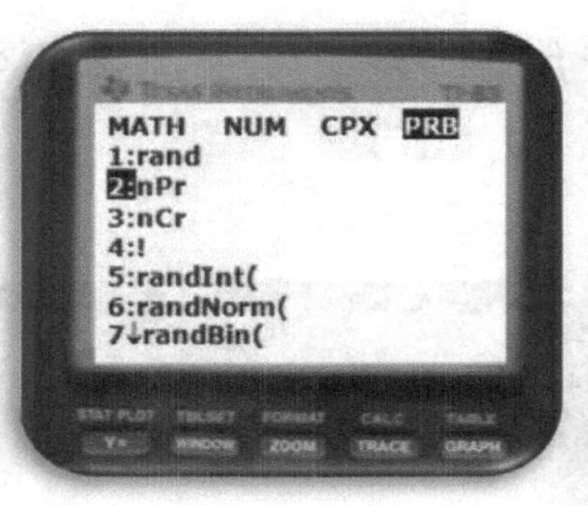

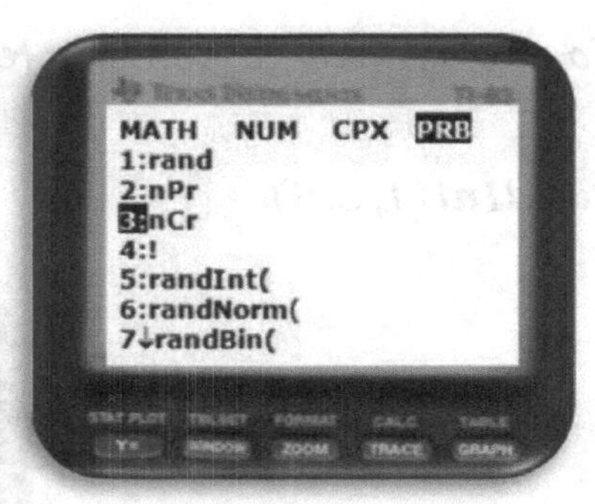

For example to find the number permutations and combinations, we could use the formulas $nPr = \frac{n!}{(n-r)!}$ and $nCr = \frac{n!}{r!(n-r)!} = \frac{nPr}{r!}$, or use the formulas predefined in the $TI-83$. Let $n = 4$ and $r = 3$, then we have:

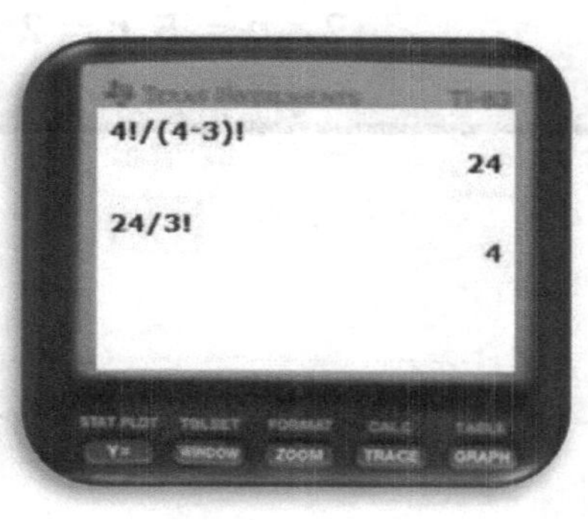

That is, there are **24** permutations of four objects taken three at a time, and only **4** distinct combinations. These are the same results we would obtain using nPr and nCr, respectively. Note here, the key strokes are to *enter the value of n,* ***4****, then under* ***MATH*** *over to* ***PRB*** *down to* **2:***nPr* *or* **3:***nCr, followed by the final number,* ***3****.*

TI 83 — BASIC COMMANDS FOR COUNTING

- **MATH > PRB**
  - RANDOM INTEGERS

    randInt(<minimum integer>**,**<maximum integer>**,** <sample size>**)**
  - FACTORIAL <number>**!**
  - PERMUTATIONS

    <# of trials> **nPr** <# selected>
  - COMBINATIONS

    <# of trials> **nCr** <# selected>

Using Technology in Discrete Probability C5

Discrete Probabilities using EXCEL

You will need to use the accompanying **Excel** file **"Excel Chapter 5 Using Technology in Discrete Probability"** to generate the information need for many of the following questions.

FORMAT: Bold key words to be **emphasized**, **label figures** and **tables**, and **paginate**.

Question 1: A raffle usually has one grand prize and several second, third and fourth place prices; the less the value, the greater the count in terms of number of winning tickets. Using the generator in the worksheet "**Raffle**", change the number in the cell highlighted yellow and press **ENTER**; then using the random values given, determine the following information. Be sure to include the chart with your simulated data and determine how many winning tickets are in this raffle? Moreover, if we assume there are 1000 tickets sold, what is the expected winning for a given ticket?

Given the value of the prices, the number of each price and the total number of tickets sold, we compute the proportion of times each price will be won, and this is the relative frequency.

	E	F	G	H
1			Value	Tickets
2		Grand Prize	9000	1
3		Second Place Prize	200	90
4		Third Place Prize	80	30
5		Fourth Place Prize	20	100
6				
7				1000

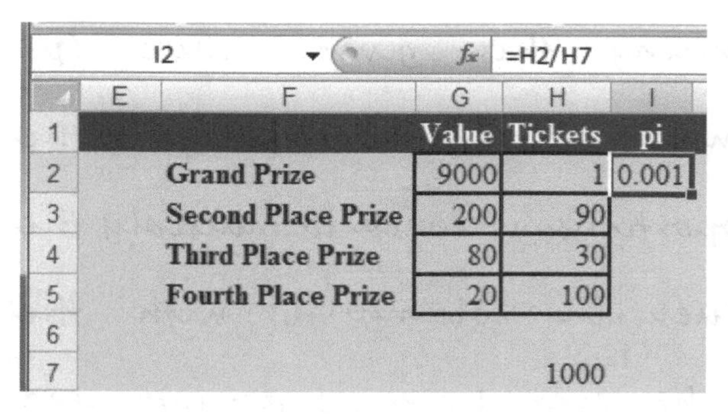

I2 | f_x =H2/H7

	E	F	G	H	I
1			Value	Tickets	pi
2		Grand Prize	9000	1	0.001
3		Second Place Prize	200	90	
4		Third Place Prize	80	30	
5		Fourth Place Prize	20	100	
6					
7				1000	

Hence, we want 1 over 1000, 90 over 1000, 30 over 1000 and 100 over 1000. Here, each of the frequencies given in cells **H2:H5** each need to be divided by **H7**; however, if we compute the relative frequency for the Grand Prize in **I2** as **H2/H7** and try to Copy/Paste down, the cell **H7** will change to **H8**, **H9** and **H10** – which is not what we need, we always want to divided by **H7**, so we need to put a stopper on the row (the number 7) and then, the code **=H2/H$7**, when Copy/Pasted or dragged down, the top row will change accordingly, from Grand Prize to Second Place Prize, so forth and so on, but it will always divide by the value in row 7, specifically **H7**. The probability will not sum to one as there are many losing tickets with **0$** in prize money.

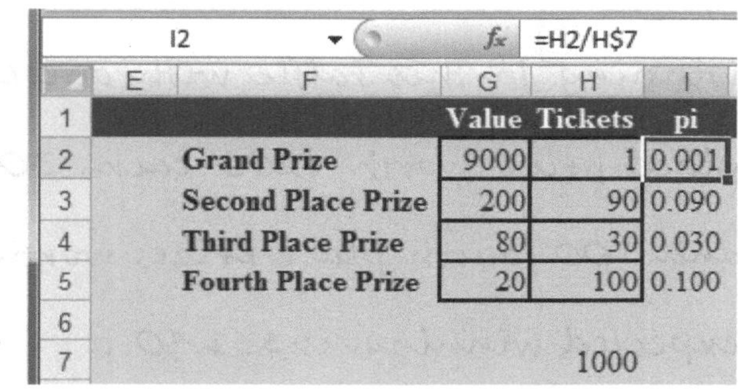

I2 | f_x =H2/H$7

	E	F	G	H	I
1			Value	Tickets	pi
2		Grand Prize	9000	1	0.001
3		Second Place Prize	200	90	0.090
4		Third Place Prize	80	30	0.030
5		Fourth Place Prize	20	100	0.100
6					
7				1000	

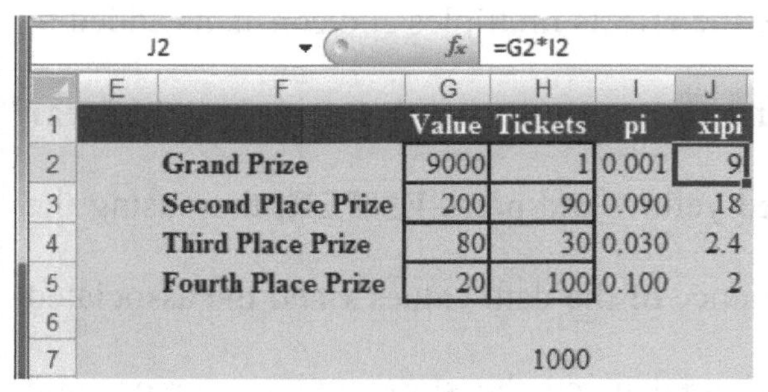

J2 | f_x =G2*I2

	E	F	G	H	I	J
1			Value	Tickets	pi	xipi
2		Grand Prize	9000	1	0.001	9
3		Second Place Prize	200	90	0.090	18
4		Third Place Prize	80	30	0.030	2.4
5		Fourth Place Prize	20	100	0.100	2
6						
7				1000		

Hence, using the formula for expected value, $E(x) = \sum x_i p_i$, we must also compute the products of the prize value (x) and the probability of

J7 | f_x =SUM(J2:J5)

	E	F	G	H	I	J
1			Value	Tickets	pi	xipi
2		Grand Prize	9000	1	0.001	9
3		Second Place Prize	200	90	0.090	18
4		Third Place Prize	80	30	0.030	2.4
5		Fourth Place Prize	20	100	0.100	2
6						
7				1000		31.4

winning this given value (**p**). Similar to computing the proportions, we need to multiply the values in column **G** with the probabilities compute in column **I**; however, here we do not need stoppers.

Then we can compute the sum of these values to determine the expected winning. In this raffle with one Grand Prize worth \$9000, 90 second place prize worth \$200 each, 30 third place prizes worth \$80 each and 100 fourth place prizes worth \$20 each and 1000 tickets sold, the expected winnings is \$31.40.

Question 2: Using linear relationships to illustrate the effects multiples and constants added to variable on the expected value and variance - using the generator in the worksheet "**Linear Relation**", change the number in the cell highlighted yellow and press **ENTER**; then using the random values given, compute the mean and the variance of the data values x and the associated data y values, explain how this could have been figured using the slope and y-intercept and properties of expected value.

This generator creates twenty matched pairs related by the slope and intercept given. From this information and using the basic Excel codes introduced in Chapter 2, we can compute the means, variance and standard deviation.

Sum	210	740
Mean	10.5	37
Std Dev	5.63	22.51
Variance	31.67	506.67

	A	B	C	E	F
1	Information	Value		x	y
2	Slope	4		1	-1
3	Intercept	-5		2	3
4				3	7
5				4	11
6				5	15
7				6	19
8				7	23
9				8	27
10				9	31
11				10	35
12				11	39
13				12	43
14				13	47
15				14	51
16				15	55
17				16	59
18				17	63
19				18	67
20				19	71
21				20	75

Given this information, $E(y)$ should be the same as $E(4x-5) = 4E(x) - 5$, and $4(10.5) - 5$ does equal 37.

That is,

$$37 = E(y) = E(4x-5) = 4E(x) - 5 = 4(10.5) - 5 = 42 - 5 = 37.$$

However, the variance is not affected by constant additives and is affected by the multiple-squared. That is, $V(y) = (4)^2V(x) - 0$ or more simplistically, $V(y) = 16V(x)$. Is this true in our example?

$$506.67 = V(y) = 16V(x) = 16(31.67) = 506.67.$$

This should verify the relationships: given $y = ax + b$ then $E(y) = aE(x) + b$ and $V(y) = a^2V(x)$.

Question 4: Discrete probability distributions: **Binomial, Poisson** and **Geometric**. Using the generator in the worksheet "**Distributions,**" determine the **expected value**, the **variance** and the **standard deviation** for each of the three distributions. What is the probability of the given number of successes or success on the given try? Show calculations and interpret results. Graph and discuss the Poisson probability distribution.

This question is an exercise in manipulation of the simulated data.

Binomial Probability Distribution

Information Binomial	Value
Probability of Success	0.11
Sample Size	962
Number of Success	110

Given the information for the binomial probability distribution, the expected mean is equal to np, the variance is $np(1-p)$, the standard deviation is the square-root of the variance and $P(x) = \binom{n}{x} p^x (1-p)^{n-x}$, where $\binom{n}{x}$ is combinations ${}_nC_x$. Hence, given the probability of success $P(S)$ in $G2$ and the sample size in $G3$, we can compute the mean (expected count) in cell $J2$ using the code $= G2 * G3$.

Similarly, we can compute the variance in cell $J3$ using the code $= G3 * G2 * (1 - G2)$, the

J2 | f_x =G2*G3

	E	F	G	H	I	J
1	EXAMPLE	Information Binomial	Value			
2		Probability of Success	0.11		Mean	105.8
3		Sample Size	962		Variance	94.2
4		Number of Success	110		Std Dev	9.7
5					P(110)=	0.0368

standard deviation in cell **J4** using the code $= J3\text{^}0.5$ or $= SQRT(J3)$. As for the final probability,

	fx =BINOMDIST(G4,G3,G2,0)			
F	G	H	I	J
Information Binomial	Value			
Probability of Success	0.11		Mean	105.8
Sample Size	962		Variance	94.2
Number of Success	110		Std Dev	9.7
			P(110)=	0.0368

we can either code the formula or use ***BINOMDIST*** in Excel.

Note: The **binomial probability distribution** of the desired number of successes in cell **G4** is based on the $P(S)$ in cell **G2**, the **sample size** in cell **G2**, and since we are interested in the single probability, this is indicated by the **0** whereas a **1** is indicative of the **cumulative probability distribution**.

ANSWER: The **expected value** is 106 (**105.8**); that is, out of a sample of size **962**, given an 11% success rate, we **expect** approximately **106** successes. With a **variance** of 94.2 and **standard deviation** of **9.7**, 110 is within one **standard deviation** of the expected number of successes. The probability of exactly 110 successes out of 962 trials is 3.68%.

CALCULATIONS: $\mu = np = 962 \times 0.11 = 105.8$

$$\sigma^2 = np(1-p) = 962 \times 0.11 \times 0.89 = 94.2$$

$$\sigma = \sqrt{94.2} = 9.7$$

$$\mu - \sigma = 96.1 \quad \text{and} \quad \mu + \sigma = 115.5$$

Geometric Probability Distribution

Given the information for the geometric probability distribution, the expected count (mean) is equal to $\mathbf{1/p}$, the variance is $(\mathbf{1-p})/\mathbf{p^2}$, the standard deviation is the square-root of the variance and $\mathbf{P(n)} = \mathbf{p(1-p)^{n-1}}$.

J8 | f_x | =1/G8

	F	G	H	I	J
7	**Information Geometric**	**Value**			
8	**Probability of Success**	0.07		**Mean**	14.3
9	**Number of Trials**	4		**Variance**	189.8
10				**Std Dev**	13.8
11				**P(4)=**	0.0563

Hence, given the probability of success $\boldsymbol{P(S)}$ in $\mathbf{G8}$ and the number of trials is given in cell $\boldsymbol{G9}$, we can compute the mean (expected count) in cell $\boldsymbol{J8}$ using the code $= \mathbf{1/G8}$, the variance in cell J9 is calculated using the code $= (\mathbf{1} - \boldsymbol{G8})/\boldsymbol{G8}\mathbf{\^{}2}$ and standard deviation in cell $\boldsymbol{J10}$ is the square-root of the variance found using the code $= \boldsymbol{SQRT(J9)}$.

To compute the probability of success on the nth trial, as given in **J4** we can compute this using the code $= G8 * (1 - G8)^\wedge(G9 - 1)$, where **G8** is the probability of success and **G9** is the number of trials.

	F	G	H	I	J
7	Information Geometric	Value			
8	Probability of Success	0.07		Mean	14.3
9	Number of Trials	4		Variance	189.8
10				Std Dev	13.8
11				P(4)=	0.0563

J11 =G8*(1-G8)^(G9-1)

ANSWER: The **expected value** is 15 (**14.3**); that is, in order to find success, we **expect** to have to try and try again – in fact, we expect to have to try 15 times (here we round us as if you must try 0.3 times, you must try one more time.) However, the **variance** is **189.8** and the **standard deviation** is **13.8**. That is, we can **expect** to have to try between 1 and 28 times. The **probability** of success on the fourth try is only **5.63%**.

CALCULATIONS: $\mu = \frac{1}{p} = \frac{1}{0.07} = 14.3$

$$\sigma^2 = \frac{(1-p)}{p^2} = \frac{1-0.07}{0.07^2} = 189.8$$

$$\sigma = \sqrt{189.8} = 13.8$$

$\mu - \sigma = 0.5$ and $\mu + \sigma = 28.1$

Poisson Probability Distribution

Given the information for the Poisson probability distribution, the expected count (mean) is equal to λ, the variance is λ, the standard deviation is the square-root of the variance and $P(x) = \frac{\lambda^x e^{-\lambda}}{x!}$.

J14 | f_x =G14

	F	G	H	I	J
13	Information Poisson	Value			
14	Mean number of Success	5.6		Mean	5.6
15	Number of Success	3		Variance	5.6
16				Std Dev	2.4
17				P(3)=	0.1082

Hence, given the mean number of successes in **G14** the mean given in cell **J14** is redundant as this is simply **G14**, the variance in cell **J15** is also **G14** and standard deviation in cell **J16** is the square-root of the variance found using the code $= SQRT(J15)$.

Coding the equation for the Poisson probability distribution $P(x) = \frac{\lambda^x e^{-\lambda}}{x!}$ requires the exponential function as well as factorials. The exponentiation base e is given by the code $\boldsymbol{EXP}(< value >)$ and factorials by the code $\boldsymbol{FACT}(< number >)$.

J17 fx =G14^G15*EXP(-1*G14)/FACT(G15)

	F	G	H	I	J	K
13	**Information Poisson**	**Value**				
14	**Mean number of Success**	5.6		**Mean**	5.6	
15	**Number of Success**	3		**Variance**	5.6	
16				**Std Dev**	2.4	
17				**P(3)=**	0.1082	

ANSWER: The expected value is 5.6; that is, given that the mean number of successes is specified as 5.6, the mean is 5.6 (rather redundant), what is more interesting is that this measure is also the variance - the exponential decay cause the spread to also be dictated by this mean value. Hence, the standard deviation is 2.4 and the probability of only three successes when 5.6 are expected is 10.82%. Given 5.6 successes are expected on average, anywhere between 4 and 8 are highly likely, relatively speaking.

	A	B	C	D	E
1	**Information Poisson**	**Value**		X	P(X)
2	**Mean number of Success**	5.6		0	0.003698

CALCULATIONS: $\mu = \lambda = 5.6$

$$\sigma^2 = \lambda = 5.6$$

$$\sigma = \sqrt{5.6} = 2.4$$

$\mu - \sigma = 3.2$ *and* $\mu + \sigma = 8$

*We can combine this with the graphics capabilities in Excel to better illustrate these measures. In the accompanying worksheet labeled "**Poisson Graphics**" there are two columns, **D** and **E**, coded in such a way that it will extend up to a probable number and then using the filter to remove all remaining blanks, the graph is given in the worksheet labeled "**Chart 1**". Once the mean number of successes is set, then select the filter on column **D**.*

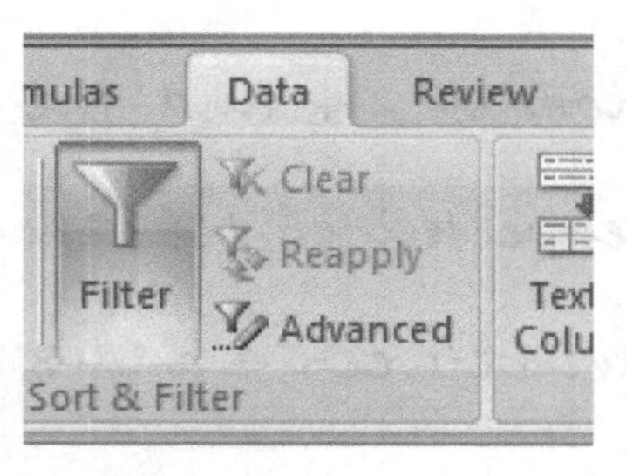

*Note: to turn on a filter, select the desired columns and under **Data**, select the **Filter**.*

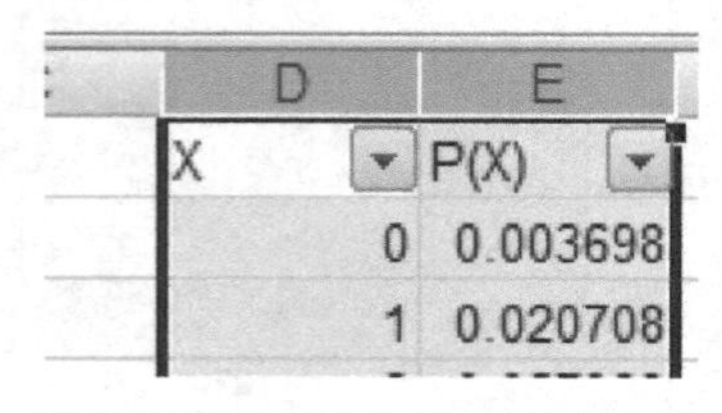

D	E
X	P(X)
0	0.003698
1	0.020708

Now, with the filter set to select all as show, you can change the mean number of success.

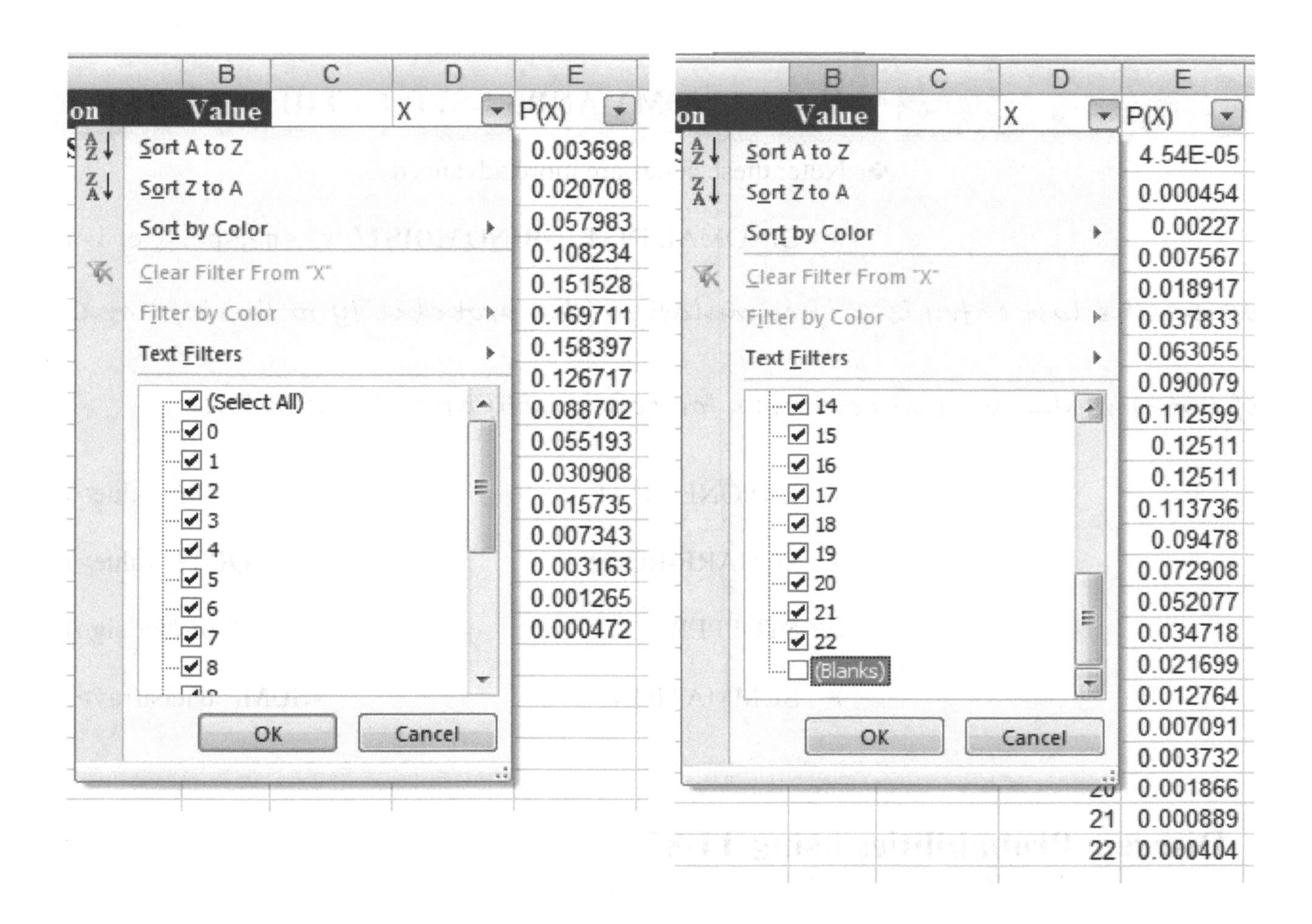

Then, once the worksheet has completely regenerated, using the Filter, unselect the blank entries and the chart will correctly display the new histogram.

Once the new graphic is in the worksheet named **Chart 1**, then this image can be copied and pasted into **Paint** or **Word**.

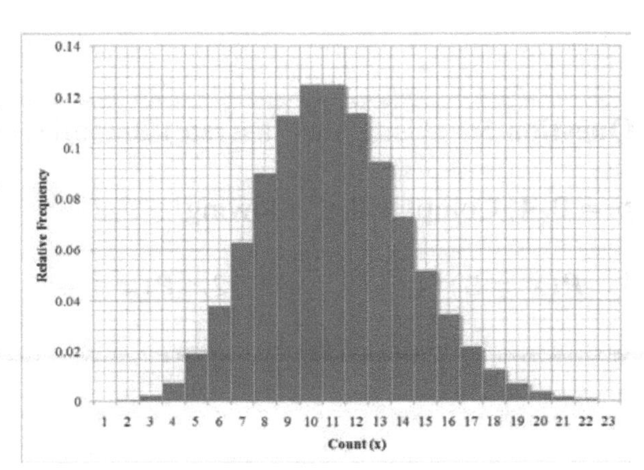

EXCEL — BASIC COMMANDS USED IN THIS SECTION

❖ Note: these codes are more advanced

- BINOMAL DIST. **=BINOMDIST(**<x>,<n>,<p>,<0 or 1>**)**

where the last entry is 1 if cumulative (the probability to the left) or 0 if not cumulative, but corrected for continuity at a single value.

- EXPONENTIAL **=EXP(**<value>**)**
- SQUARE-ROOT **=SQRT(**<value>**)**
- STOPPER $ (dollar sign)
- SUMMATION **=SUM(**<data array>**)**

Discrete Probabilities using TI-83

The $TI-83$ *calculator is capable of computing* ***discrete probability distributions*** *such as the* ***binomial***, ***Poisson*** *and the* ***geometric probability distributions.***

Question 5: Using the (discrete) Binomial probability distributions, given $\boldsymbol{n = 10}$ and $\boldsymbol{p = 0.4}$. Compute the following

1. $\boldsymbol{P(x = 5)}$
2. $\boldsymbol{P(x \leq 4)}$
3. $\boldsymbol{P(x = i), i = 0, 1, \ldots, 10}$

Using the $TI-83$, these values can reality be computing either entering the formula, or using the $DISTR$ (2nd $VARS$) down to **0:** $binomialpdf($ or **A:** $binomalcdf($.

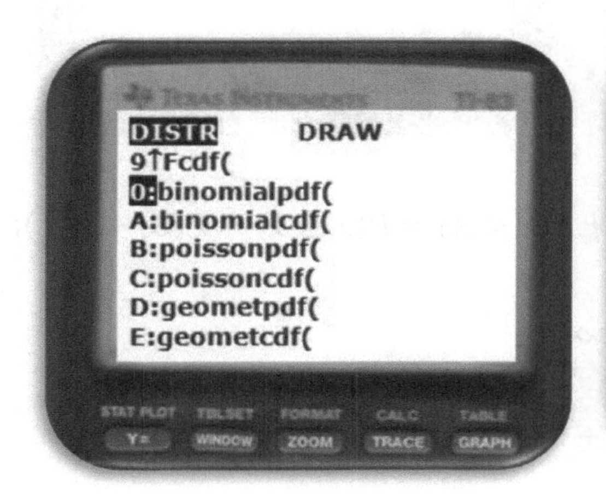

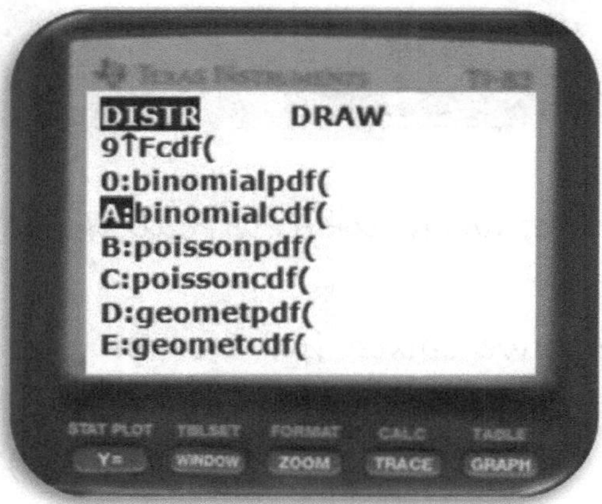

For example, given $n = 5$ and $p = 0.6$. Compute the following

1. $P(x = 3)$ 2. $P(x < 2)$ 3. $P(x = i), i = 0, 1, \dots, 5$

For part 1, we could have entered the code $5C3 * .6^3 * (1-.6)^(5-3)$ to obtain the final results, or we can use the code $binomialpdf(5, .6, 3)$ under $DISTR$ (2nd $VARS$) down to **0:** $binomialpdf($.

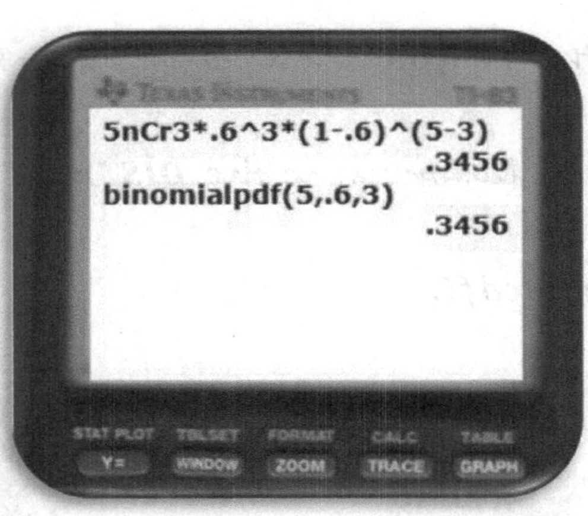

For part 2, we must first realist that $\boldsymbol{P(x < 2) = P(x \leq 1) = P(0) + P(1)}$;

therefore, we could have enter the code

$$\boldsymbol{5C0 * .6^\wedge 0 * (1-.6)^\wedge(5-0) + 5C1 * .6^\wedge 1 * (1-.6)^\wedge(5-1)}$$

to obtain the final results, or we can use the code $\boldsymbol{binomialcdf(5, .6, 2)}$

under $\boldsymbol{DISTR}$ $\boldsymbol{(2^{nd}\ VARS)}$ *down to* **A:***binomialcdf*(.

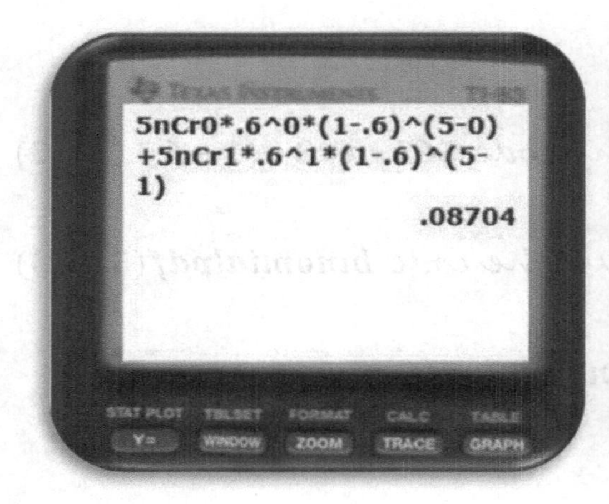

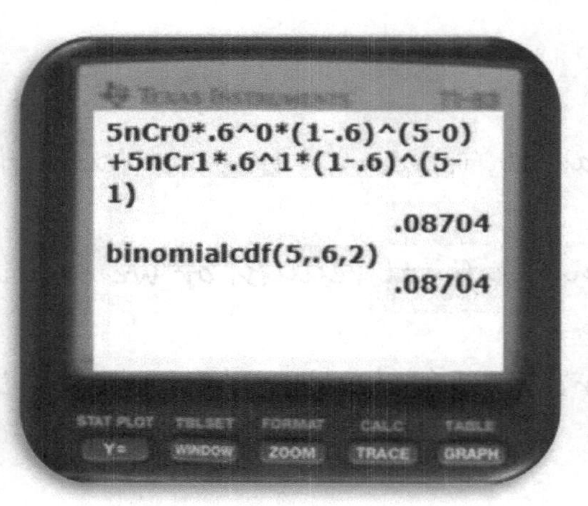

For part 3, we could repeat the procedure outlined in part 1, or we can use lists to simplify this issue as follows:

First, we must put the counts into a list. Under ***AT EDIT***, we can create a list using **1:*Edit*** and place the data in a list, say ***L1*** and then quit (2nd ***MODE***).

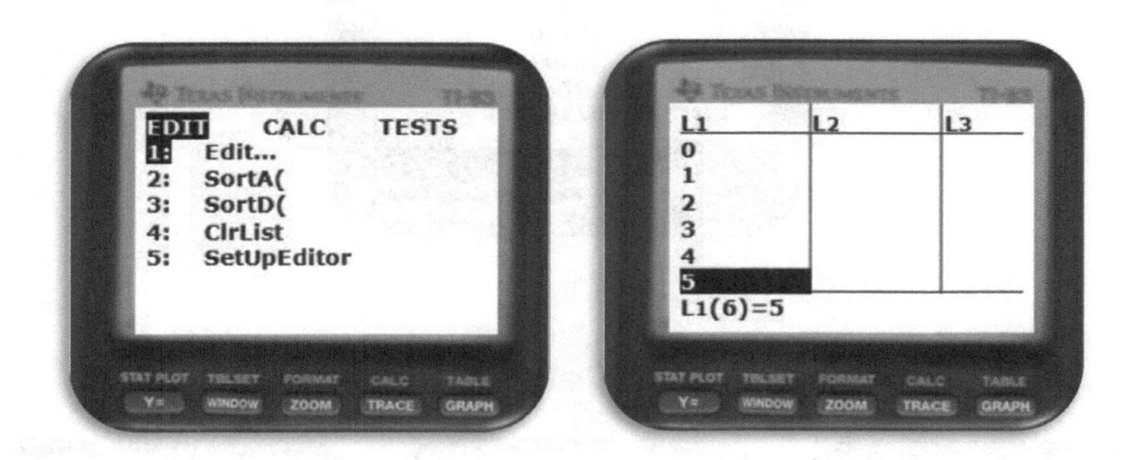

Then, using the second list, move up on top of the list and then press ***DISTR*** (2nd ***VARS***) down to **0:*binomialpdf***(and ***ENTER***. Then, you can add the parameters and number of successes by typing the number of trials, "**5**", followed by the number of successes a comma, ",", the probability of success, **.6**, a comma, ",", then list 1, ***L1*** (2nd **2**), ending with the closing parenthesis, ")" and ***ENTER***.

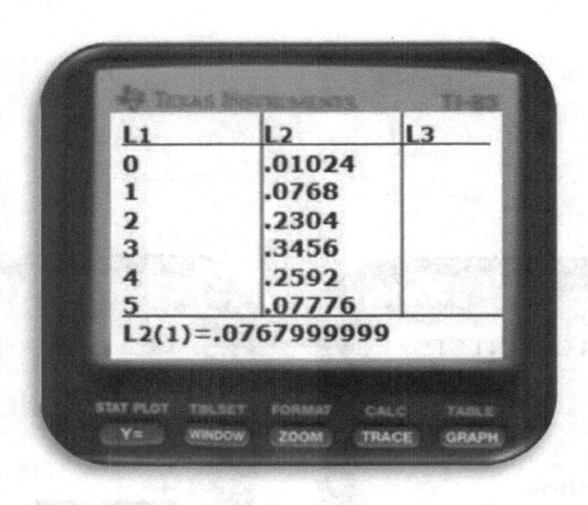

TEXAS INSTRUMENTS
TI-83
L1
L2
L3
0
.01024
1
.0768
2
.2304
3
.3456
4
.2592
5
.07776
L2(1)=.0767999999
STAT PLOT
TBLSET
FORMAT
CALC
TABLE
Y=
WINDOW
ZOOM
TRACE
GRAPH

L1
L2
L3
0
1
2
3
4
5
L2=
Y=
WINDOW
ZOOM
TRACE
GRAPH

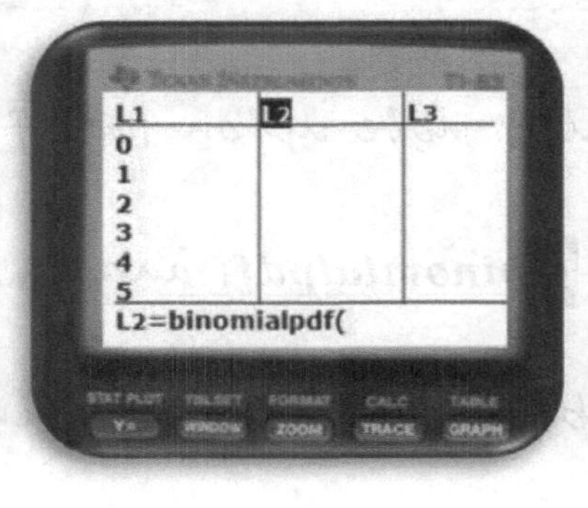

L1
L2
L3
0
1
2
3
4
5
L2=binomialpdf(
Y=
WINDOW
ZOOM
TRACE
GRAPH

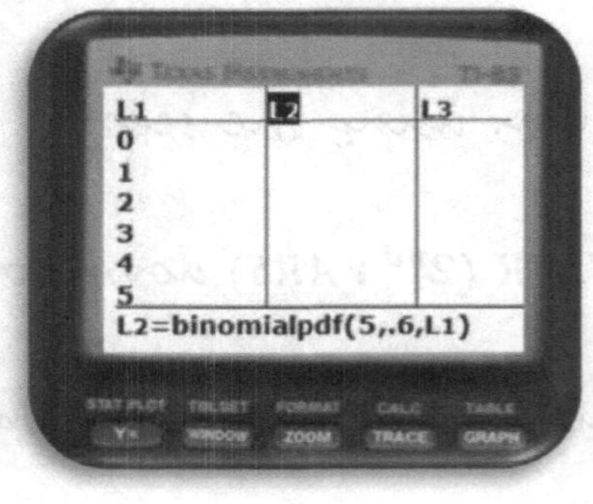

L1
L2
L3
0
1
2
3
4
5
L2=binomialpdf(5,.6,L1)
Y=
WINDOW
ZOOM
TRACE
GRAPH

Note, here we are given the answers to all three parts: part 1)

$$P(x = 3) = 0.3456,$$

for Part 2,

$$P(x < 2) = \mathrm{P}(0) + \mathrm{P}(1) = 0.01024 + 0.0768 = 0.08704$$

and for Part 3.

$$P(x = 0) = 0.01024$$

$$P(x = 1) = 0.0768$$

$$P(x = 2) = 0.2304$$

$$P(x = 3) = 0.3456$$

$$P(x = 4) = 0.2592$$

and

$$P(x = 5) = 0.07776.$$

Question 6: Using the (discrete) Poisson probability distributions, given $\lambda = 4.7$. Compute the following

1. $P(x = 5)$
2. $P(x \leq 5)$
3. $P(x = i), i = 0, 1, \ldots, 10$

*Using the $TI-83$, these values can reality be computing either entering the formula, or using the **DISTR** (2nd **VARS**) down to* **B:poissonpdf(** *or* **C:poissoncdf(**.

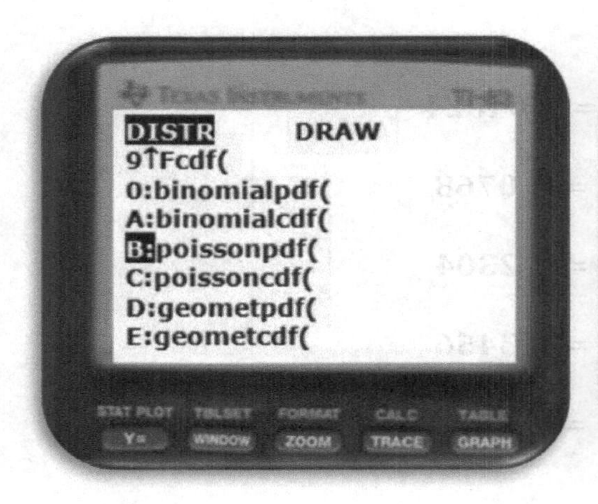

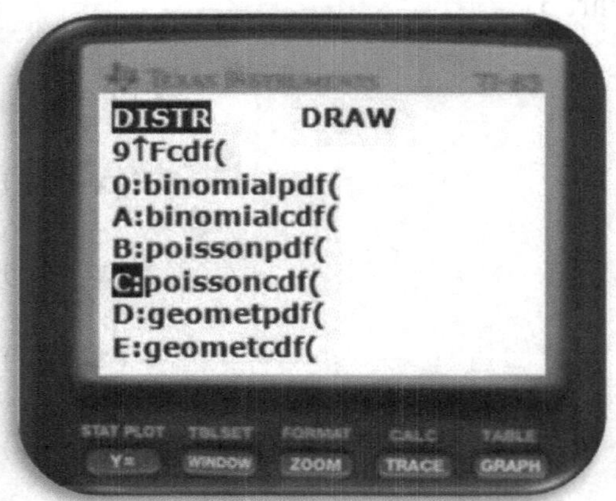

For example, given $\lambda = 4.7$, *compute the following*

1. $P(x = 3)$ 2. $P(x \leq 2)$ 3. $P(x = i), i = 0, 1, \ldots, 5$

For part 1, we could have enter the code $4.7\text{^}3 * e\text{^}(-4.7)/3!$ *to obtain the final results, or we can use the code* **poissonpdf**(5, .6, 3) *under* **DISTR** (2nd **VARS**) *down to* **B:poissonpdf(** *and the factorial "!" is under* **MATH** *over to* **PROB** *down to* **4:!**, *see Using Technology in Probability, Chapter 4.*

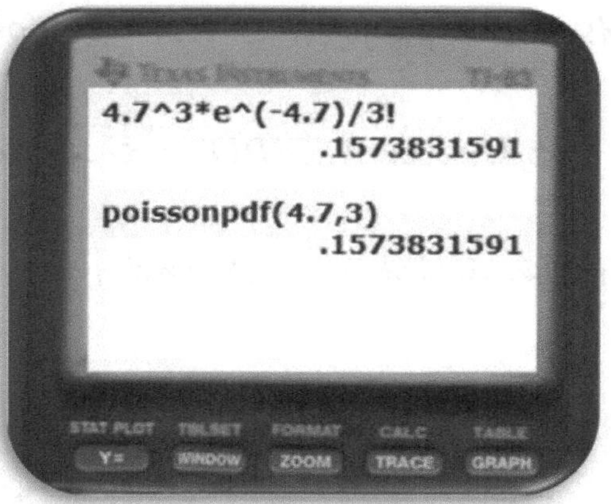

For part 2, we must first realist that $P(x \leq 2) = P(0) + P(1) + P(2)$;

therefore, we could have enter the code

$$4.7^\wedge 0 * e^\wedge(-4.7)/0! + 4.7^\wedge 1 * e^\wedge(-4.7)/1! + 4.7^\wedge 2 * e^\wedge(-4.7)/2!$$

to obtain the final results, or we can use the code $\boldsymbol{poissoncdf}(4.7, 2)$.

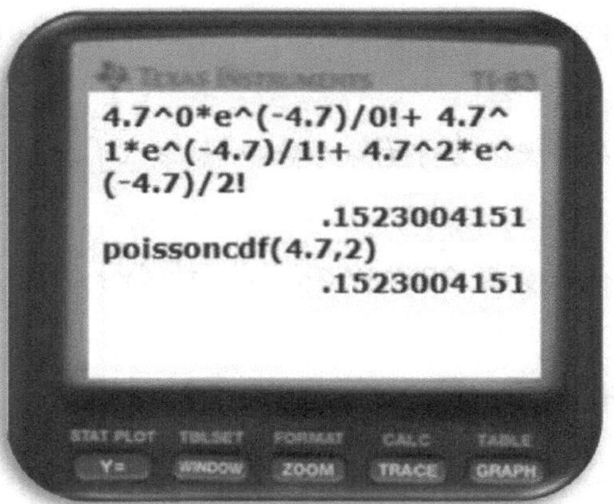

For part 3, we could repeat the procedure outlined in part 1, or we can use lists to simplify this issue as follows: first, we must put the counts into a list. Under *AT EDIT*, we can create a list using **1:*Edit*** and place the data in a list, say ***L1*** and then quit (**2nd *MODE***).

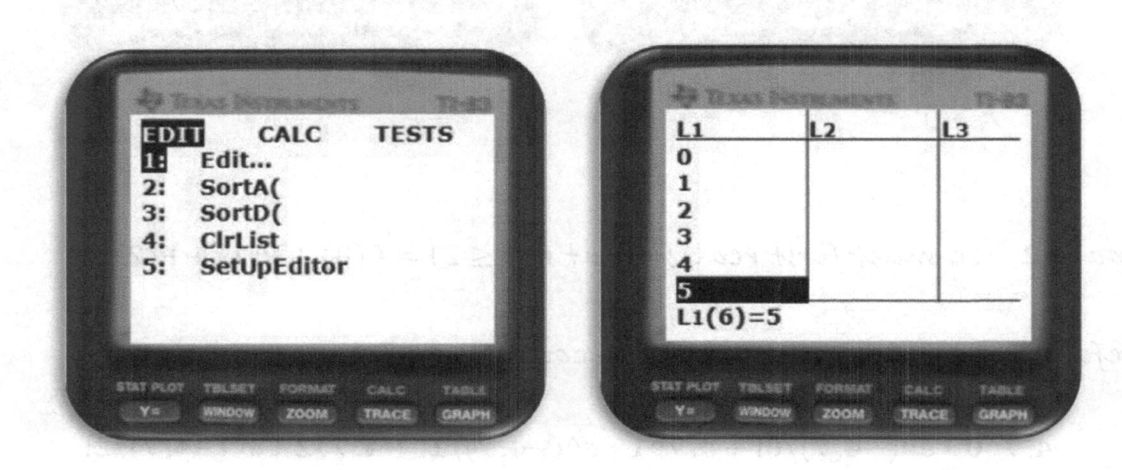

Then, using the second list, move up on top of the list and then press ***DISTR*** (**2nd *VARS***) down to **0:*poissonpdf*(** and ***ENTER***. Then, you can add the parameters and number of successes by typing the number of trials, "**5**", followed by the number of successes a comma, ",", the probability of success, .6, a comma, ",", then list 1, ***L1*** (**2nd 2**), ending with the closing parenthesis, ")" and ***ENTER***.

$$\boldsymbol{poissonpdf(4.7, L_1)}$$

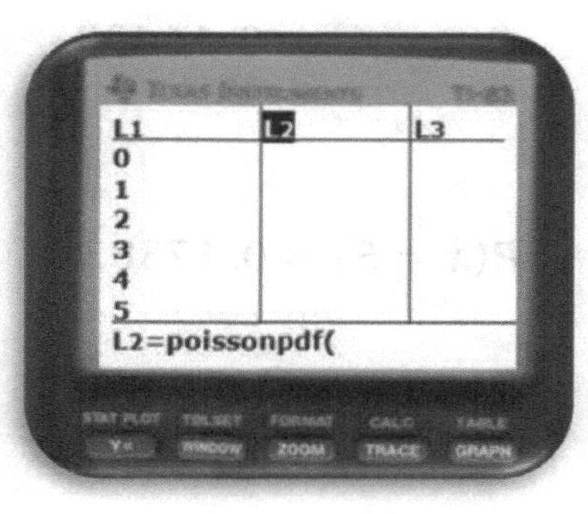

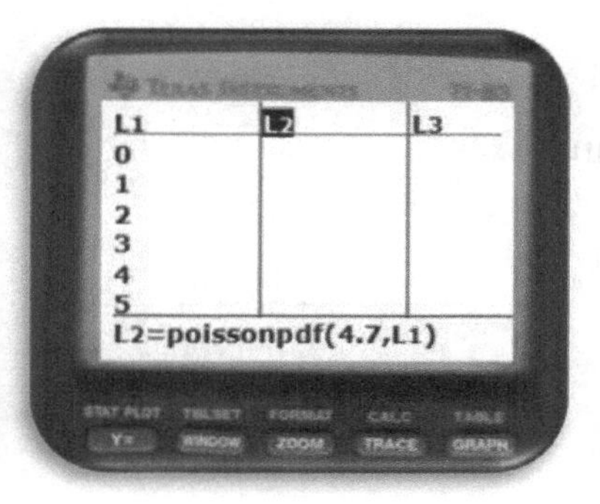

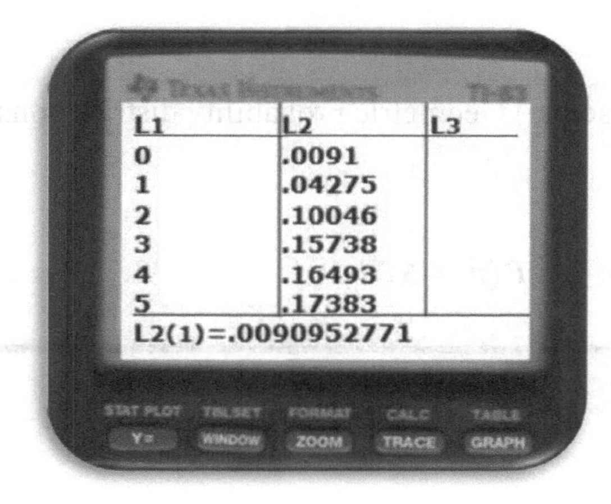

Note, here we are given the answers to all three parts: part 1)

$$P(x = 3) = 0.15738,$$

For Part 2,

$$P(x \leq 2) = \text{P}(0) + \text{P}(1) + \text{P}(2) = 0.0091 + 0.04275 + .10046 = 0.1523$$

and for Part 3,

$$P(x = 0) = 0.0091$$

$$P(x = 1) = 0.04275$$

$$P(x = 2) = 0.10046$$

$$P(x = 3) = 0.15738$$

$$P(x = 4) = 0.16493$$

and

$$P(x = 5) = 0.17383.$$

Question 7: Using the (discrete) Geometric probability distributions, given $p = 0.05$.

Compute the following

1. $P(n = 5)$ 2. $P(n = 10)$ 3. $P(n > 20)$

*Using the $TI - 83$, these values can reality be computing either entering the formula, or using the **DISTR** (2nd **VARS**) down to **D:geometpdf(** or **E:geometcdf(**.*

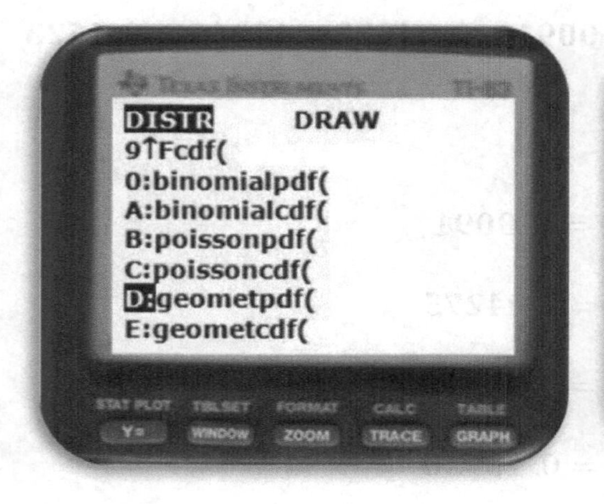

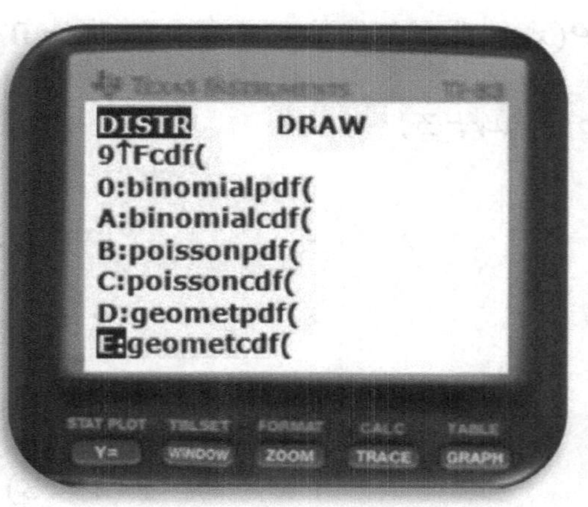

For example, given $p = 0.04$, compute the following

1. $P(n = 5)$

2. $P(x > 5)$

For part 1, we could have entered the code $(1-.04)^{5-1} *.04$ to obtain the final results, or we can use the code $\boldsymbol{geometpdf}(.04, 5)$ under *DISTR* (2nd *VARS*) down to **D:***geometpdf*(.

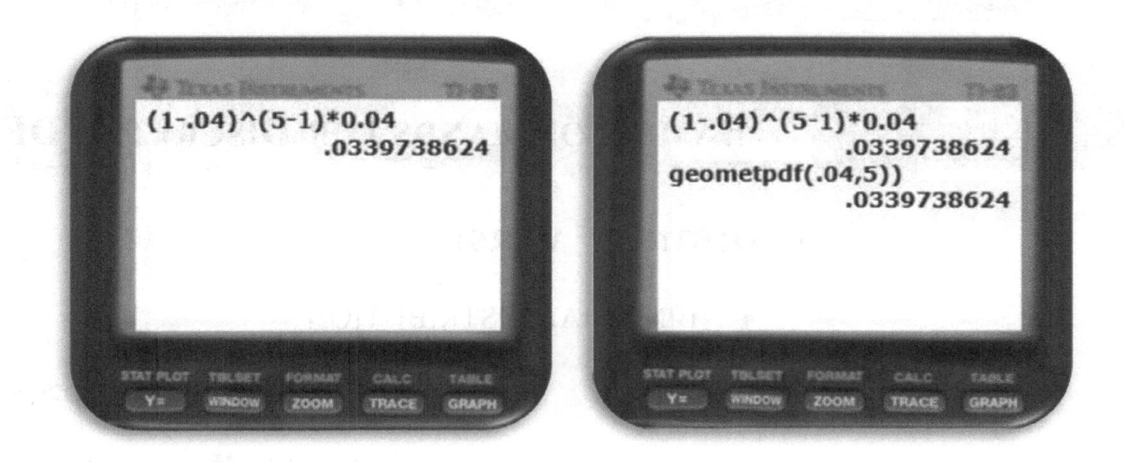

For part 2, it is unrealistic to find $P(x > 5) = P(6) + P(7) + P(8) + \cdots$;

hence, using the complement we have

$P(x > 5) = 1 - P(x \leq 5) = 1 - [P(1) + P(2) + P(3) + P(4) + P(5)]$;

therefore, we could have enter the code

$$1 - ((1-.04)^\wedge(1-1) *.04 + (1-.04)^\wedge(2-1) *.04 + (1-.04)^\wedge(3-1) *.04$$
$$+ (1-.04)^\wedge(4-1) *.04 + (1-.04)^\wedge(5-1) *.04)$$

or we can use the code $1 - \boldsymbol{geometcdf}(.04, 5)$.

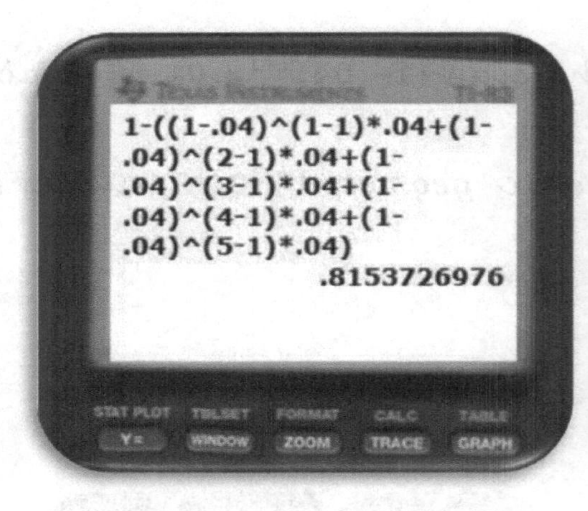

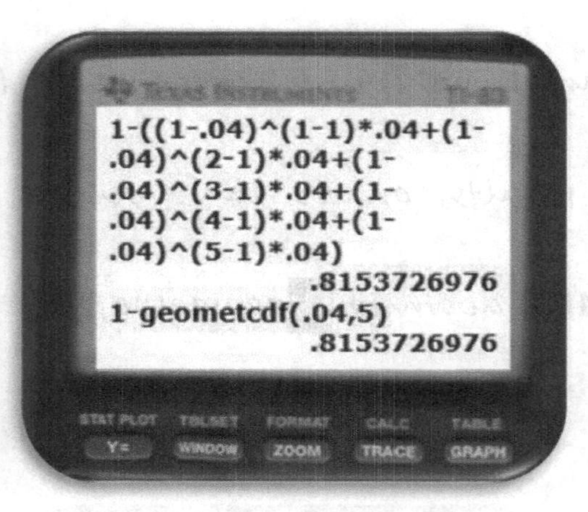

TI 83 | BASIC COMMANDS FOR DISCRETE PDFs

- **DISTR (2nd VARS)**
  - BINOMIAL DISTRIBUTION

    binomialpdf(<n>,<p>,<r>**)**

    binomialcdf(<n>,<p>,<r>**)**
  - POISSON DISTRIBUTION

    poissonpdf(<lambda>,<x>**)**

    poissoncdf(<lambda>,<x>**)**
  - GEOMETRIC DISTRIBUTION

    geometpdf(<p>,<n>**)**

    geometcdf(<p>,<n>**)**

Using Technology in Continuous Probability C6

Continuous Probabilities using Excel

You will need to use the accompanying **Excel** file "Excel Chapter 6 Using Technology in Continuous Probability" to generate the information need for many of the following questions.

FORMAT: Bold key words to be **emphasized**, **label figures** and **tables**, and **paginate**.

Question 1: Using the worksheet "**Normal Random Generator**", generate 100 simulated data values by setting the mean and standard deviation to 125 and 20, respectively. Compute the **sample mean** and the **sample standard deviation**, establish the three confidence intervals $(\mu - k\sigma, \mu + k\sigma)$ for $k = 1,2,3$ and then determine the **count** and thus the **relative frequency** of each of these intervals. Compare the parameters to the statistics as well as compare the **relative frequencies** obtained to the **empirical rule**.

This question is to demonstrate the Empirical Rule in a sample. Recall, the Empirical Rule states: (under the assumption of symmetric and bell shaped – i.e. Normal), approximately 68% of the data will fall within one-standard deviation, approximately 95% of the data will fall within two-standard deviations and approximately of the data 99.7% will fall within three-standard deviations.

E2 | =IF(D2="","",INT(NORMINV(RAND(),B$3,B$4)))

	A	B	D	E	G	H	I	K	L	
1	Parameters		Count	Simulation	EXAMPLE	Count		Count	Simulation	Co
2	Sample Size	10	1	7		1	99	1	99	
3	Mean	10	2	5		2	99	2	99	
4	Std Dev	5	3	7		3	94	3	94	
5	Variance	25	4	8		4	110	4	110	

Using Excel there is a control panel that, given the (input) sample size, mean and standard deviation, will generate a sample based on the probability structure (a simulation) using the code for (inverse) normal distribution which gives the random variable value based on a given probability using the code NORMINV(<probability>,<mean>,<standard deviation>). Here we are also using the ***RAND***() function introduce in Chapter 4 Using Technology in Probability and made the generation of the data point conditional to the count..

Once we have generated 100 data points with the specified mean and standard deviation, we can compute the sample mean and the sample standard deviation using Excel codes introduced in Chapter 2; then compute the various intervals $(\hat{\mu} - k\hat{\sigma}, \hat{\mu} + k\hat{\sigma})$ for $k = 1,2,3$ and count how many data values fall within these intervals.

Steps 1: Compute the sample mean and sample standard deviation. - given the

M28 | =AVERAGE(I2:I1001)

	L	M	N	O	P	Q
28	Mean	99				
29	Std Dev	14.24				

generated sample is given in the data array in cells I2 to I1001 (allowing for a maximum of 1000 points to be generated), in the accompanying example given in Excel and highlighted in blue, are computed in cells M28 and M29, coded as $= \boldsymbol{AVERAGE}(\boldsymbol{I2}{:}\,\boldsymbol{I1001})$ and $= \boldsymbol{STDEV}(\boldsymbol{I2}{:}\,\boldsymbol{I1001})$, respectively.

	L	M	N	O	P	Q	R
28	Mean	99					
29	Std Dev	14.24					
30							
31	μ−σ=	84.76	μ−2σ=	70.52	μ−3σ=	56.28	
32	μ+σ=	113.2	μ+2σ=	127.5	μ+3σ=	141.7	
33							
34	Cum. Counts	13		2		0	
35		83		99		100	

M35 =COUNTIF($I$2:$I$1001,"<"&M32)

Step 2: Compute the upper and lower limits for each of the various intervals by simply differencing as illustrated with $\mu+3\sigma$, cell **Q32** computes the upper limit on the value using the code **=M28+3*M29**.

Step 3: Determine the cumulative counts using the conditional **COUNTIF** command. The stoppers ($) allow the code to be copied down from cell **M34** to cell **M35** (between rows) as well as allows cells **M34**:**M35** to be copied and pasted into cells **O34**:**O35** and **Q34**:**Q35** (between columns). This is why in the code $= \boldsymbol{COUNTIF}(\$I\$2{:}\$I1001, " < "\&M32)$ has stopper on both the rows **2** and **1001** as well as the column **I**. At most, we will have to edit the first counter to be "<=", that is, less than or equal to.

	L	M	N	O	P	Q
28	Mean	99				
29	Std Dev	14.24				
30						
31	μ−σ=	84.76	μ−2σ=	70.52	μ−3σ=	56.28
32	μ+σ=	113.2	μ+2σ=	127.5	μ+3σ=	141.7
33						
34	Cum. Counts	13		2		0
35		83		99		100
36						
37	Count	70		97		100

M37 =M35-M34

Step 4: Finally, the counts in each interval can be computed as the difference between the cumulative counts. For example, within one standard deviation, the count in cell **M37** is equal to the difference between cells **M35** and **M34** coded $= \boldsymbol{M35} - \boldsymbol{M34}$.

Q32 =M28+3*M29

	L	M	N	O	P	Q
28	Mean	99				
29	Std Dev	14.24				
30						
31	μ−σ=	84.76	μ−2σ=	70.52	μ−3σ=	56.28
32	μ+σ=	113.2	μ+2σ=	127.5	μ+3σ=	141.7

	L	M	N	O	P	Q
28	Mean	100				
29	Std Dev	15				
30						
31	μ−σ=	85	μ−2σ=	70	μ−3σ=	55
32	μ+σ=	115	μ+2σ=	130	μ+3σ=	145
33						
34	Cum. Counts	17		2		0
35		84		100		100
36						
37	Count	67		98		100

In these final calculations we see the Empirical Rule, 70 out of 100 is approximately 68%, 97 out of 100 is approximately 95% and 100 out of 100 is approximately 99.7%.

Note: we could have done this calculations with the true parameters for the mean and standard deviations as they are known – what is nice about Excel is that all we must do is change the numbers in cells **M28** and **M29** and each value with be recalculated and again, this illustrates the Empirical Rule. However, in the real world it is highly unlikely that both the mean and standard deviations are known and therefore we need to understand what our data tells us.

Question 2: Determine the following **probabilities** and illustrate **normal chart** – you many need to use **PAINT** or edit format in **EXCEL**. Include associated z-scores. Note: you may use the "**Normal Calculator and Graphics**" in **EXCEL** file "Chapter 6 Excel Using Technology in Continuous Probability."

1. $P(87 \leq x \leq 102 \mid \mu = 100, \sigma = 12)$
2. $P(92 \leq x \leq 112 \mid \mu = 125, \sigma = 36)$
3. $P(x \leq 52 \mid \mu = 45, \sigma = 7)$
4. $P(x \geq 67 \mid \mu = 51, \sigma = 11)$

The worksheet "**Normal Calculator and Graphics**" is a graphing calculator; by changing the numbers in the control panel (highlighted in yellow), the associated z-scores, individual probabilities, etc. are automatically updated and the graph illustrated. By setting $\boldsymbol{a} = \mathbf{10}$, $\boldsymbol{b} = \mathbf{15}$, $\boldsymbol{\mu} = \mathbf{12}$ and $\boldsymbol{\sigma} = \mathbf{4}$, the graphic generator gives the illustrate to the left and the various probabilities. For example,

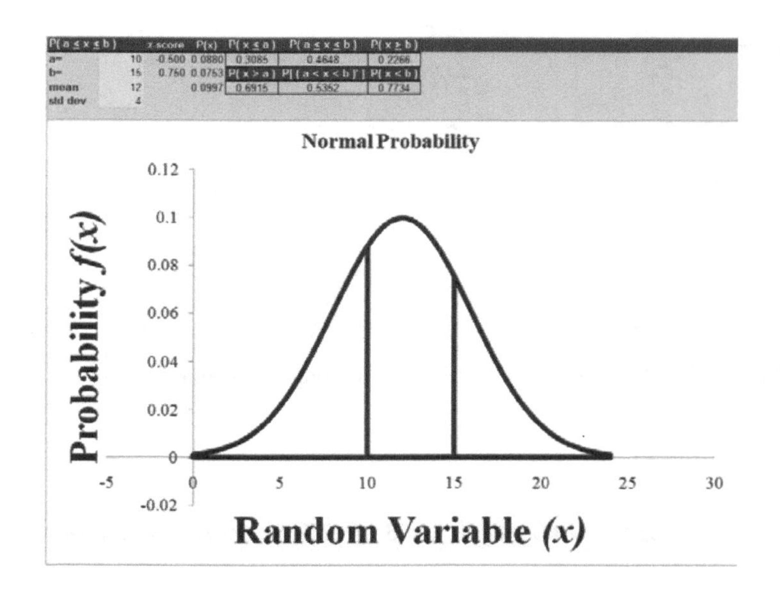

$P(x \leq 10) = 0.3085$

$P(10 \leq x \leq 15) = 0.4648$

$P(x \geq 15) = 0.2266$

$P(x > 10) = 1 - P(x \leq 10) = 0.6915$

$P[(10 < x < 15)']$

$= P(x \leq 10) + P(x \geq 15)$

$= 0.5352$

$P(x < 15) = 1 - P(x \geq 15) = 0.7734$

Note: You may need to adjust the horizontal axis.

Question 3: Compare the **binomial distribution** with $P(S) = 0.80$ and sample sizes 5, 10, 50 and 100 to their associated normal distribution. You may use the worksheet "Binomial to Normal" in the **EXCEL** file "Excel Part 3". Discuss the apparent **skewness** and how it changes as the **sample size** increase. State whether the assumptions are satisfied for each comparison. Under what condition would the **binomial distribution** be **symmetric**?

Note: The large the simulations, the more time it takes **EXCEL** to regenerate; please be sure that all calculations are renewed before you **COPY** and **PASTE SPECIAL** into another worksheet to finish remaining analysis. The % calculated is given at the bottom of the **EXCEL** window. Warning: If you are impatient, then you may copy and paste incorrect information, often zero occur in cells while the computer is recalculating the cell entries.

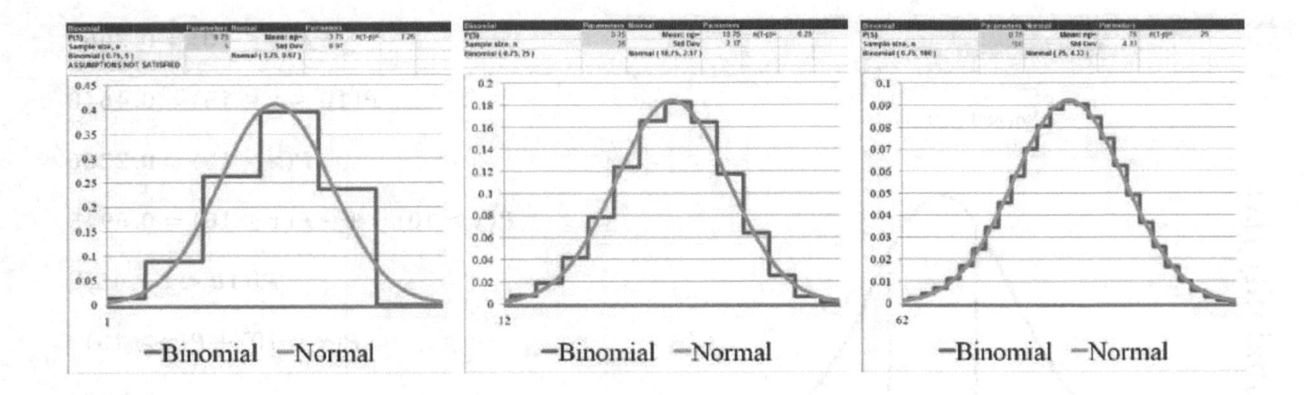

*For the given graphics above, the sample size increase from **5** to **25** to **100**; for which, the first illustration, when $n = 5$ and $p = 0.75$, the assumptions are not satisfied. That is, $np = 3.75$ and $n(1-p) = 1.25$; both less than five. However, for the second two sample sizes, the assumption is satisfied as indicated by the area represented in the binomial "histogram" (outline without the dividing lines) being approximately equal to that of the area under the smooth normal curve.*

Question 4: Using the worksheet "Control Charts", generate three random control charts with the following parameters and determine if the process is out of control.

1. $N(\mu = 32, \sigma^2 = 256)$ 2. $N(\mu = 16, \sigma^2 = 81)$ 3. $N(\mu = 16, \sigma^2 = 81)$

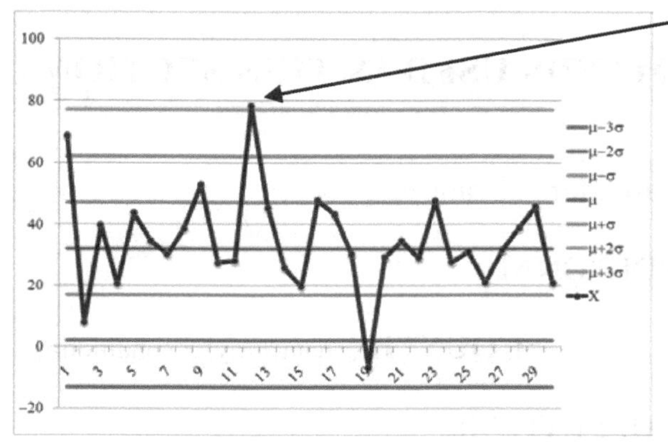

In the control chart to the left, with $x \sim N(32, 256)$ we see that there is a single data point further than three-standard deviation from the mean; this process is out of control, Signal I.

In the control chart to the left, with $x \sim N(32, 256)$ we see that there is a run of nine data points all on one side of the mean; this process is out of control, Signal II.

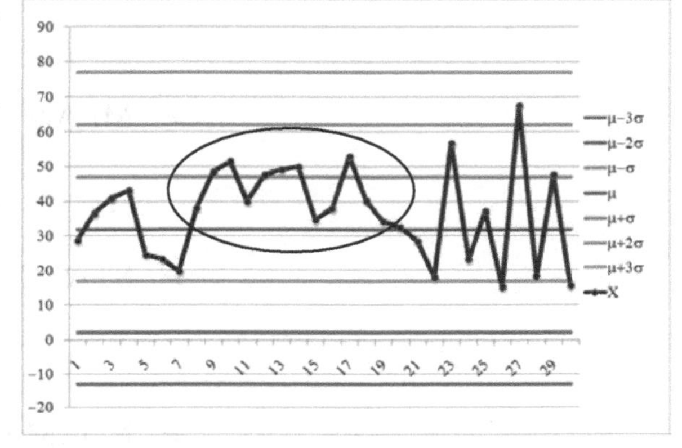

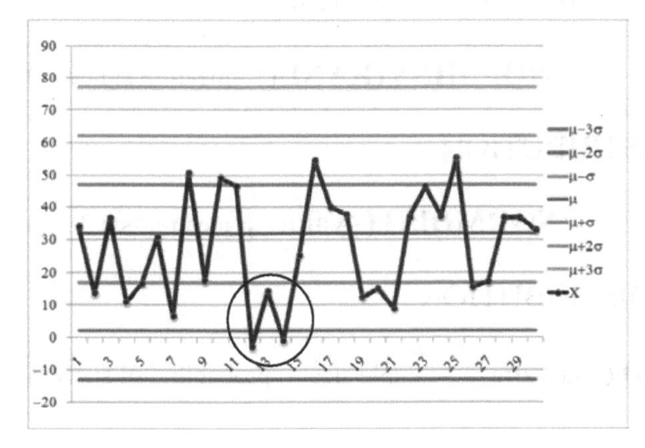

In the control chart to the left, we see that there are two data point further than two-standard deviation from the mean out of three on the same side of the mea; this process is out of control, Signal III.

EXCEL | BASIC COMMANDS USED IN THIS SECTION

- Note: these codes are more advanced
  - COUNT CONDITIONAL

    =COUNTIF(<data array>,<condition>**)**

  - CONDITIONAL STATEMENT

    =IF(<condition>,<command>,<alternative>**)**

  - MEAN

    =AVERAGE(<data array>**)**

  - STANDARD DEVIATION (STD DEV)

    =STDEV(<data array>**)**

  - NORMAL DISTRIBUTION (INVERSE)

    =NORMINV(RAND(),<mean>,<std dev>**)**

  - NORMAL DISTRIBUTION

    =NORMDIST(<value>**,**<mean>,<std dev>**)**

  - BINOMIAL DISTRIBUTION

    =BINOMDIST(<data array>,<sample size>,<probability of success>**)**

Continuous Probabilities using TI-83

The $TI-83$, under $DISTR$ (2^{ns} $VARS$), we have both the probability distributions and the **cumulative probability distributions** for the main **probability distributions** used in this text. In this section, we will illustrate the **normal cumulative probability distributions** and the **cumulative Student t-distribution** and their inverses.

Question 5: Determine the following probabilities given $x \sim N(\mu = 32, \sigma = 16)$.

1. $P(27 \le x \le 35)$ 2. $P(x \le 31)$ 3. $P(x \ge 21)$

Assume that we are given $x \sim N(\mu = 100, \sigma = 15)$, the determine the following probabilities:

1. $P(87 \le x \le 105)$ 2. $P(x \le 85)$ 3. $P(x \ge 75)$

Using the TI-83, $DISTR$ (2^{ns} $VARS$), down to **2:normalcdf(**, where this command requires, the **lower limit** followed by a comma, ",", the **upper**

limit followed by a comma ",", the **mean** followed by a comma, ",", the **standard deviation** and finally the closing parenthesis ")".

Note: be sure to use the minus sign and not the subtraction sign for negative numbers as well as to step back to the previous entry, press ***ENTRY*** (**2*nd* *ENTER***) and edit the previous entry or return to ***DISTR***.

Part 1) Part 2) Part 3)

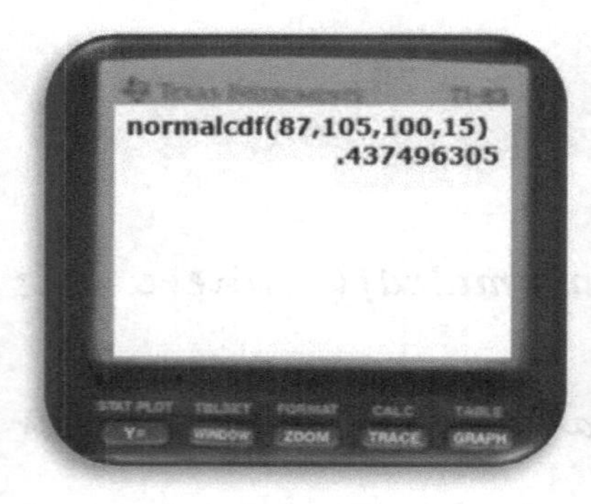

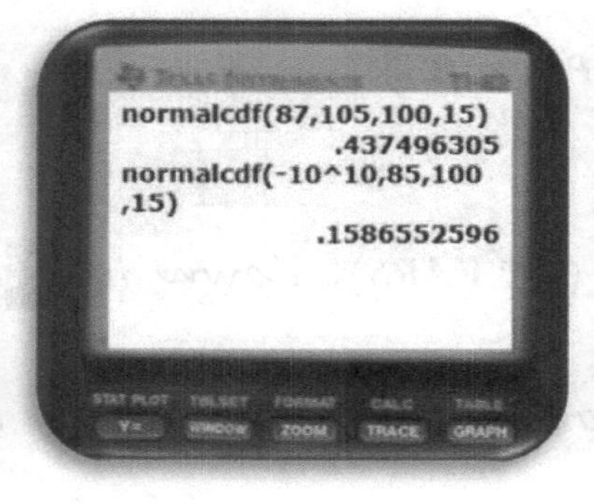

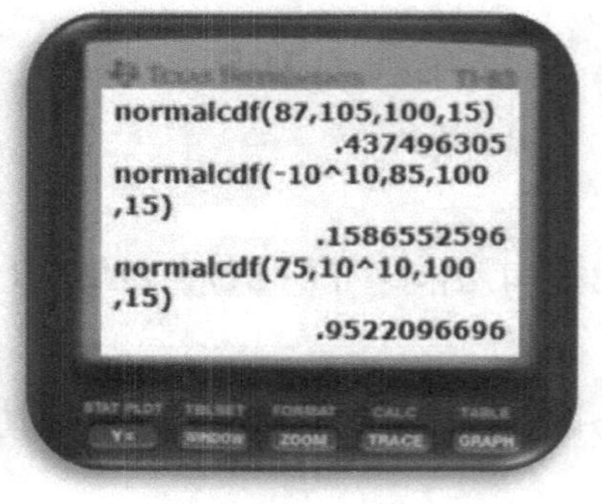

From the above, we have:

1. $P(87 \leq x \leq 105) = 0.4375$
2. $P(x \leq 85) = 0.1587$
3. $P(x \geq 75) = 0.9522$

Such use of the $TI - 83$ can be extremely useful when many calculations are needed. Without software, you would have to first convert to the standard normal and then use charts along with addition and subtraction to determine the correct probability. Moreover, the $TI - 83$ can also illustrate these probabilities; however, this does require the associated $z - \text{scores}$.

Consider $P(87 \leq x \leq 105) = P\left(\frac{87-100}{15} \leq z \leq \frac{105-100}{15}\right) = P(-0.87 \leq z \leq 0.33)$, on the calculator we have:

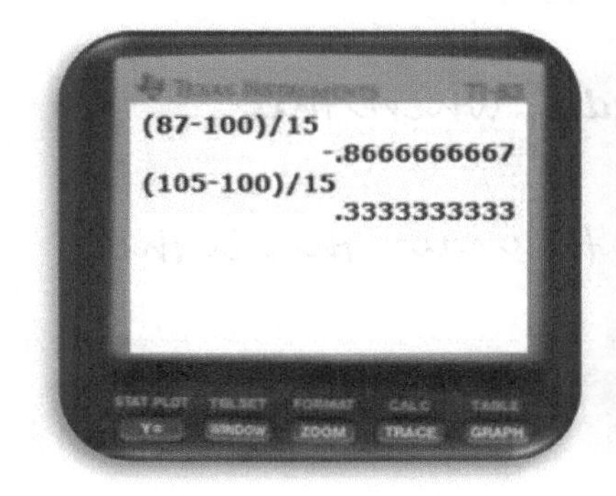

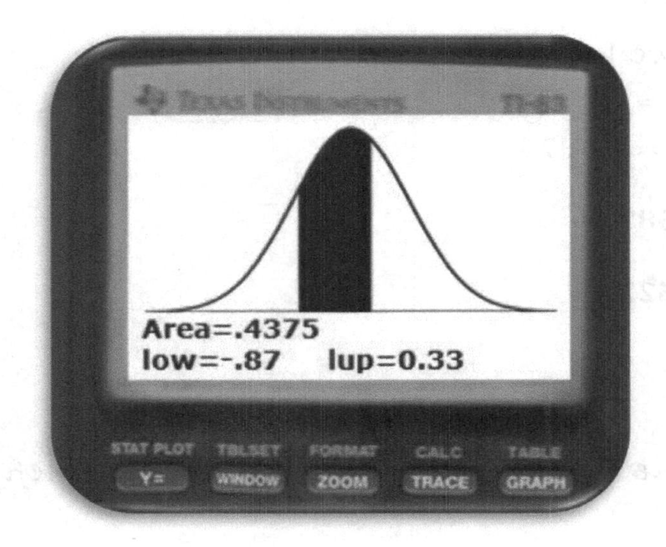

Question 6: Given the data follows the normal probability distribution, find $\boldsymbol{x = a}$, such that the following statements are true

1. $\boldsymbol{P(x \le a) = 0.80}$
2. $\boldsymbol{P(x \ge a) = 0.90}$
3. $\boldsymbol{P(-a \le x \le a) = 0.95}$

Note: to determine this value, it will suffice to find the associated $\boldsymbol{z-score}$ *such that* $\boldsymbol{P\left(z \le \frac{a-\mu}{\sigma}\right) = p}$. *For example, consider* $\boldsymbol{P(x \le a) = 0.90}$ *given* $\boldsymbol{\mu = 100}$ *and* $\boldsymbol{\sigma = 15}$. *This is equivalent to* $\boldsymbol{P\left(z \le \frac{a-100}{15}\right) = 0.90}$. *Using the TI-83, under* ***DISTR*** ($\boldsymbol{2^{ns}}$ ***VARS***), *down to* **2:normalcdf(**, *where this command requires the probability to the left. In this case, this is the*

0.90; hence, the command line is $\boldsymbol{invNorm(0.9)}$*, which returns the standard z-score which can be manipulated back to find a:* $a = \mu + z\sigma$*.*

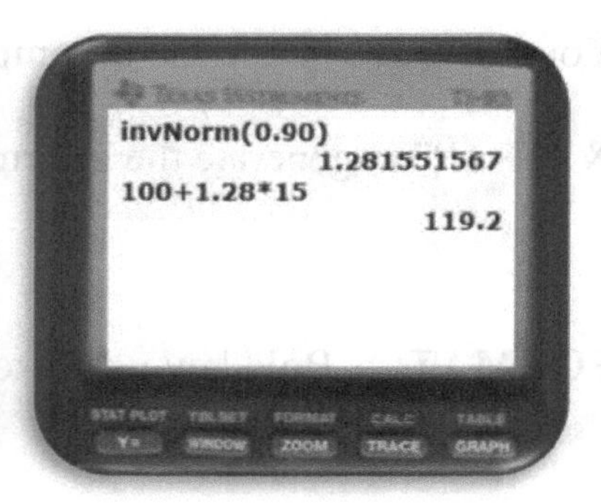

Therefore, we have that $a = 119.2$*.* ***Given the population mean is 100 and the standard deviation is 15, the probability that we observe a value less than 119.2 is approximately 90%.***

TI 83 | BASIC COMMANDS FOR CONTINUOUS PDF

- **DISTR (2nd VARS)**
  - NORMAL DISTRIBUTION

normalpdf(<value>,<μ>,<σ>**)**

normalcpf(<lower limit>,<upper limit>,<μ>,<σ>**)**

normInv(<probability to the left>**)**

CI: Means & Proportions using EXCEL

You will need to use the accompanying **EXCEL** file **"Chapter 7 & 8 Using Technology in CI & HT 1P"** to generate the information need for many of the following questions.

FORMAT: Bold key words to be **emphasized, label figures** and **tables**, and **paginate**.

Question 1: You may use the worksheet **"CI HT Means Normal"** for verification in calculations; your write up must clearly analyze the situation using the five outlined steps, discuss findings, included formulations and explanation.

A student receives an average of $\boldsymbol{\mu} = \mathbf{21.2}$ credit card offers per month. The majority of these are unsolicited. Because of the large number of complaints, the government find themselves questioning the way such businesses are run. In an effort to the number of unsolicited credit card offers, a research team established minimum qualifications and maximum mailing restrictions. One year after the new requirements was put in place, a random sample of 85 students showed that an average of $\bar{x} = 18.2$ offers per month. The tracking of all such mailings showed that the standard deviation is $\boldsymbol{\sigma} = \mathbf{16.1}$. Has the restriction had any effect? Obtain 95% confidence limits on the true mean number of credit card offers per month.

The **Chapter 7 & 8 Using Technology in CI & HT 1P** will become very useful in that you change the given information, the observed sample mean, the standard deviation, the sample size (in later in Chapter 8, the hypothesized claim), and then automatically all the necessary numbers are computed for hypothesis testing of means under the normal assumption.

CONTROL PANEL: ANYTHING IN YELLOW CAN BE CHANGED				
	90%	95%	99%	
Sample Mean	100	100	100	
Std Dev	15	15	15	
Sample Size	30	30	30	
Alpha α	10%	5%	1%	
GENERAL INFORMATION				
Zα	1.28	1.64	2.33	
Zα/2	1.64	1.96	2.58	
point estimate	100	100	100	
SE	2.7386	2.7386	2.7386	
CI				
ME	4.4913	4.4913	4.4913	
LCL	95.509	94.632	92.934	
UCL	104.491	105.368	107.066	
HT				
claim	105	105	105	
test	-1.83	-1.83	-1.83	*p-value*
one	Reject	Reject	Fail to Reject	0.0336
two	Reject	Fail to Reject	Fail to Reject	0.0672

Setting the information in the yellow highlighted cells; that is, $\bar{x} = 100, \sigma = 15$ and $n = 30$, Excel automatically computes the confidence intervals for all three common degrees of confidence: 90%, 95% and 99%.

Interpret this chart and discover that each step is computed for multiple scenarios.

- ⇨ The critical statistics for all three levels and both one-tail and two-tail
- ⇨ The standard error, margin of error, lower and upper confidence limits
- ⇨ Among other vital statistics.

Warning: Some statistics are repeated as well as algorithmically driven – be careful not to cause processing error – if you change the underlying code, please reload the original file

Question 2: You may use the worksheet "**Summary Generator**" to create the necessary summary information and the worksheet "**CI HT Means Student t**" for verification in calculations for the CI, your write up must clearly analyze the situation using the five outlined steps, discuss findings, included formulations and explanation.

Based on the annual report of a research company, the research and development department wished to estimate how much time the average customer waits in line. A random sample of 12 where observed as the stood in line. The times recorded in minutes were 56, 59, 60, 61, 64, 67, 68, 104, 110, 117, 122, and 128. Obtain a 90% confidence interval for the true mean waiting time of a customer.

Again, the **Chapter 7 & 8 Using Technology in CI & HT 1P** *will become very useful. First, the* ***Summary Generator*** *can handle* $100 \times 20 = 2,000$ *data values (but must be placed in the* 100×20 *block of cells highlighted in yellow; cells* $(A11{:}T110)$*. Note: you must put more than one data point in to be able to measure the sample variance, sample standard deviation, and the various quartiles, including the extremes.*

	A	B	C	D	E	F	G	H
1		CONTROL PANEL: ANYTHING IN YELLOW CAN BE CHANGED						
2		Sample Mean	6.17					
3		Sample Variance	4.57					
4		Sample Standard Deviation	2.14					
5		Count	6					
6		Minimum	4					
7		Q1	4.25					
8		Median	6					
9		Q3	7.75					
10		Maximum	9					
11								
12		5	4	8	4	9	7	
13								

Placing the six numbers:

5, 4, 8, 4, 9 and 7

in the arbitrary cells $B12{:}G12$*,*

Excel computes:

- the **sample mean** to be $\bar{x} = 6.17$
- the **sample variance** to $s^2 = 4.57$
- the **sample standard deviation** to be $s = 2.14$
- the **count** or **sample size** to be $n = 6$
- the **minimum**, 4
- $Q_1 = 4.25$
- $M = 6$
- $Q_3 = 7.75$
- the **maximum**, 9

Second, this information can then be used to construct such graphics as the **box plot**, or in conjunction with "**CI HT Means Normal**" or "**CI HT Means Student t**" to produced confidence limits and perform hypothesis testing (Chapter 8) for any given data set $n \leq 2000$. As here, n=6, we will use "**CI HT Means Student t**" which gives the following summary chart once the statistics in yellow are set.

	A	B	C	D	E	F	G
1		CONTROL PANEL: ANYTHING IN YELLOW CAN BE CHANGED					
2			90%	95%	99%		
3		sample mean	6.17	6.17	6.17		
4		std dev	2.14	2.14	2.14		
5		sample size	6	6	6		
6		alpha	10%	5%	1%		
7		GENERAL INFORMATION				Sign.	
8		Tα	1.4759	2.015	3.3649	4	
9		Tα/2	2.0150	2.5706	4.0321		
10		point estimate	6.17	6.17	6.17		
11		SE	0.8737	0.8737	0.8737		
12		CI					
13		ME	1.7604	1.7604	1.7604		
14		LCL	4.410	3.924	2.647		
15		UCL	7.930	8.416	9.693		
16		HT					
17		claim	4	4	4		
18		test	2.48	2.48	2.48	*p-value*	
19		one	Reject	Reject	Fail to Reject	0.0279	
20		two	Reject	Fail to Reject	Fail to Reject	0.0558	
21							

We see that at the 90% degree of confidence, with a sample mean of 6.17 and a margin of error of 1.76, we are confident the true mean is between 4.41 and 7.93.

Excel computes:

- ⇨ the critical statistic to be $t_{\frac{\alpha}{2}} = 2.015$
- ⇨ the standard error to $\frac{s}{\sqrt{n}} = 0.8737$
- ⇨ the margin of error to be $ME = 1.76$
- ⇨ $LCL = 4.41$
- ⇨ $UCL = 7.93$

This information can then be used to obtain confidence limits for all three degrees of confidence: 90%, 95% and 99%.

Question 3: You may use the worksheet **"CI HT Proportions"** for verification in calculations and graphics; however, your write up must clearly analyze the situation using the five outlined steps, discuss findings, included formulations and explanation.

Before 1940, the proportion of female rats in the general population was about 60%; however, after 1970, a widespread effort to destroy rats. In a recent sample of 48 rats, there were only 23 females. At the 0.01 level of significance, do these data indicate that the population proportion of female rats is now less than 60% in the region?

The **Chapter 7 & 8 Using Technology in CI & HT 1P** will also obtain confidence limits for proportions. In the worksheet "CI HT Proportions", simply place the observed number of successes, x, and the total number of trials, n, in the appropriate cells (**C3**: **C4**), and all necessary statistics will be generated.

In the example to the right, given $x = 43$ and $n = 75$, we are at least 99% confident the true proportion is between 0.4260 and 0.7207.

	A	B	C	D	E	F	G
1		CONTROL PANEL: ANYTHING IN YELLOW CAN BE CHANGED					
2			90%	95%	99%		
3		*x*	43	43	43		
4		*n*	75	75	75		
5		alpha	10%	5%	1%		
6		GENERAL INFORMATION					
7		Zα	1.28	1.64	2.33		
8		Zα/2	1.64	1.96	2.58		
9		point estimate	0.57333	0.57333	0.57333		
10		SE	0.05711	0.05711	0.05711		
11		CI					
12		LCL	0.4797	0.4614	0.4260		
13		UCL	0.6670	0.6853	0.7207		
14		HT					
15		claim	0.7	0.7			
16		test	-2.39	-2.39			
17		one	Reject	Reject		0.0084	
18		two	Reject	Reject	Fail	0.0168	
19							

Warning: Some statistics are repeated as well as algorithmically driven – be careful not to cause processing error – if you change the underlying code, please reload the original file

EXCEL | BASIC COMMANDS USED IN THIS SECTION

- Note: these are just a few of the codes used in this section.
  - STANDARD NORMAL Inv — **=NORMSINV(**<z-score>**)**
  - ABSOLUTE VALUE — **=ABS(**<value>**)**
  - ROUND — **=ROUND(**<value >,<sig. fig.>**)**
  - SQUARE ROOT — **=SQRT(**<value>**)**
  - t-DISTRIBUTION — **=TDIST(**<value>, <*v*>**)**

CI: Means & Proportions using TI-83

The $TI-83$ can obtain **confidence limits** for both **means** (using both the normal probability distribution and the Student t-distribution) and **proportions**.

Question 4: In an experiment, it is found that in a group of 50 individuals, the average height is 5.4 ft. Given the standard deviation is known to be 3 inches (0.25 inches), obtain 95% confidence limits on the true mean height.

Consider the example, in an experiment, a sample size of 36, $\mathbf{n = 36}$, shows a sample mean of $\bar{x} = 70$ and the standard deviation is known to be $\sigma = 15$. Assuming normality, using the $TI-83$, we go under ***STAT*** over to ***TESTS***, down to **7:ZInterval**. Enter the given statistics, we have the following results.

We are at least 95% **confident** that the true mean is between 65.1 and 74.9. The TI-83 gives the **lower** and **upper confidence limits** and restates the **sample mean** and **sample size**. These additional measures are more useful when listed data is used instead of summary statistics.

Question 5: In an experiment, the following information is gathered - 85, 82, 71, 94, 61. Obtain 90% confidence intervals for the true population mean.

In an experiment, the following information was obtained:

101, 107, 95, 92, 110, 85.

First, we must put this information into a list. Under ***STAT EDIT***, we can create a list using **1:** ***Edit*** and place the data in a list, say ***L1*** and then quit (**2nd** ***MODE***).

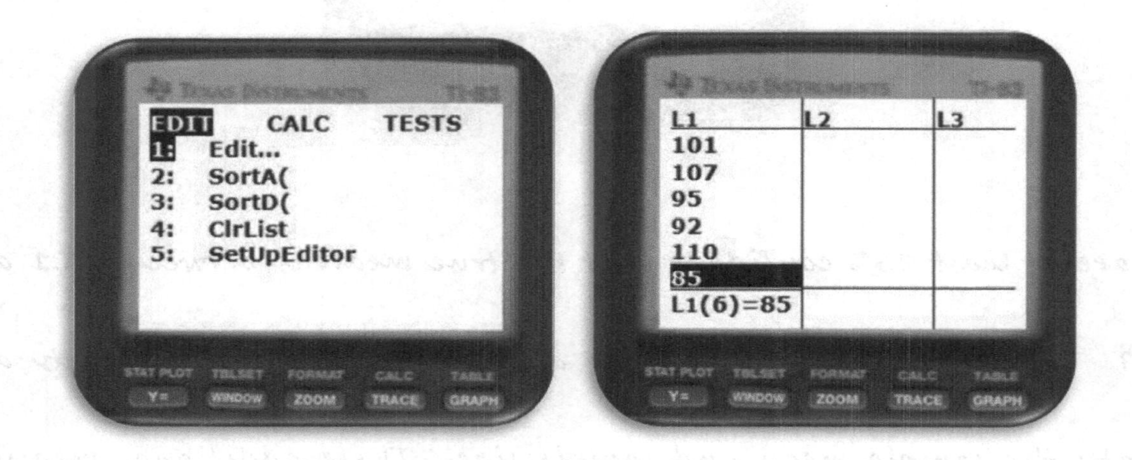

Here, we cannot assume normality, using the ***TI − 83***, we go under ***STAT*** over to ***TESTS***, down to **8:*****TInterval***. Enter the given statistics, we have the following results.

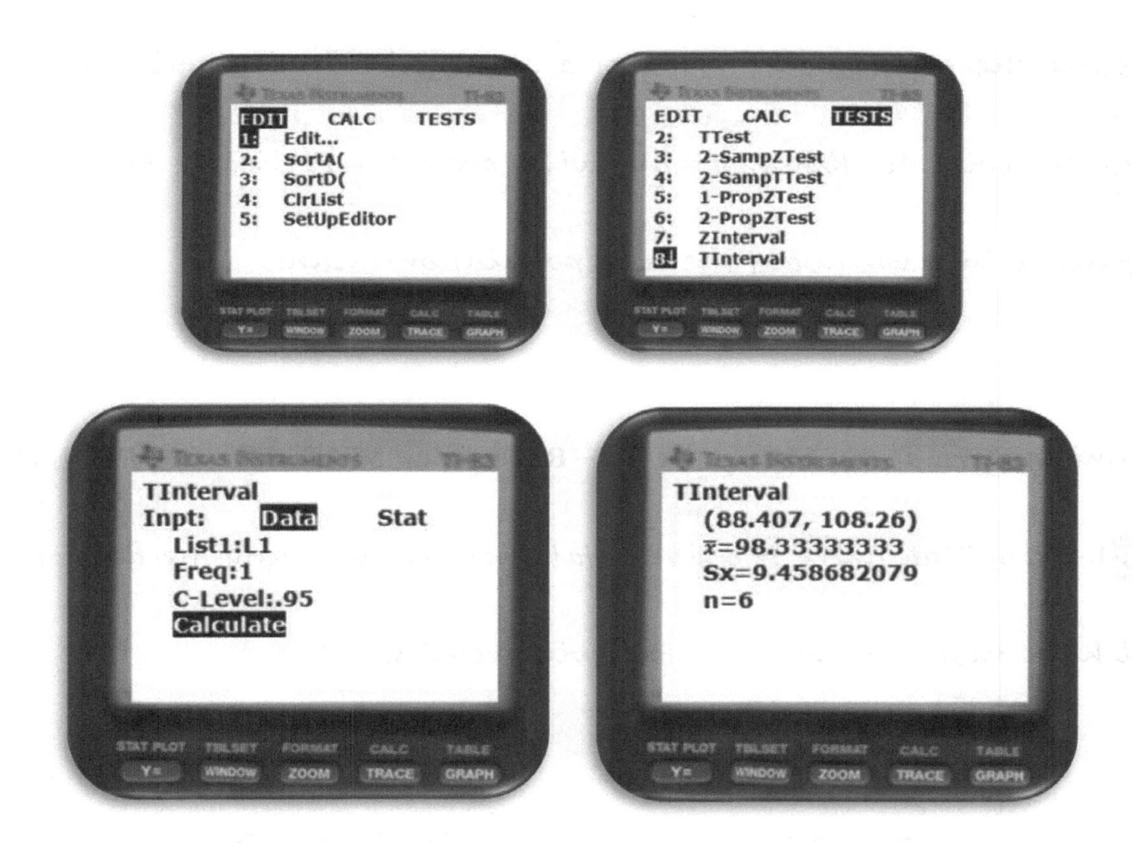

We are at least 95% confident that the true mean is between 88.41 and 108.26. The TI-83 gives the lower and upper confidence limits, the sample mean, sample standard deviation and sample size.

Question 6: On a test, a student earned 157 out of two hundred points (a C+), however the student which to argue a solid B (85%). Find 99% confidence limits on the true proportion (percent earned).

Consider the experiment: to test if a damaged coin is a fair, a student tosses the coin 40 times, $\mathbf{n = 40}$, with only $\boldsymbol{x} = \mathbf{19}$ heads. Find a 99% confidence interval about the true population mean.

Assuming normality, using the $\boldsymbol{TI-83}$, under $\boldsymbol{STAT}$ over to $\boldsymbol{TESTS}$, down to **A:1 − *PropZInt***. Enter the given statistics and selecting the appropriate null hypothesis, we have the following results.

We are at least 99% confident that the true proportion of heads is **between 0.2716 and 0.6784,** *while this does favor tails with only 47.5% heads, 50% is within reason. We can conclude that while damaged, the coin may still be fair.*

TI 83 | BASIC COMMANDS FOR GRAPHICS

- **STAT > TESTS**
  - NORMALLY DISTRIBUTION CONFIDENCE LIMITS

ZInterval

<sample mean>

<sample size>

  - STUDENT T-DISTRIBUTION CONFIDENCE LIMITS

TInterval

<sample mean>

<sample standard deviation>

<sample size>

  - ONE PROPORTION CONFIDENCE LIMITS

1-PropZInt

<number of successes>

<number of trials>

Using Technology in Hypothesis Testing C8

HT: Means & Proportion using EXCEL

You will need to use the accompanying **EXCEL** file **"Chapter 7 & 8 Using Technology in CI & HT 1P"** to generate the information need for many of the following questions.

FORMAT: Bold key words to be **emphasized, label figures** and **tables**, and **paginate**.

Question 1: You may use the worksheet **"CI HT Means Normal"** for verification in calculations; your write up must clearly analyze the situation using the eight outlined steps, discuss findings, included methods and interpretations.

A student receives an average of $\mu = 21.2$ credit card offers per month. The majority of these are unsolicited. Because of the large number of complaints, the government find themselves questioning the way such businesses are run. In an effort to the number of unsolicited credit card offers, a research team established minimum qualifications and maximum mailing restrictions. One year after the new requirements was put in place, a random sample of 85 students showed that an average of $\bar{x} = 18.2$ offers per month. The tracking of all such mailings showed that $\sigma = 16.1$. Has the restriction had any effect? Use a 5% level of significance to test the claim that there has been a reduction in the average number of credit card offers sent per month per student.

The **Chapter 7 & 8 Using Technology in CI & HT 1P** is also extremely useful in hypothesis testing of means under the normal assumption.

CONTROL PANEL: ANYTHING IN YELLOW CAN BE CHANGED				
	90%	95%	99%	
Sample Mean	100	100	100	
Std Dev	15	15	15	
Sample Size	30	30	30	
Alpha α	10%	5%	1%	
GENERAL INFORMATION				
Zα	1.28	1.64	2.33	
Zα/2	1.64	1.96	2.58	
point estimate	100	100	100	
SE	2.7386	2.7386	2.7386	
CI				
ME	4.4913	4.4913	4.4913	
LCL	95.509	94.632	92.934	
UCL	104.491	105.368	107.066	
HT				
claim	105	105	105	
test	-1.83	-1.83	-1.83	*p-value*
one	Reject	Reject	Fail to Reject	0.0336
two	Reject	Fail to Reject	Fail to Reject	0.0672

Setting the information in the yellow highlighted cells; that is, $\bar{x} = 100, \sigma = 15$ and $n = 30$, and the hypothesized claim: $H_0: \mu = 105$. Excel automatically computes the hypothesis testing (both one-tail and two-tail) for all three common levels of significance: 10%, 5% and 1%, including the **p-value** and the appropriate decision.

Interpret this chart and discover that each step is computed for multiple scenarios.

- ⇨ The **critical statistics** for all three levels and both one-tail and two-tail
- ⇨ The **standard error, margin of error, lower** and **upper confidence limits**
- ⇨ The **test statistic**
- ⇨ The **decision: reject** or **fail to reject**.

Warning: Some statistics are repeated as well as algorithmically driven - be careful not to cause processing error - if you change the underlying code, please reload the original file

Question 2: You may use the worksheet **"CI HT Means Student t"** for verification in calculations, your write up must clearly analyze the situation using the five outlined steps, discuss findings, included formulations and explanation.

Based on the annual report of a research company, the research and development department wished to estimate how much time the average customer waits in line. A random sample of 12 where observed as the stood in line. The times recorded in minutes were 56, 59, 60, 61, 64, 67, 68, 104, 110, 117, 122, and 128. Using a 10% level of significance, test the claim that the mean wait time is less than 95 minutes.

Using the same chart we used to obtain confidence limits, we can test a given hypothesis: $H_0: \mu = 4$.

	A	B	C	D	E	F	G
1		CONTROL PANEL: ANYTHING IN YELLOW CAN BE CHANGED					
2			90%	95%	99%		
3		sample mean	6.17	6.17	6.17		
4		std dev	2.14	2.14	2.14		
5		sample size	6	6	6		
6		alpha	10%	5%	1%		
7		GENERAL INFORMATION				Sign.	
8		Tα	1.4759	2.015	3.3649	4	
9		Tα/2	2.0150	2.5706	4.0321		
10		point estimate	6.17	6.17	6.17		
11		SE	0.8737	0.8737	0.8737		
12		CI					
13		ME	1.7604	1.7604	1.7604		
14		LCL	4.410	3.924	2.647		
15		UCL	7.930	8.416	9.693		
16		HT					
17		claim	4	4	4		
18		test	2.48	2.48	2.48	p-value	
19		one	Reject	Reject	Fail to Reject	0.0279	
20		two	Reject	Fail to Reject	Fail to Reject	0.0558	
21							

Here, at the 10% level of significance, we reject the null hypothesis. However, at the 1% level of significance, we would fail to reject, with a **p-value** of 0.0279 (assuming one-tail), the probability of Type I Error is rather unlikely, lying between 0.01 and 0.05. However, assuming the two-tail hypothesis, the **p-value** increases to 0.0558, greater than 0.05, but still less than 0.10. Note: here the degree of freedom is assumed to be $\boldsymbol{v} = \boldsymbol{n} - \mathbf{1}$.

Question 3: You may use the worksheet "CI HT Proportions" for verification in calculations; however, your write up must clearly discuss all the eight steps outlined in this section for hypothesis testing of proportions.

Before 1940, the proportion of female rats in the general population was about 60%; however, after 1970, a widespread effort to destroy rats. In a recent sample of 48 rats, there were only 23 females. At the 0.01 level of significance, do these data indicate that the population proportion of female rats is now less than 60% in the region?

The **Chapter 7 & 8 Using Technology in CI & HT 1P** will also perform hypothesis testing for proportions. In the worksheet "**CI HT Proportions**", simply place the observed number of successes, x, and the total number of trials, n, in the appropriate cells ($\boldsymbol{C3}$: $\boldsymbol{C4}$), and all necessary statistics will be generated including the critical statistic for hypothesis testing assuming normal approximate to the binomial, the test statistic and the final decision.

In the example to the right, given $x = 43$ and $n = 75$, at the 1% level of significance, test the claim that the true proportion is 70%, that is, $H_0\!: p = 0.70$.

	A	B	C	D	E	F	G
1		CONTROL PANEL: ANYTHING IN YELLOW CAN BE CHANGED					
2			90%	95%	99%		
3		*x*	43	43	43		
4		*n*	75	75	75		
5		alpha	10%	5%	1%		
6		GENERAL INFORMATION					
7		Zα	1.28	1.64	2.33		
8		Zα/2	1.64	1.96	2.58		
9		point estimate	0.57333	0.57333	0.57333		
10		SE	0.05711	0.05711	0.05711		
11		CI					
12		LCL	0.4797	0.4614	0.4260		
13		UCL	0.6670	0.6853	0.7207		
14		HT					
15		claim	0.7	0.7	0.7		
16		test	-2.39	-2.39	-2.39	*p-value*	
17		one	Reject	Reject	Reject	0.0084	
18		two	Reject	Reject	Fail to Reject	0.0168	
19							

Using the information provided in the chart, we are at the 1% level of significance, there is sufficient evidence to show that the true proportion is less than the claimed 70% ($p = 0.70$).

Warning: Some statistics are repeated as well as algorithmically driven - be careful not to cause processing error - if you change the underlying code, please reload the original file

EXCEL — BASIC COMMANDS USED IN THIS SECTION

- Note: these are just a few of the codes used in this section.
  - STANDARD NORMAL INVERSE
  - **=NORMSINV(**<z-score>**)**
  - ABSOLUTE VALUE **=ABS(**<value>**)**
  - ROUND **=ROUND(<**value >,<sig. fig.>**)**
  - SQUARE ROOT **=SQRT(**<value>**)**
  - t-DISTRIBUTION **=TDIST(**<value>, <*ν*>**)**

HT: Means & Proportion using TI-83

The ***TI* – 83** can perform **hypothesis testing** for both **means** (using both the normal probability distribution and the Student t-distribution) and **proportions**.

Question 4: In an experiment, it is found that in a group of 50 individuals, the average height is 5.4 ft. Given the standard deviation is known to be 3 inches (0.25 inches), at the 5% level of significance, test the claim that the average height is 5.5 ft.

Consider the example, given a sample size of 36, $n = 36$*, with a sample mean of* $\bar{x} = 70$ *and the standard deviation is known to be* $\sigma = 15$*. At the 5% level of significance, we wish to test the hypothesis that the population mean is 75,* $H_0: \mu = 75$*.*

Assuming normality, using the ***TI – 83****, under* ***STAT*** *over to* ***TESTS****, the first option is* ***ZTest****. Enter the given statistics and selecting the appropriate null hypothesis, we have the following results.*

At the 5% level of significance there is sufficient evidence to reject the null hypothesis. That is, with a **p − value** of **0.0455**, the observed sample mean is significantly different than 75. Now the question becomes is it significantly greater than. We can quickly perform this test by following the steps above and selecting the second option for hypothesis testing.

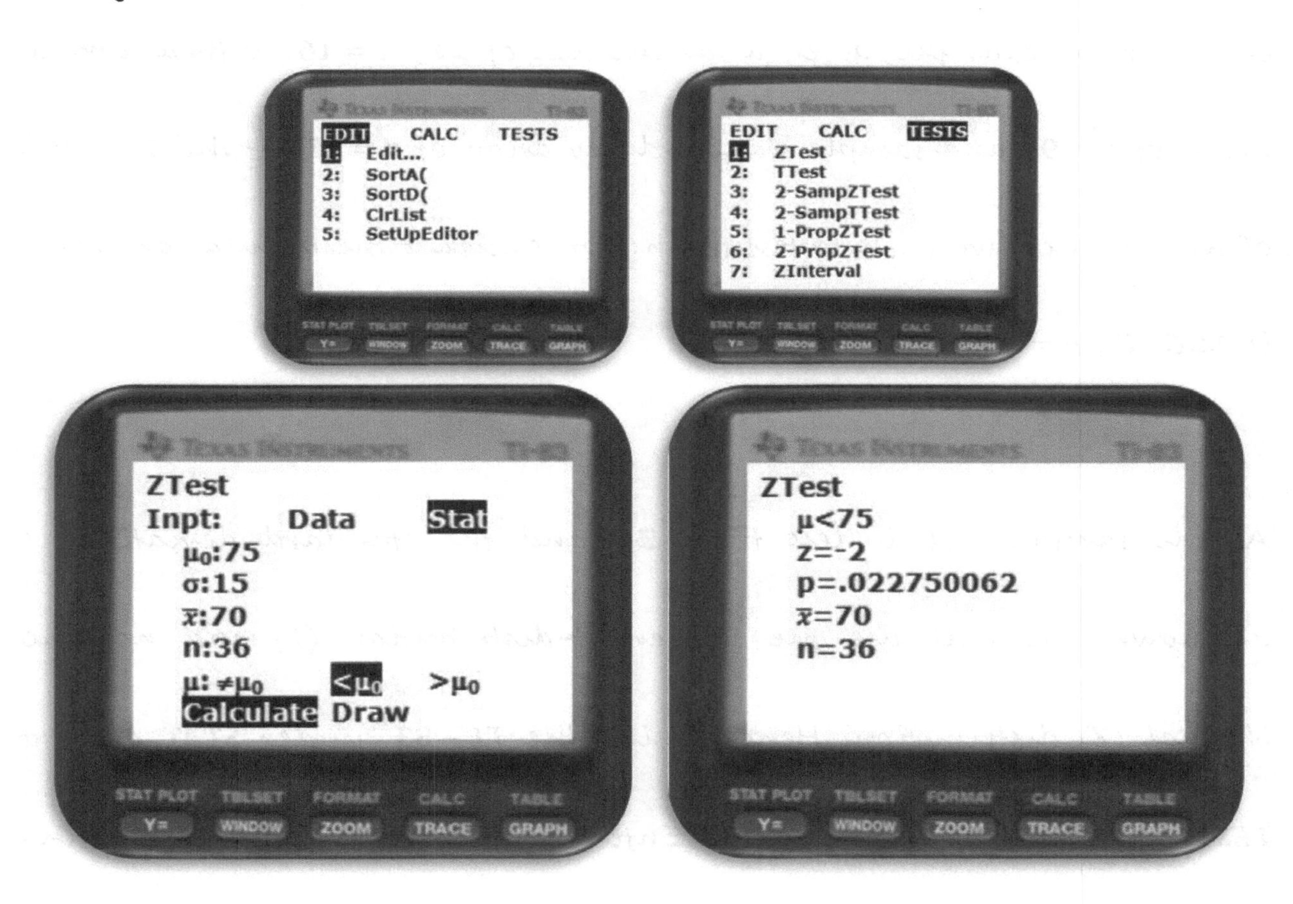

Note that the only change in values is the **p − value**; it is exactly half of that found in the one-tail hypothesis.

Question 5: In an experiment, it is found that in a group of 10 patients, the average weight is 175 lbs and an estimated standard deviation of 15 lbs, at the 1% level of significance, test the claim that the average weight is 180 lbs.

Consider the example, given a sample size of 16, $\mathbf{n = 16}$, with a sample mean of $\bar{\mathbf{x}} = \mathbf{92}$ and sample standard deviation of $\mathbf{s = 15}$. At the 1% level of significance, we wish to test the hypothesis that the population mean is 100, $\boldsymbol{H_0: \mu = 100}$.

As the sample size is less than 30 and the standard deviation is unknown, we will use the **Student t-distribution** (T) and not the Normal $(\boldsymbol{Z})$ distribution. Hence, using the $\boldsymbol{TI-83}$, under $\boldsymbol{STAT}$ over to $\boldsymbol{TESTS}$, the second option is $\boldsymbol{TTest}$. Enter the given statistics and selecting the appropriate null hypothesis, we have the following results.

At the 5% level of significance there is insufficient evidence to reject the null hypothesis. That is, with a $\mathbf{p-value}$ *of* **0.0298***, the observed sample mean is not significantly different than 100 at the 1% level of significance. Note, however, at the 5% level of significance, this observed outcome is significantly different from 100.*

Question 6: On a test, a student earned 157 out of two hundred points (a C+), however the student which to argue a solid B (85%). Test this hypothesis at the 5% level of significance.

Consider the experiment: to test if a damaged coin is a fair, a student tosses the coin 40 times, $n = 40$, with only $x = 19$ heads. At the 5% level of significance, we wish to test the hypothesis that the coin is fair, that is, $H_0: p = 0.50$ versus the alternative, $H_1: p < 0.50$.

Assuming normality, using the $TI - 83$, under **STAT** over to **TESTS**, down to **5:** ***1PropZTest***. Enter the given statistics and selecting the appropriate null hypothesis, we have the following results.

At the 5% level of significance there is insufficient evidence to reject the null hypothesis. With a $\mathbf{p-value}$ *of* $\mathbf{0.3759}$*, the observed sample proportion is not significantly different than the 50-50 split expected in a fair dice.*

TI 83 | BASIC COMMANDS FOR GRAPHICS

- **STAT > TESTS**
  - TESTING USING NORMALLY DISTRIBUTION

    ZTest

    Data or **Stats**
  - TESTING USING STUDENT T-DISTRIBUTION

    TTest

    Data or **Stats**
  - TESTING FOR ONE PROPORTION

    1-PropZTest

    Stats

CI & HT: Difference of Means & Proportions using EXCEL

You will need to use the accompanying **EXCEL** file **"Chapter 9 Using Technology in CI & HT 2P"** to generate the information needed for many of the following questions.

FORMAT: Bold key words to be **emphasized, label figures** and **tables**, and **paginate**.

Question 1: You may use the worksheet **"CI & HT 2P Means Case I & II"** for verification in calculations. Your write up must clearly discuss all the points outlined for both confidence and significance. That is, give confidence limits and test the given claim.

In the experiment, subjects were randomly divided into two groups to test a new drug created to reduce blood pressure: the experimental group received a new drug and the control group received a placebo. There were $n_1 = n_2 = 50$ subjects in each group. For the experimental group, the mean drop in blood pressure was $\bar{x}_1 = 27.9$ with sample standard deviation $s_1 = 4.8$. For the control group, the mean drop in blood pressure was $\bar{x}_2 = 25.9$ with sample standard deviation $s_2 = 5.2$. Use a 5% level of significance to test the hypothesis that there was no difference (either way) in scores between the two groups.

Using the Excel file "**Chapter 9 Using Technology in CI & HT 2P** ", we can use the first worksheet "**CI & HT 2P Means Normal**" to quickly answer such questions as the one posted above.

	A	B	C	D	E
1		CONTROL PANEL:			
2		ANYTHING IN YELLOW CAN BE CHANGED			
3			Population 1	Population 2	
4		Sample Size	30	30	
5		Sample Mean	155	162	
6		Std Dev	25	15	
7		Alpha	5%		
8		Confidence	95%		
9				Sig. fig.	
10		Difference of Means	7.0000	4	
11		Std Error	5.3229	4	
12		Zα/2=±	1.960		
13		Zα=	1.645		
14		CI			
15		ME=	10.433		
16		LCL=	-3.433		
17		UCL=	17.433		
18		HT			
19		Claim	0		
20		Test Statistic z=	1.32		
21		TAILS	DECISION	*p-value*	
22		one-tail	Fail to Reject	0.0942	
23		two-tail	Fail to Reject	0.1884	
24					

In the example to the left, $n_1 = 30$ $\bar{x}_1 = 155$, $\sigma_1 = 25$, $n_2 = 30$, $\bar{x}_2 = 162$, and $\sigma_2 = 15$. Here, we see that we are 95% confident the true difference in means is $\bar{x}_2 - \bar{x}_1 = 7$ (the point estimate) and the standard error associated with differences of means (assuming normality) of $\sqrt{\frac{\sigma_1^2}{n_1} + \frac{\sigma_2^2}{n_2}} = 5.32$ and a **margin of error** of $ME = 8.72$. Hence, we are at least 95% confident that the true difference in means is between -3.43 and 17.43. At the 5% level of significance, there is insufficient evidence to reject the claim that the true difference in means is in fact zero.

Question 2: You may use the worksheet "CI & HT 2P Means Case III t" for verification in calculations. Your write up must clearly discuss all the points outlined in hypothesis testing for difference of means (independent selection) and determine if the **difference of means** is 0. You select the level of significance.

Sample	RV 1	RV 2
1	91	127
2	107	109
3	73	91
4	49	110
5	68	96
6	102	119
7	142	139
8	105	103
9	115	53
10	132	88
11	112	88
12	89	59
13	39	46
14	123	70
15	99	121
16	161	65
17	99	116
18	83	65
19	89	163
20	93	101

Once you obtain the summary statistics for the two populations (RV1 and RV2), we can quickly determine the best decision based on various degrees of freedom; namely,

$$v_1 = \frac{\left(\frac{s_1^2}{n_1}+\frac{s_2^2}{n_2}\right)^2}{\frac{\left(\frac{s_1^2}{n_1}\right)^2}{n_1-1}+\frac{\left(\frac{s_2^2}{n_2}\right)^2}{n_2-1}},\ v_2 = \min\{n_1-1, n_2-1\} \text{ and } v_p = n_1+n_2-1$$

In the example to the right, $n_1 = 20$ $\bar{x}_1 = 155$, $s_1 = 25$, $n_2 = 20$, $\bar{x}_2 = 165$, and $\sigma_2 = 15$.

Excel computes:

$$v_1 = 31.11$$

$$v_2 = 19$$

$$v_p = 38$$

	A	B	C	D	E	F
1		CONTROL PANEL: ANYTHING IN YELLOW CAN BE CHANGED				
2			Population 1	Population 2	Sig. fig.	
3		Sample Size	20	20	1	
4		Sample Mean	155	165	Pooled s_p	
5		Std Dev	25	15	20.6	
6		Degree of Freedom	31.11	19	38	
7			df (1)	df (2)		
8		Alpha	1%		Sig. fig.	
9		Difference of Means	10		2	
10			$\sigma_1=\sigma_2$	$\sigma_1\neq\sigma_2$		
11		Std Error	6.51	6.52	2	
12		Estimates				
13		Tα=	2.45	2.54	2.43	
14		Tα/2=±	2.74	2.86	2.71	
15		CI				
16		ME=	17.86	18.65	17.64	
17		LCL=	-5.970	-8.650	-7.640	
18		UCL=	25.970	28.650	27.640	
19		HT				
20		Claim	0		Sig. fig.	
21			$\sigma_1=\sigma_2$	$\sigma_1\neq\sigma_2$	4	
22		Test Statistic t=	1.54	1.53		
23		DECISION				
24		one-tail	Fail to Reject	Fail to Reject	Fail to Reject	
25		two-tail	Fail to Reject	Fail to Reject	Fail to Reject	
26		*p-value(s)*	$\sigma_1\neq\sigma_2$	$\sigma_1\neq\sigma_2$	$\sigma_1=\sigma_2$	
27		TAILS	df (1)	df (2)	with s_p	
28		one-tail:	0.0681	0.0712	0.0659	
29		two-tail:	0.1362	0.1424	0.1318	
30						

Among other critical statistics which can be used to formulate a decision regarding the difference of means. In the above example, at the 5% level of significance, it is clear that there is insufficient evidence to reject the null hypothesis (according to all possible degrees of freedom.)

Question 3: Rework Question 2 assuming dependent selection; you may use the worksheet **"CI & HT 2P Means Case IV t"** which makes all necessary calculations. Your write up must clearly discuss all the points outlined in hypothesis testing for difference of means (dependent selection) and determine if the **mean difference** is 0. You select the level of significance.

As shown in the example below, Excel will compute the differences of the matching pairs (highlighted in yellow) and will make the necessary calculations. Here we are given ***point estimate*** $\bar{d} = 6.84$ *with an estimated* ***sample standard deviation*** $s_d = 13.63$. *We are at least 90%* ***confident the true mean difference is between 2.18 and 11.50.*** *That is, there is a positive difference, the second population data tends to be larger than the first population data.*

	B	C	D	E	F	I	J	K
1	CONTROL PANEL: ANYTHING IN YELLOW CAN BE CHANGED					Pop 1	Pop 2	
2	Sample size	25	25	25		375	357	18
3	Sample Mean Difference	6.84	6.84	6.84	2	223	247	-24
4	Sample Std Deviation	13.63	13.63	13.63	2	631	628	3
5	Degree of Confidence	90%	95%	99%	Sign.	643	639	4
6	Level of Significance	10%	5%	1%		541	556	-15
7	GENERAL INFORMATION					653	642	11
8	Tα	1.32	1.71	2.49	2	819	822	-3
9	Tα/2	1.71	2.06	2.80		812	818	-6
10	Point Estimate	6.84	6.84	6.84		660	665	-5
11	SE	2.7260	2.7260	2.7260		733	735	-2
12	CI					703	702	1
13	ME	4.6615	4.6615	4.6615		319	296	23
14	LCL	2.18	1.22	(0.79)		597	577	20
15	UCL	11.50	12.46	14.47		705	694	11
16	HT					604	602	2
17	Claim	0	0	0		771	756	15
18	Test Statistic	2.51	2.51	2.51	*p-value*	478	475	3
19	one-tail	Reject	Reject	Reject	0.0096	1040	1010	30
20	two-tail	Reject	Reject	Fail to Reject	0.0192	624	603	21
21						666	669	-3
22						706	692	14
23						807	772	35
24						749	736	13
25						657	650	7
26						72	74	-2

Interpret this chart and discover that each step is computed for multiple scenarios.

⇨ The **critical statistics** for all three levels and both one-tail and two-tail

⇨ The **point estimate**

⇨ The **standard error**

For CI:

⇨ **Margin of error**

⇨ **lower confidence limit**

⇨ **Upper confidence limit**

For HT:

⇨ **Test statistic**

⇨ **Decision: reject or fail to reject**

⇨ **p-value(s)**

Warning: Some statistics are repeated as well as algorithmically driven - be careful not to cause processing error - if you change the underlying code, please reload the original file

Question 4: You may use the worksheet "**CI & HT 2P Prop Case V z**" for verification in calculations. Your write up must clearly discuss all the points outlined for both confidence and significance. That is, give confidence limits and test the given claim.

In the experiment, subjects were randomly divided into two groups to test a new drug created to reduce blood pressure: the experimental group received a new drug and the control group received a placebo. There were $n_1 = n_2 = 50$ subjects in each group. For the experimental group, the drug works for 37 patients. For the control group, the drug works for 27 patients. Use a 5% level of significance to test the hypothesis that there was no difference (either way) in percent of individuals for which the treatment was successful in reducing the blood pressure.

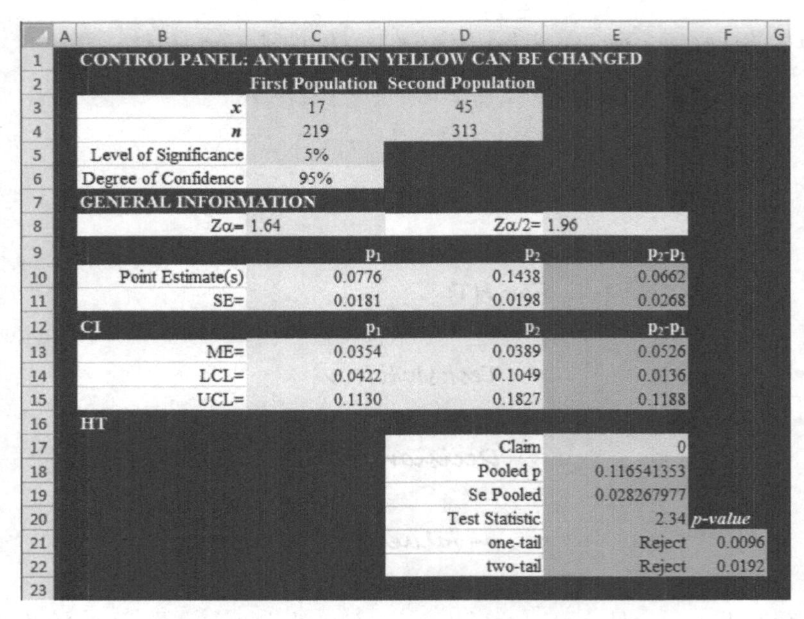

	B	C	D	E	F
1	CONTROL PANEL: ANYTHING IN YELLOW CAN BE CHANGED				
2		First Population	Second Population		
3	x	17	45		
4	n	219	313		
5	Level of Significance	5%			
6	Degree of Confidence	95%			
7	GENERAL INFORMATION				
8	Zα= 1.64		Zα/2= 1.96		
9		p_1	p_2	p_2-p_1	
10	Point Estimate(s)	0.0776	0.1438	0.0662	
11	SE=	0.0181	0.0198	0.0268	
12	CI	p_1	p_2	p_2-p_1	
13	ME=	0.0354	0.0389	0.0526	
14	LCL=	0.0422	0.1049	0.0136	
15	UCL=	0.1130	0.1827	0.1188	
16	HT				
17			Claim	0	
18			Pooled p	0.116541353	
19			Se Pooled	0.028267977	
20			Test Statistic	2.34	*p-value*
21			one-tail	Reject	0.0096
22			two-tail	Reject	0.0192
23					

In the example to the left, $x_1 = 17, n_1 = 219, x_2 = 45$, and $n_2 = 313$; the null hypothesis set for is $H_0: p_2 - p_1 = 0$.

INTERPRETATION:

At the 5% level of significance, there is sufficient evidence to reject the null hypothesis.

According to the analysis, the **first estimated population proportion** is $p_1 = 0.0776$ and the **second population proportion** is $p_2 = 0.1438$ (nearly double); hence the **difference in proportions** is estimated to be $p_2 - p_1 = 0.0662$. **We are at least 95% confident that the first population proportion is between 0.0422 and 0.1130** whereas **we are at least 95% confident that the second population proportion is between 0.1049 and 0.1827**. While there is a slight overlap, there is not enough to declare that there is any significant difference. Upon further analysis, **we are at least 95% confident that the true difference in proportion is between 0.0136 and 0.1188**. With a **p-value of 0.0096**, the second population proportion is significantly greater than the first population proportion.

EXCEL — BASIC COMMANDS USED IN THIS SECTION

- Note: these are just a few of the codes used in this section.
  - ABSOLUTE VALUE **=ABS(**<value>**)**
  - ROUND **=ROUND(<**value >,<sig. fig.>**)**
  - SQUARE ROOT **=SQRT(**<value>**)**
  - STANDARD NORMAL INVERSE =**NORMSINV(**<z-score>**)**
  - t-DISTRIBUTION **=TDIST(**<value>, <*v*>**)**

CI & HT: Difference of Means & Proportions using TI-83

In terms of the ***two populations****, the* ***TI – 83*** *can give both* ***confidence limits*** *as well as* ***hypothesis testing*** *using both the* ***normal probability distribution*** *and the* ***Student t-distribution****.*

Question 5: In an experiment, a sample of 16 males results in a sample mean of 15 and a sample of 12 females results in a sample mean of 22. Obtain 95% confidence limits on the true difference of means given that data's distribution follows the normal probability distribution and the standard deviation for males is known to be 6 and for females, 5.

Consider the example, an experiment consisting of two populations, from the first population a random sample of 25 is taken, $n_1 = 25$, with a **sample mean** of $\bar{x}_1 = 100$, and from a random sample of 36, $n_2 = 36$, has a mean of $\bar{x}_1 = 125$. Given the **population standard deviations** are known to be $\sigma_1 = 4$ and $\sigma_2 = 14$, obtain 95% confidence limits on the difference of means.. In general, the code for computing confidence limits can simply be done using the standard key pad; that is, $LCL = (100 - 105) - 1.96 * \sqrt{}(4\text{^}2/25 + 14\text{^}2/36)$ and $UCL = (100 - 1055) - 1.96 * \sqrt{}(4\text{^}2/25 + 14\text{^}2/36)$, where **1.96** is the critical statistic, $z_{\frac{\alpha}{2}} = z_{0.025} = \mp 1.96$. Note, we could use the TI-83 to find this value using ***DISTR*** (***2nd VARS***) and

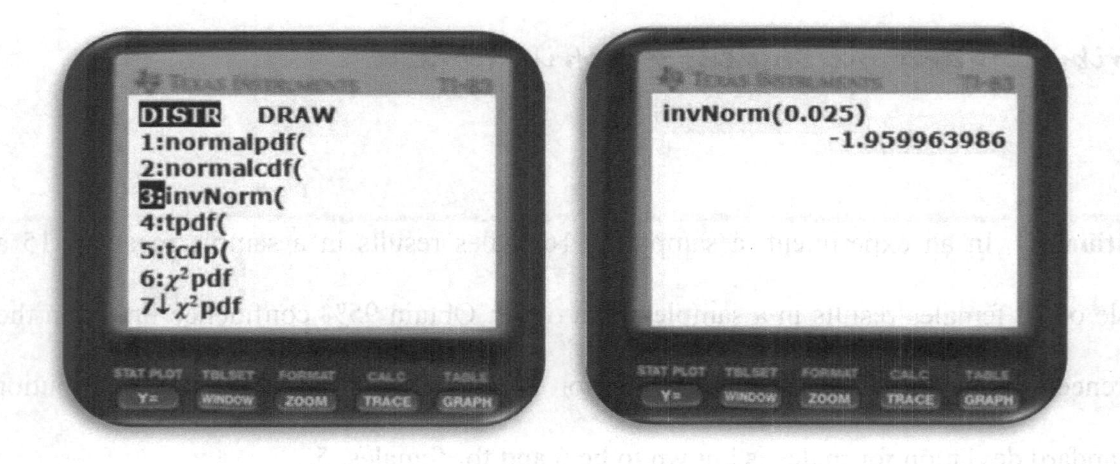

Once you type the first one, you can press ***ENTRY*** (2nd ***ENTER***), the calculator will go back a step to the last line of code and you will be able to change the − to a +.

Therefore, **we are at least 95% confident that the true difference in means is between** -29.835 **and** -20.165. However, there is an easier way using ***STAT***. Go over to ***TESTS*** and down to **9:** $2-SampZInt$ where you will be given the option to enter the data into lists or from statistics as in the example above.

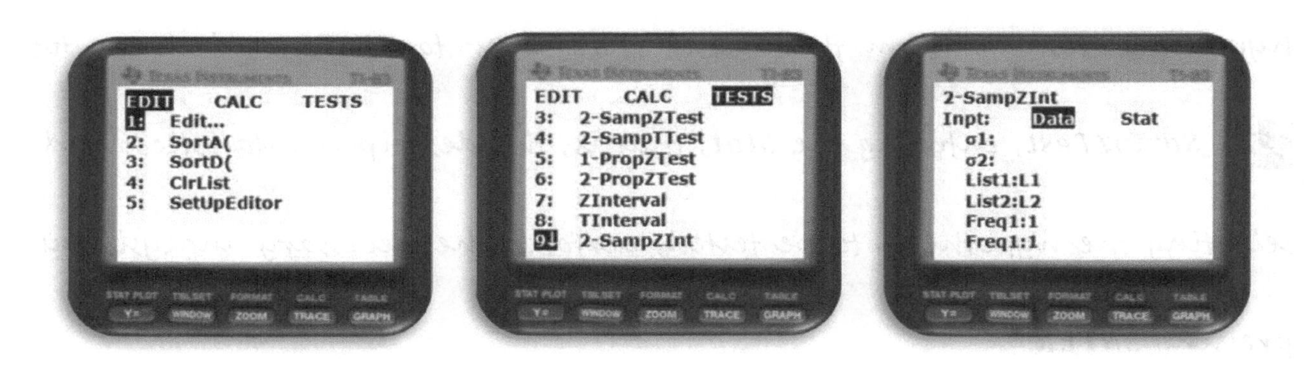

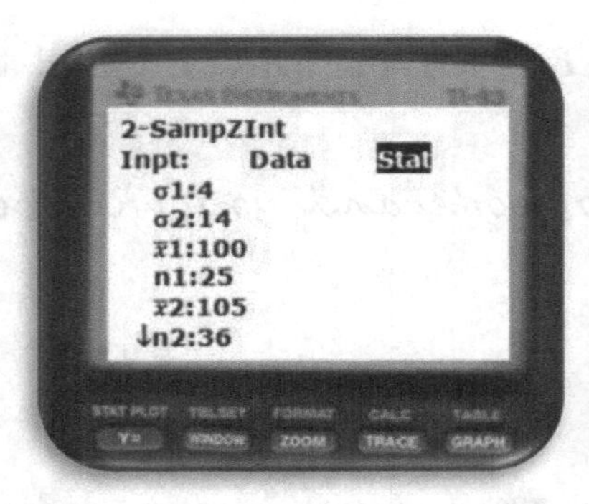

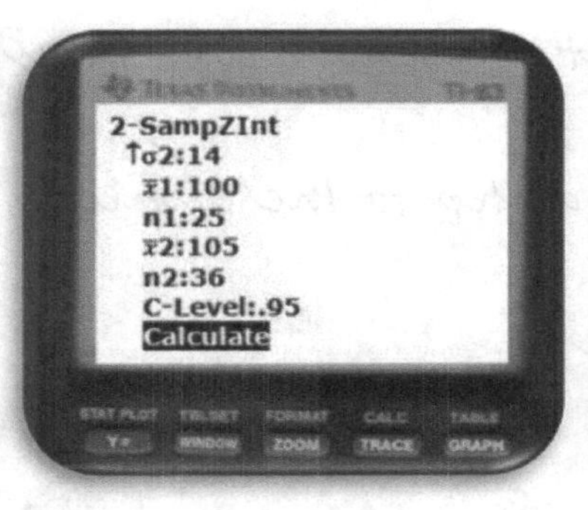

These are exactly the same, up to rounding as when we used the key pad and enter the formulations by hand.

Question 6: In an experiment, a sample of 16 males results in a sample mean of 15 and a sample of 12 females results in a sample mean of 22. Test the claim that there is no significant difference given that data's distribution follows the normal probability distribution and the standard deviation for males is known to be 6 and for females, 5.

*Once the information is in the calculator, whether it is in lists or in the form of summary statistics, the analysis can be extended to hypothesis testing. From the menu **STAT**, over to **TESTS** and down to **3:2 – SampZTest**, entering the **Stat**, that is, the descriptive statistics, and selecting the hypothesis to be tested, perform the necessary analysis by pressing **ENTER**.*

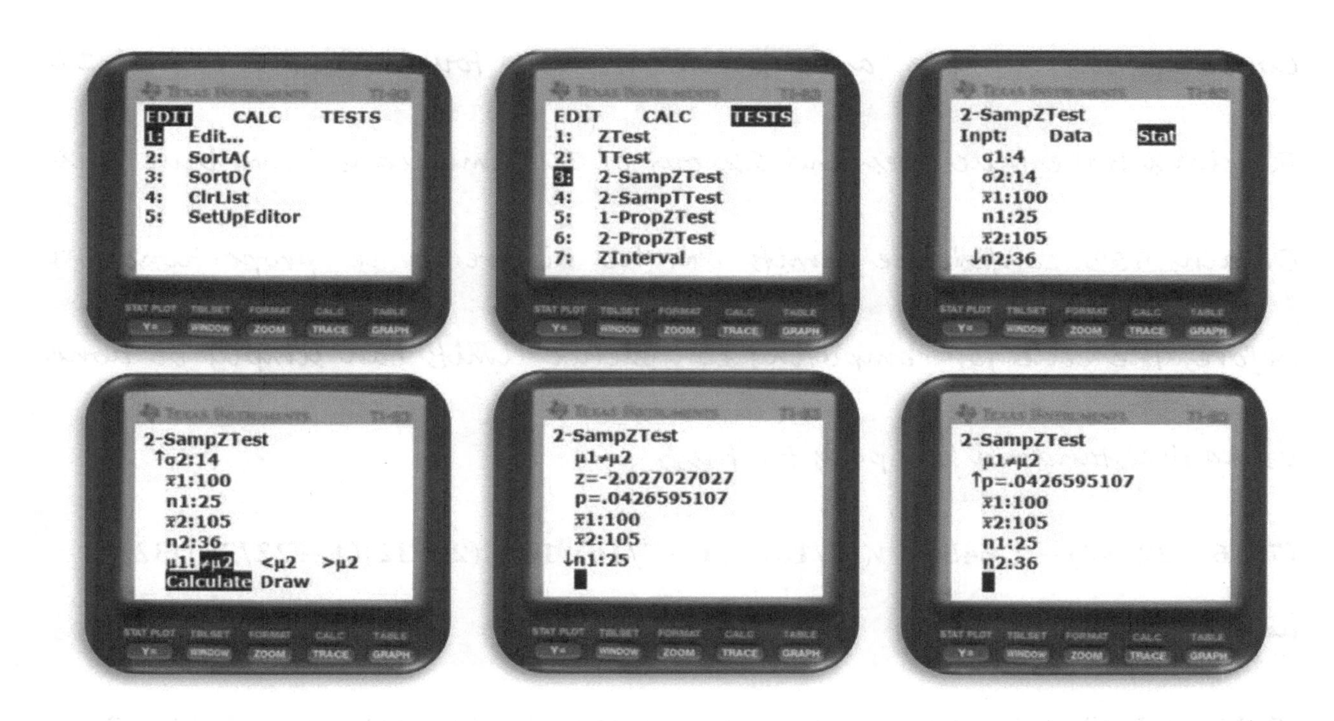

We can directly conclude at the 5% level of significance, there is sufficient evidence to reject the null hypothesis. With a **p − value** of **0.0427**, there is a significant difference in means. This conclusion is consistent with our confidence interval.

Question 7: In a poll, out of 200 republicans and 197 democrats, is was found that 153 of the republicans voted for a tax increase and 137 democrats voted for a tax increase. Obtain 90% confidence limits on the true difference in proportion.

Consider the example, an experiment, it is found that 7 out of 16 Russians have blue eyes and 22 out of 32 Americans have blue eyes. Obtain 95% confidence limits on the difference in proportions. As before, the code for computing confidence limits can simply be done using the standard key pad; that is,

$$(7/16 - 22/32) - 1.6456 * \sqrt{}((7/16) * (1 - 7/16)/16 + (22/32)(1 - 22/32)/32)$$

and

$$(7/16 - 22/32) + 1.6456 * \sqrt{}((7/16) * (1 - 7/16)/16 + (22/32) * (1 - 22/32)/32)$$

where 1.645 is the critical statistic, $z_{\frac{\alpha}{2}} = z_{0.05} = 1.645$. Once you type the first one, you can press ***ENTRY*** (**2**nd ***ENTER***), the calculator will go back a step to the last line of code and you will be able to change the − to a +.

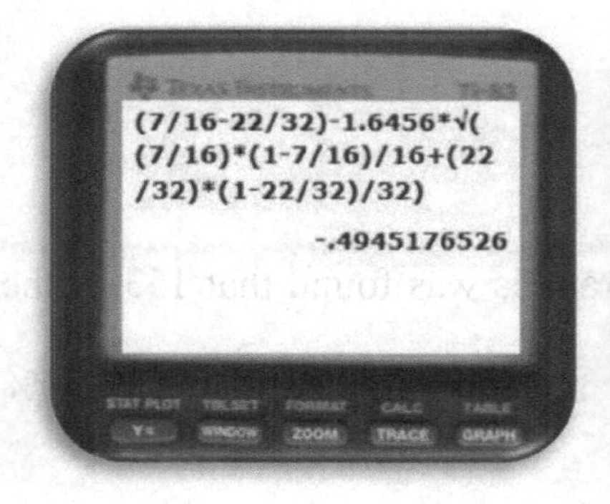

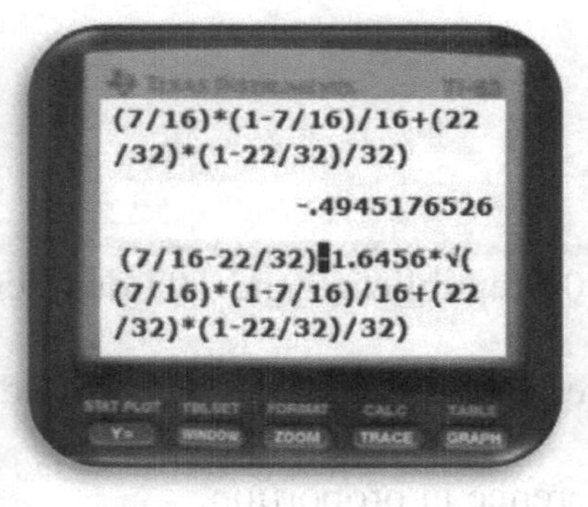

Therefore, we are at least 95% confident that the true difference in proportions is between -0.4945 and -0.0055. To make this a little easier, you could have used ***STO→*** and store the fractions into, say A and B, using the code $\mathbf{7/16}\boldsymbol{STO} \rightarrow \boldsymbol{A}$ and $\mathbf{22/32}\boldsymbol{STO} \rightarrow \boldsymbol{B}$; to get to the green letters for storage, use ***ALPHA MATH*** and ***ALPHA MATRIX***, respectively.

Then the previous calculations become

$$LCL = (A - B) - 1.6456 * \sqrt{(A * (1 - A)/16 + B * (1 - B)/32)}$$

and

$$UCL = (A - B) + 1.6456 * \sqrt{(A * (1 - A)/16 + B * (1 - B)/32)}.$$

To obtain the same results, however, there is an easier way: using **STAT** go over to **TESTS** and down to **B:2 – PropZInt** where you will be given the option to enter the information.

These are exactly the same, up to rounding as when we used the key pad and enter the formulations by hand.

Question 8: In a poll, out of 200 republicans and 197 democrats, is was found that 153 of the republicans voted for a tax increase and 137 democrats voted for a tax increase. At the 10% level of significance, test the hypothesis that these proportions are equal.

Using the same information in the previous example, the analysis can be extended to hypothesis testing. From the menu ***STAT***, over to ***TESTS*** and down to **6:**2 − ***SampZTest***, entering the necessary information and selecting the hypothesis to be tested, perform the necessary analysis by pressing ***ENTER***.

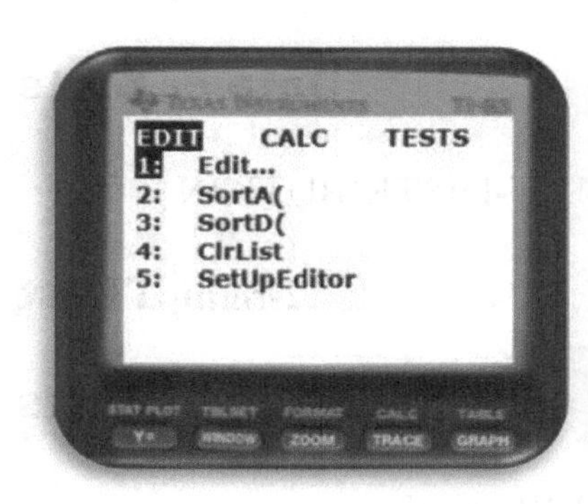

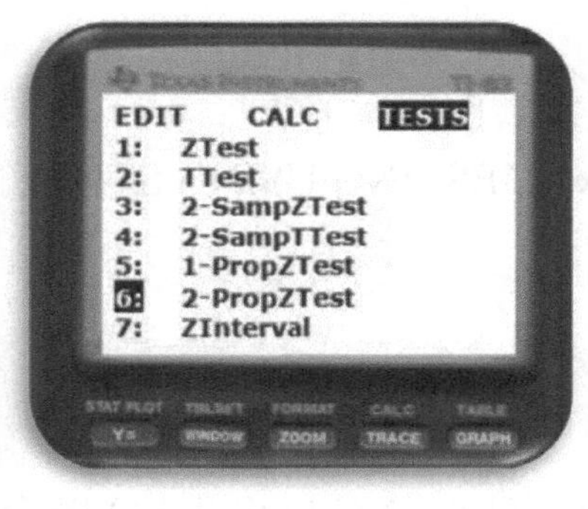

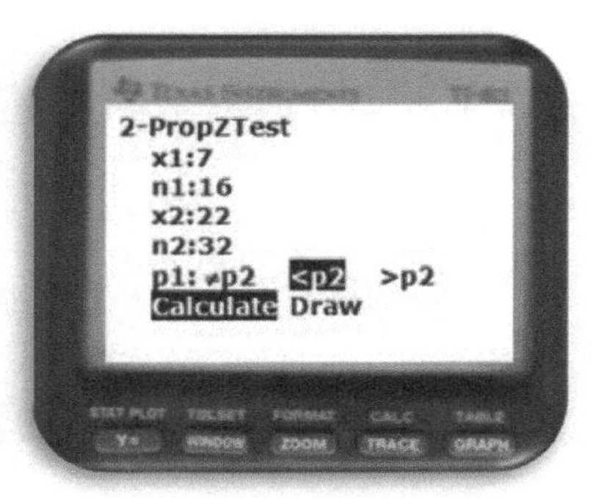

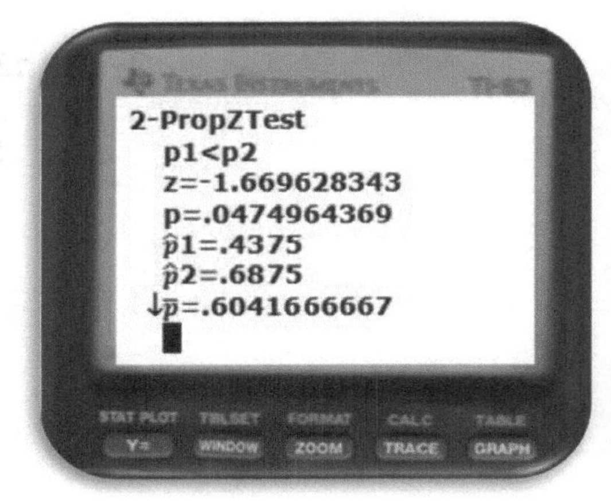

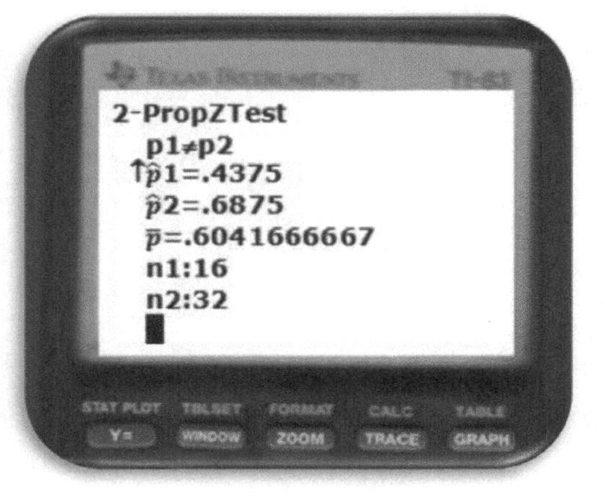

We can directly conclude at the 10% level of significance, there is sufficient evidence to reject the null hypothesis. With a p – value of **0.0475**, *there is a significant difference in proportions. This conclusion is consistent with our confidence interval.*

TI 83 | BASIC COMMANDS FOR GRAPHICS

- **STAT > TESTS**
  - TESTING USING NORMAL DISTRIBUTION

    2-SampZTest

    Data or **Stats**
  - TESTING USING STUDENT T-DISTRIBUTION

    2-SampTTest

    Data or **Stats**
  - TESTING FOR TWO PROPORTION

    2-PropZTest

    Stats

Using Technology in Additional Hypothesis Testing C10

CI & HT using Chi-square and F-distribution using EXCEL

You will need to use the accompanying **EXCEL** file **"Chapter 10 Using Technology Additional CI & HT"** to generate the information needed for many of the following questions.

FORMAT: Bold key words to be **emphasized**, **label figures** and **tables**, and **paginate**.

Question 1: The electronic connection in a computer must be re-soldered when wear on these parts indicates too much variability in the current as it passes through the circuits. A large computer contains thousands of electronic connections, and safety regulation requires that variability measurements on the population of all electronic connections not exceed 0.12 ampere. An inspector took a random sample of 31 electronic connections with a sample variance 0.18 ampere. Using a 0.01 level of significance, is the inspector justified in claiming that all the electronic connection should be re-soldered?

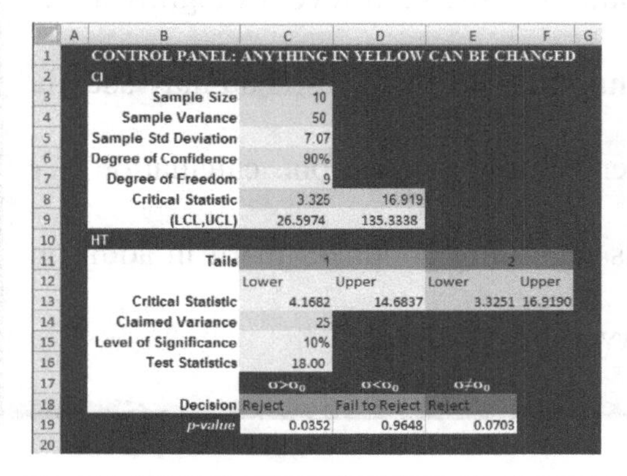

B	C	D	E	F
CONTROL PANEL: ANYTHING IN YELLOW CAN BE CHANGED				
CI				
Sample Size	10			
Sample Variance	50			
Sample Std Deviation	7.07			
Degree of Confidence	90%			
Degree of Freedom	9			
Critical Statistic	3.325	16.919		
(LCL,UCL)	26.5974	135.3338		
HT				
Tails	1		2	
	Lower	Upper	Lower	Upper
Critical Statistic	4.1682	14.6837	3.3251	16.9190
Claimed Variance	25			
Level of Significance	10%			
Test Statistics	18.00			
	$\sigma > \sigma_0$	$\sigma < \sigma_0$	$\sigma \neq \sigma_0$	
Decision	Reject	Fail to Reject	Reject	
p-value	0.0352	0.9648	0.0703	

In the example to the left, using the worksheet **"CI & HT Variance"** *in the file* **"Solver Chapter 10"**, *anything in yellow can* be changed and hence setting $n = 10$, $s^2 = 50$ and $\alpha = 0.05$, Excel has computed the following: $s \approx 7.07, v = 9, \chi_L^2 = 2.700$ and $\chi_U^2 = 19.023$. Therefore, we have the lower and upper confidence limits on the true variance; that is, **we are at least 90% confident that the true variance is between 26.5974 and 135.3338.** At the 10% level of significance, we **reject the hypothesis that the true variance is actually equal to 25** in favor of either the weaker statement, **the variance is not equal to 25** and the stronger statement, **the variance is in fact greater than 25** as indicated by the associated **p-values**, 0.0703 and 0.0352, respectively.

Question 2: M&M EXPERIMENT the **M&M/Mars Company** claims that the proportions of **M&Ms** in bags of mini-packs are as follows in the table below; that is, the null hypothesis is that the desired distribution "fits" the data. You will need to purchase a King Size bag (or larger) bag of Plain M&Ms and test the goodness-of-fit of the distribution at the 0.05 level of significance. Note: the degrees of freedom, $\boldsymbol{v = m - 1}$ where $\boldsymbol{m}$ is the number of categories. You may use the worksheet "***HT Goodness of Fit***" to check your answer. Show at least one calculation per column and include all parts outline for testing hypothesis regarding goodness-of-fit in addition to a bar chart illustrating the candy color distribution observed.

Color	Expected Percent	Expected Frequency E	Observed Frequency O	Observed Relative Frequency	$\frac{(O-E)^2}{E}$
Brown	13%				
Red	13%				
Yellow	14%				
Green	16%				
Orange	20%				
Blue	24%				
TOTAL	100%			100%	___

Using the worksheet "**HT Goodness of Fit**" in the file "**Solver Chapter 10**", by placing the recorded information into the various columns, Excel will perform hypothesis testing for goodness-of-fit. Information required include: **categories** (up to 10), **observed frequencies** (O) and the **expected percentages** (E%). Excel will compute the **expected frequencies** (E), the **errors** (**differences: $Diff$**), the **difference-squared** ($Diff^2$) the **relative error** (χ_i^2) for each category, the **test statistic**, χ^2, the **critical statistic**, χ_α^2, the **p-value**, and gives the final decision: **reject** or **fail to reject**.

Consider the experiment, two fair tokens are painted with nail polish (both on the side of heads) in an effort to skew the probability distribution. After 10 coats, the coins are tossed 100 times with the following results: zero heads 15 times, one head 64 times and two heads 19 times. To determine if the coins would still be deemed "fair", we test to see if the expected 25%-50%-25% split amount the three categories: 0, 1 and 2 will be tested at the 5% level of significance.

Entering this information into the cells highlighted in yellow, yields the following results (illustrated in the graphic below). The final conclusion, **at the 5% level of significance, is that there is sufficient evidence to reject the null hypothesis.** At the 5% level of significance, with 2 **degrees of freedom**, the **critical statistic** is $\chi^2_\alpha = \mathbf{5.99}$. Therefore, the **test statistic** $\chi^2 = \mathbf{9.51}$ lies in the rejection region. Thus, with a p-value of 0.0086, we conclude that the coins have successfully been skewed. It appears that the probability distribution

CONTROL PANEL: ANYTHING IN YELLOW CAN BE CHANGED

Category	O	E%	E	Diff	Diff²	χ² error
0	15	25.0%	24.5	-9.5	90.25	3.68
1	64	50.0%	49	15	225	4.59
2	19	25.0%	24.5	-5.5	30.25	1.23
3	98	1			Test Statistic χ^2=	9.51
					Alpha α=	5%
					Degree of freedom ν=	2
					Critical Statistic $\chi^2_{\nu,\alpha}$=	5.99
					p-value	0.0086
					Decision	Reject

associated with two fair coins does not fit the observed distribution.

Question 3: Use $\chi^2 = \sum \frac{(O-E)^2}{E}$ with degrees of freedom, $v = (r-1)(c-1)$ to determine if in the clinical trials a success recovery is **independent** of the drug prescribed; that is, the null hypothesis is the events are independent. You may use the worksheet **"HT Independence"** to check your answer. Show at least one calculation per chart.

O-Observation Drug	Successful Recovery	Not Successful
A	61	39
B	51	49
C	73	27

Using **"HT Independence"** *we can readily measure the expected frequencies and the relative errors for a contingency table that is* 15×6 $(C3{:}H17)$*. This will generate the expected counts in cells* $C21{:}H35$ *and the relative errors in cells* $C39{:}H53$*, each illustrated below.*

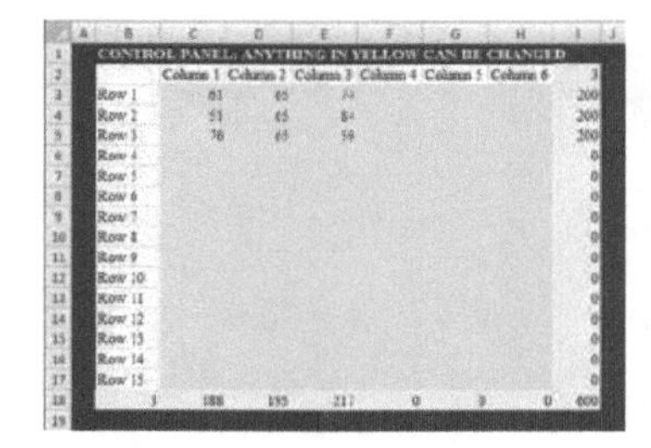

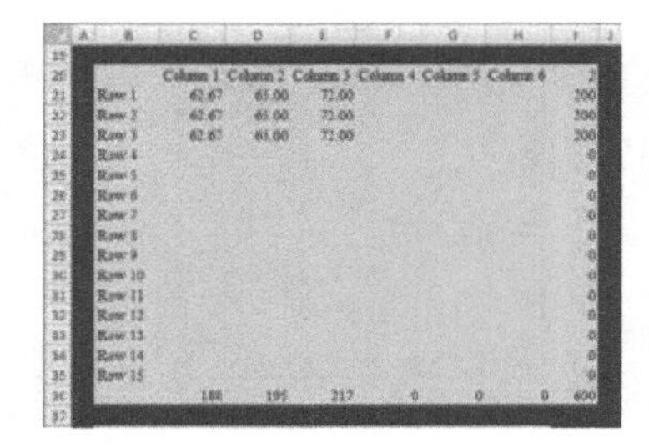

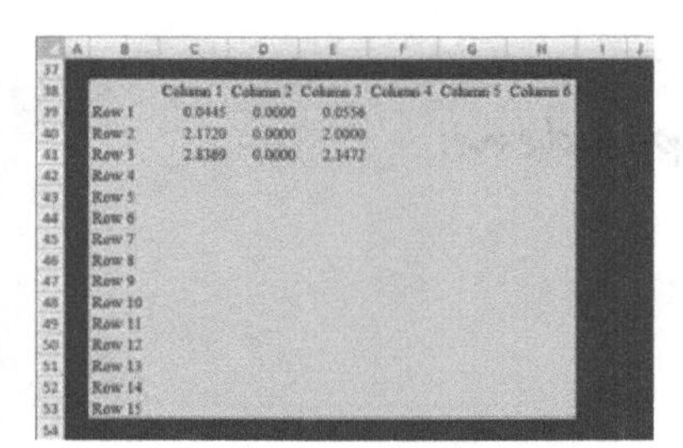

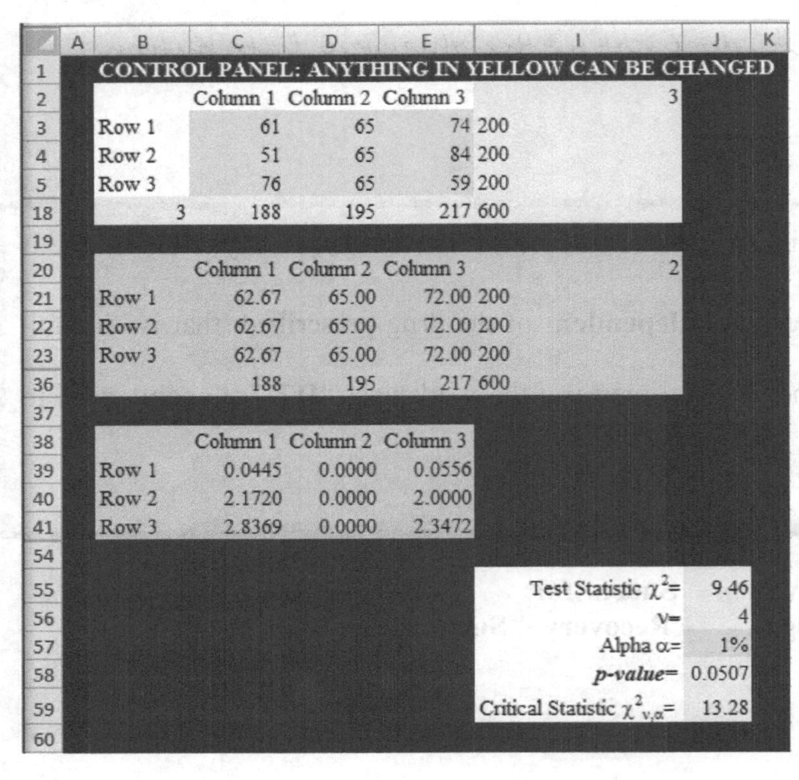

CONTROL PANEL: ANYTHING IN YELLOW CAN BE CHANGED

		Column 1	Column 2	Column 3		3
Row 1		61	65	74	200	
Row 2		51	65	84	200	
Row 3		76	65	59	200	
	3	188	195	217	600	

	Column 1	Column 2	Column 3		2
Row 1	62.67	65.00	72.00	200	
Row 2	62.67	65.00	72.00	200	
Row 3	62.67	65.00	72.00	200	
	188	195	217	600	

	Column 1	Column 2	Column 3
Row 1	0.0445	0.0000	0.0556
Row 2	2.1720	0.0000	2.0000
Row 3	2.8369	0.0000	2.3472

Test Statistic χ^2=	9.46
ν=	4
Alpha α=	1%
p-value=	0.0507
Critical Statistic $\chi^2_{v,\alpha}$=	13.28

In the given example, we have a 3×3 contingency table. At the 1% level of significance and with $\nu = (3-1) \times (3-1) = 4$, we have $\chi^2_{v,\alpha} = \chi^2_{4,0.01} = 13.28$; hence with a **test statistic** $\chi^2 = 9.46$ we fail to reject the null hypothesis at the 1% level of significance. With a **p-value** of 0.0507, **at the 1% level of significance there is sufficient evidence to reject the null hypothesis** that the events represented in the rows (the first factor) is independent of the events represented in the columns (the second factor). Therefore, **we conclude that the events are dependent.**

Question 4: To better understand human anatomy, an experiment is conducted to determine if variance in the population of men is equal to the variance in the population of women, 12 men and 18 women had their height measured (to the cm) in the morning, afternoon and evening. Using this information, the sample variance among the men was found to be 0.15 cm and among the women, 0.21. At the 5% level of significance, test the hypothesis that variances are equal. You may use the worksheet **"CI & HT 2P Variances F"** to check your answer.

Using the worksheet "CI & HT 2P Variance F" *in the file* "**Chapter 9 Using Technology in CI & HT 2P**", *with just a few edits in the given information, we can make a decision using the F-statistic given the summary provided in the spreadsheet.*

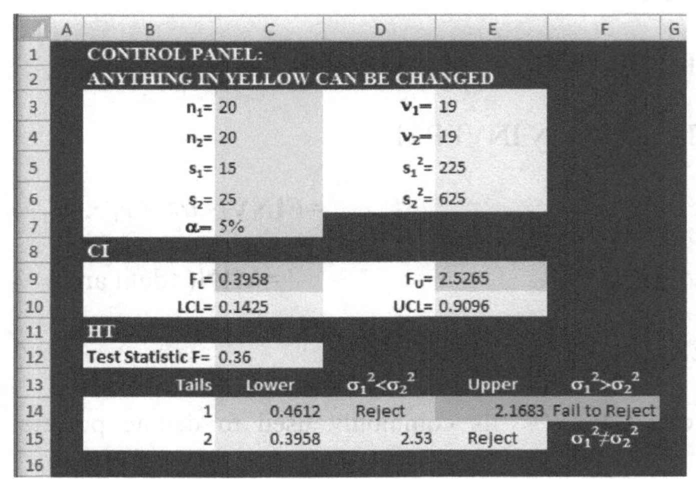

	A	B	C	D	E	F	G
1		CONTROL PANEL:					
2		ANYTHING IN YELLOW CAN BE CHANGED					
3		n_1=	20	v_1=	19		
4		n_2=	20	v_2=	19		
5		s_1=	15	s_1^2=	225		
6		s_2=	25	s_2^2=	625		
7		α=	5%				
8		CI					
9		F_L=	0.3958	F_U=	2.5265		
10		LCL=	0.1425	UCL=	0.9096		
11		HT					
12		Test Statistic F=	0.36				
13		Tails	Lower	$\sigma_1^2<\sigma_2^2$	Upper	$\sigma_1^2>\sigma_2^2$	
14		1	0.4612	Reject	2.1683	Fail to Reject	
15		2	0.3958	2.53	Reject	$\sigma_1^2\neq\sigma_2^2$	
16							

In the example to the left, if we set $n_1 = n_2 = 20$, $s_1 = 15$ *and* $s_2 = 25$, *and the level of significance to 5%, Excel gives the lower and upper confidence limits,* $F_L = 0.3958$ *and* $F_U = 2.5265$, *and gives the 95% confidence limits on the ratio of variance,* ***we are at least 95% that the true ratio of variances is between 0.1425 and 0.9096****, which supports* *the claim that there is a difference in variance. Furthermore, with an F-statistic of 0.36, we reject the null hypothesis in favor of the alternative hypothesis that* $\sigma_1^2 < \sigma_2^2$.

EXCEL — BASIC COMMANDS USED IN THIS SECTION

❖ Note: these are just a few of the codes used in this section.

- ABSOLUTE VALUE **=ABS(**<value>**)**
- CHI-SQUARED DISTRIBUTION **=CHIDIST(**<test value>,<ν>**)**
- CHI-SQUARED INVERSE **=CHIINV(**<probability in tail>,<ν>**)**
- DIVISION /
- F-DISTRIBUTION **=FDIST(**<test statistic>,<ν_1>,<ν_2>**)**
- F-DISTRIBUTION INVERSE **=FINV(**<α>,<ν_1>,<ν_2>**)**
- MINIMUM **=MIN(**<data array>**)**
- POWER ^

Note: the carrot key "^" is commonly used to denote powers: $x\text{^}2 = x^2$ and therefore, $50\text{^}0.5 = SQRT(50)$

- ROUND **=ROUND(**<value >,<sig. fig.>**)**
- SQUARE ROOT **=SQRT(**<value>**)**
- SUBTRACTION -

CI & HT using Chi-square and F-distribution using TI-83

In terms of the ***chi-squared distribution****, the* $TI-\mathbf{83}$ *is limited to that of hypothesis testing for* ***independence****. However, under* **DISTR** *we can directly use both the* ***chi-squared*** *and the* ***F-distributions****.*

> **Question 5:** The electronic connection in a computer introduced in question 1 has a test statistic of $\chi^2 = \mathbf{45}$, with $\nu = \mathbf{31} - \mathbf{1} = \mathbf{30}$. Determine the probability of type one error; that is, the $p-value$, the probability of the observed test statistic or something more extreme.

In general, the code for the ***chi-square cumulative probability*** *is* $\chi^2 \boldsymbol{cdf}(< lower\ limit >, < upper\ limit >, < \nu >)$. *If the* ***upper limit*** *is infinity, then we can set the* ***upper limit*** *to an extremely large number like* **10^10**. *For example, to find* $\boldsymbol{P}(\chi^2 > 10|\nu = 5)$ *we would use the following key strokes:* ***DISTR*** $(2^{nd}$ ***VARS***$)$ *down to* **7:** $\chi^2\boldsymbol{cdf}$, *then* ***ENTER*** *followed by the lower limit,* **10**, *a comma, ",", the upper limit,* **10^10**, *a comma, ",", the degree of freedom,* **5**, *and final the closing parenthesis or simply just* ***ENTER***.

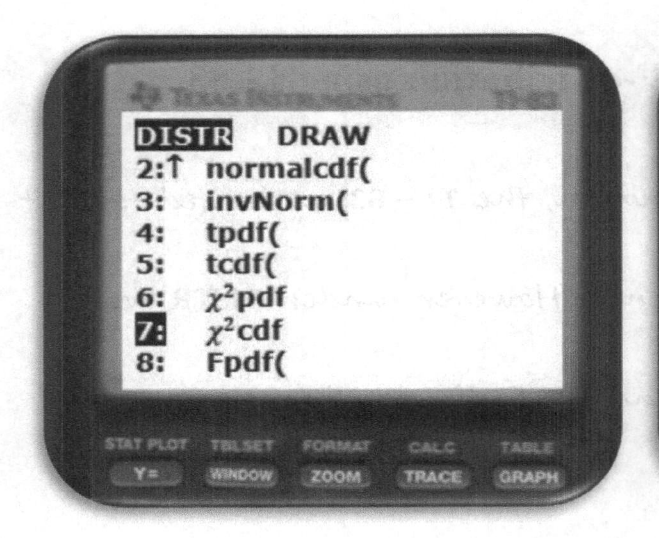

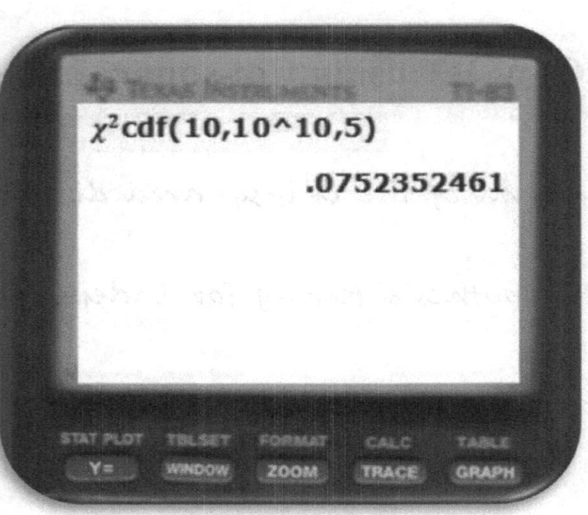

$$P(\chi^2 > 10|\nu = 5) \approx \mathbf{0.7524}$$

Note: the $TI - 83$ does not have the inverse function for the chi-square distribution.

Question 6: The events A and B are believed to be independent of the events X and Y. To test this hypothesis, a sample of 50 events are observed and categorized into the following contingency table. Perform hypothesis testing for independence and compute the $p - value$.

Observed	X	Y
A	5	7
B	25	13

Using the $TI-83$, we must first take the time to compute the **expected frequencies**. The calculator assumes that the both the matrix (contingency table) of **observed frequencies** are in one matrix, say $[A]$, and the **expected frequencies** are in another matrix, say $[B]$. For example, assume the following two matrices for the observed and expected frequencies are given below:

Observed	X	Y
A	15	17
B	25	13

Expected	X	Y
A	18.29	14.00
B	21.71	16.00

To put these matrices into the calculator, under **MATRIX**, over to **EDIT** and press **ENTER**; then, after selecting the desired matrix, set the dimensions $(2 \to 2$ for $2 \times 2)$ and using **ENTER**, enter the numbers into the matrix and then **QUIT** (2nd **MODE**). The $TI-83$ denotes matrices with a capital letter offset by brackets [ ].

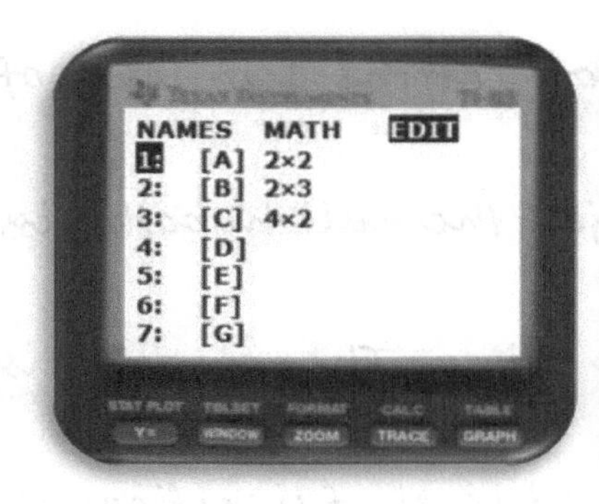

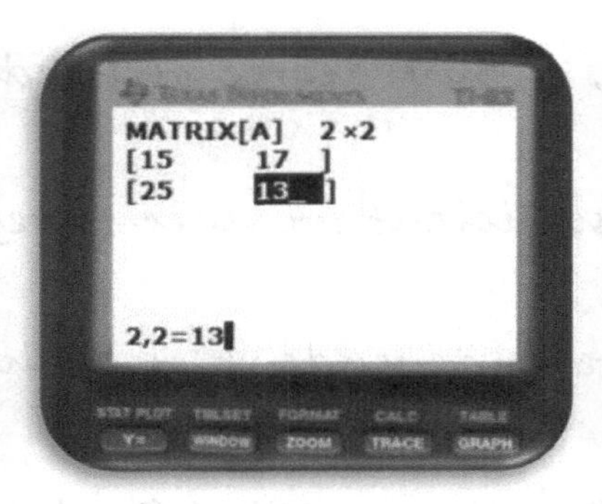

Under ***STAT***, move over to ***TESTS*** down to $\chi^2 -$ ***Test*** which will take you to the screen where we name the matrix; to change the matrix, use ***MATRIX*** and select the appropriate matrix.

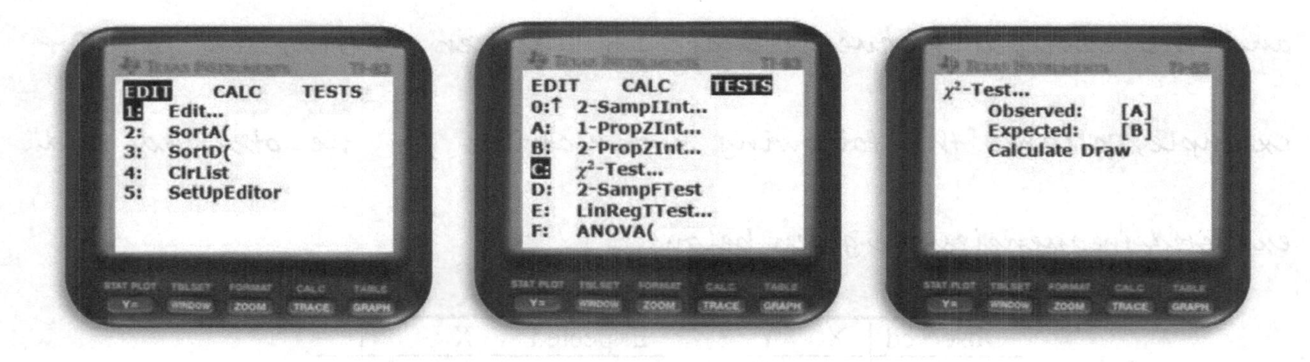

Then move to ***Calculate*** and press ***ENTER***.

Hence, in this example, with **1 degree of freedom, at the 10% level of significance, there is insufficient evidence to reject the null hypothesis**, that is, these events are independent of each other. The p-value is 0.1111; which is greater than any commonly used level of significance.

Had we selected ***DRAW*** instead, then we would see the graph of the given distribution including the **test statistic** and the $\boldsymbol{p-value}$, but not the **degree of freedom**.

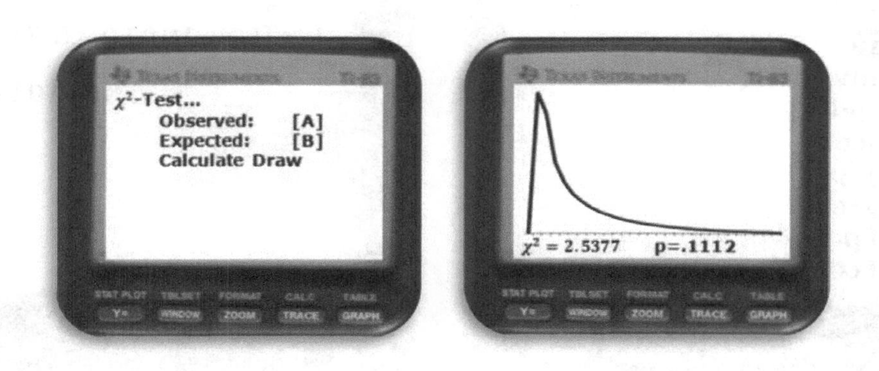

Question 7: The human anatomy study conducted in question 4 has a test statistic of $\boldsymbol{F = 1.4}$, assuming $\boldsymbol{v_1 = 5}$ and $\boldsymbol{v_2 = 7}$. Determine the probability in the tail, that is, the $\boldsymbol{p - value}$.

In general, the code for the F-distribution is $\boldsymbol{Fcdf}(< \text{lower limit} >, < \text{upper limit} >, < \boldsymbol{v_1} >, < \boldsymbol{v_2} >)$, if the **upper limit** is infinity, then we can set the **upper limit** to an extremely large number like **10^10**. For example, to find $\boldsymbol{P}(\boldsymbol{F} > 14|\boldsymbol{v_1} = \mathbf{10}, \boldsymbol{v_2} = \mathbf{7})$ we would following the use key strokes: ***DISTR*** (2 ^nd^ ***VARS***) down to **9:** $\boldsymbol{Fcdf}$, then ***ENTER*** followed by the lower limit, **14**, a comma, ",", the upper limit, **10^10**, a comma, ",", the degree *of freedom,* **10***, a comma, ",", the degree of freedom,* **7***, and finally the closing parenthesis or simply just* ***ENTER***.

$$P(F > 14|\nu_1 = \mathbf{10}, \nu_2 = \mathbf{7}) \approx \mathbf{0.0010}$$

Note: the $\boldsymbol{TI-83}$ *does not have the inverse function for the* **F**-*distribution.*

Question 8: In the human anatomy study conducted in question 4 in the population of 12 men and 18 women, we have sample variance among the men of 0.15 cm and among the women, 0.21 cm. At the 10% level of significance, test the hypothesis that variances are equal.

To put this information into the calculator, under ***STAT****, move over to* ***TESTS*** *down to* **D:2 – SamplF – Test** *which will take you to the screen* where we enter the necessary statistics. For example, consider the claim that two population variances are equal given $n_1 = 10, \sigma_1^2 = 15$, $n_2 = 9$, and $\sigma_1^2 = 29$ versus the alternative, the variances are not equal.

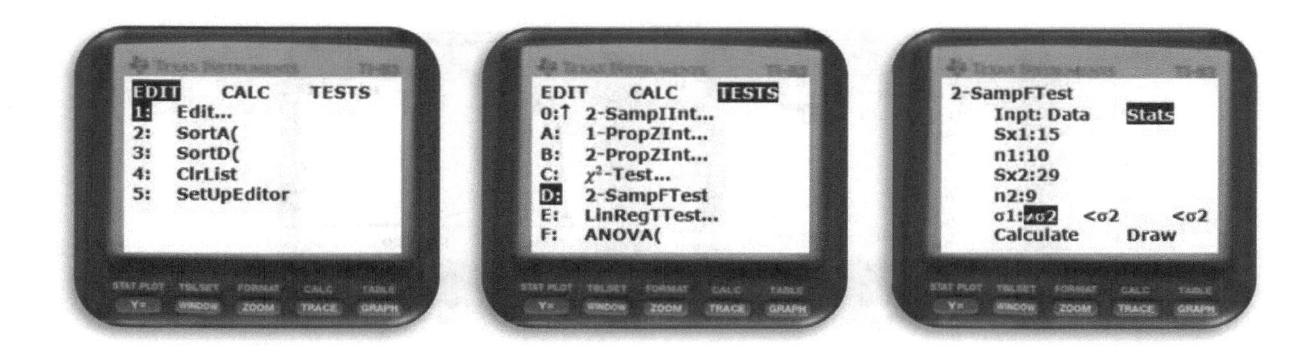

Then move to ***Calculate*** and press ***ENTER***.

Hence, in this example, at the 10% level of significance, there is **sufficient evidence to reject the null hypothesis**, that is, the variances are not equal. Note: this is not the case at the 5% level of significance. The $p-value$ is 0.06599; which is between 0.05 and 0.10.

Had we selected **DRAW** instead, then we would see the graph of the given distribution including the **test statistic** and the **p – value**, but not the **degree of freedom**.

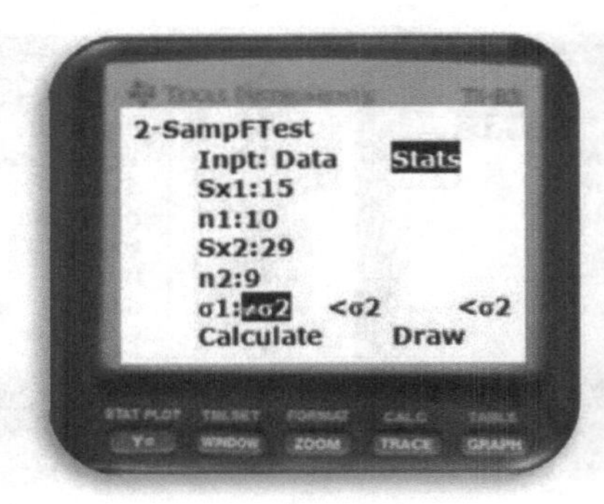

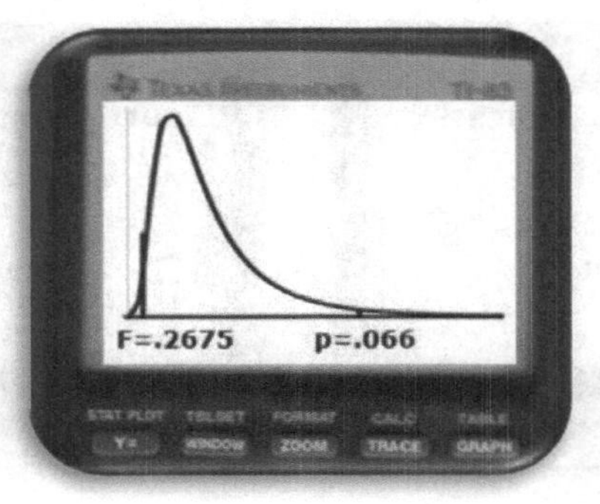

Question 9: Analyze the information given in the following table. Is the variance of ***X*** equal to the variance of ***Y***? Test the hypothesis at the 1% level of significant.

X	*Y*
3	2
7	6
3	5
1	9
4	2

Using the TI-83, using the techniques outlined in Chapter 3 Using Technology in Graphical Representations of Data, put the data values and the frequencies in two distinct lists, say **L1**, and **L2**.

Under ***STAT***, move over to ***TESTS*** down to **D:2 – SamplF – Test** which will take you to the next menu where you select the ***Data*** option.

Therefore, we have that the test statistic is $F = 2.4$ and with a ***p – value*** of 0.3587, **at any common level of significance, there is insufficient evidence to reject the null hypothesis**, that is, there is no significant difference in variance between these two data sets.

- **STAT > TESTS**

  - TESTING USING CHI-SQUARE DISTRIBUTION

χ^2-Test

Independence only

  - TESTING USING CHI-SQUARE DISTRIBUTION

2-SampFTest

Regression using EXCEL

You will need to use the accompanying **EXCEL** file **"Chapter 11 Using Technology in Regression"** to generate the information needed for many of the following questions.

FORMAT: Bold key words to be **emphasized**, **label figures** and **tables**, and **paginate**.

Question 1: Using the worksheet **"Matched Pairs Random Generator"** to generate at least two graphs that illustrate **positive** and **negative** correlation as well as **weak** and **strong** correlation; your write up must clearly discuss the following. To adjust the slope and the variability set the **Marginal Change** to (1) a positive and (2) a negative in conjunction with setting **Std Y** and **Std X** to varying positive value.

a) State the estimated **correlation coefficient** r.

b) Does the correlation coefficient indicate a low (weak), moderate, high (strong) correlation? Is this correlation positive or negative?

c) State the regression model $\hat{y} = b_0 + b_1 x$..

d) Give the 95% confidence interval for β_1 and interpret.

e) In testing the null hypothesis, $H_0: \beta_1 = 0$; state the $p - value$ and at the 0.05 level of significance determine whether the explanatory variable x significantly contributes to the response variable x.

f) In the statistical model, $\boldsymbol{y} = \boldsymbol{\beta}_0 + \boldsymbol{\beta}_1\boldsymbol{x}$, where $\boldsymbol{\beta's}$ are the weights that drive the estimates of the response variable, and the observed values, $\boldsymbol{y}_i = \boldsymbol{\beta}_0 + \boldsymbol{\beta}_1\boldsymbol{x}_i + \boldsymbol{\varepsilon}_i$ where $\boldsymbol{\varepsilon}$ is the random error. State the assumption with respect to ε and how the accompanying figures (residual plot and PP plot) illustrate this point. Explain.

g) Use the above model to estimate the response that is an **interpolation.**

h) Use the above model to estimate the response that is an **extrapolation.**

To generate a positive correlation, set the ***marginal change*** *(C4) to a positive value; to generate a negative correlation, set the* ***marginal change*** *to a negative value; you can also change the correlation coefficient by change the other parameters highlighted in yellow.*

	A	B	C	D	E
1		CONTROL PANEL: ANYTHING IN YELLOW CAN BE CHANGED			
2		Parameters			
3		Sample Size	100		
4		Marginal Change	2		
5		Intercept	5		
6		Mean x	10		
7		Std x	5		
8		Std y	25		
9		Confidence Level (1-α)%=	95%		

This will randomly generate 100 *matched pairs in cells* ***C51*: *D150***. *To fix the information*, ***Copy*** *and* ***Paste Special*, *Values***.

Then the following information is provided:

	A	B	C	D	E	F	G	H
1		**CONTROL PANEL: ANYTHING IN YELLOW CAN BE CHANGED**						
2		**Parameters**						
3		Sample Size	100					
4		Marginal Change	2					
5		Intercept	5					
6		Mean *x*	10					
7		Std *x*	5					
8		Std *y*	25					
9		Confidence Level (1-α)%=	95%					
10		**Statistics**	X	Y				
11		Sample Mean	10.67	26.19				
12		Sample Standard Deviation	4.26	25.16				
13		**Correlation**						
14		Sample Correlation r=	0.2247		S_e	24.65		
15		Test statistic t (H_0:ρ=0)	2.2831		Σx	1066.7		
16		*p-value*	0.0123		Σx^2	13177.2		
17		Decision	Proceed		SE	1798.7039		
18		**LRM**						
19		Estimated Slope	1.327					
20		Estimated Intercept	12.040					
21		Critical Statistic	1.9845			LCL	UCL	
22		ME (β)=	1.1532			0.17	2.48	
23		Test statistic t (H_0:β=0)	2.283					
24		*p-value*	0.0123					
25		**Five Number Summary**	X	Y	Y^	LCL	UCL	
26		Min	(0.05)	(31.71)	11.97	6.60	17.35	
27		Q_1	7.77	7.62	22.35	19.94	24.76	
28		Median	10.93	27.84	26.53	24.54	28.53	
29		Q_2	13.36	42.67	29.76	27.40	32.11	
30		Max	22.91	86.83	42.44	36.40	48.47	
31		Extrapolation	50.00		78.38	59.96	96.80	
32								

State the estimated **correlation coefficient** r. *The estimate of the true correlation coefficient is given* $\boldsymbol{C14}$. *In the above example with an estimated correlation coefficient of* $\boldsymbol{r = 0.2247}$, *there is some correlation between the two variables.*

Does the correlation coefficient indicate a low (weak), moderate, high (strong) correlation? Is this correlation positive or negative? *There is moderate to weak correlation in the given example, and performing hypothesis testing for* $\boldsymbol{\rho}$ *we find that it is significantly different from zero. There is enough correlation to proceed as indicated by cell* $\boldsymbol{C17}$ *which states* ***proceed*** *or* ***no linear trend*** *based on the degree of confidence set and the associated level of significance.*

State the regression model $\hat{\boldsymbol{y}} = \boldsymbol{b_0} + \boldsymbol{b_1 x}$. *Using the information provided in the printout, cells* $\boldsymbol{C19{:}C20}$ *we have* $\hat{\boldsymbol{y}} = \boldsymbol{12.040 + 1.327x}$.

Give the 95% confidence interval for $\boldsymbol{\beta_1}$ and interpret. *In the* ***linear regression model*** $(\boldsymbol{LRM})$, *we are given the* ***critical statistic***, *the* ***margin of error***, *the* ***test*** *statistic and the* $\mathbf{p-value}$; *and then, in cells* **F22:G22**, *we are given the* **LCL** *and the* **UCL** *for* β_1 *are given. Hence,* ***we are at least 95% confident the true marginal change is between*** 0.17 *and* 2.48, *not zero.*

In testing the null hypothesis, $H_0: \beta_1 = 0$; state the p-value and at the 0.05 level of significance determine whether the explanatory variable x significantly contributes to the response variable y. *For hypothesis testing of the* ***parameter*** β_1, *we look at the cells* **C23** *and* **C24**, *which give the* ***test statistic*** *and the accompanying* $\mathbf{p-value}$. *With a* $\mathbf{p-value}$ *of* **0.0123**, ***at the 5% level of significance, there is sufficient evidence to reject the null hypothesis,*** $\beta_1 = 0$ *for the alternative, that there is* ***marginal change*** *either way.*

In the statistical model, $y = \beta_0 + \beta_1 x$, where $\beta's$ are the weights that drive the estimates of the response variable, and the observed values, $y_i = \beta_0 + \beta_1 x_i + \varepsilon_i$ where ε is the random error. State the assumption with respect to ε and how the accompanying figures (PP plot and residual plot) illustrate this point. Explain. *Using the* ***scatter plot*** *worksheet labeled* ***RG Scatter Plot,*** *and hiding columns M:R in worksheet* ***Matched Pairs Random Generator***, *we have the following image along* with the **PP Plot** and the **Residual Plots**, see worksheets **RG PP Plot** and **RG Residuals**.

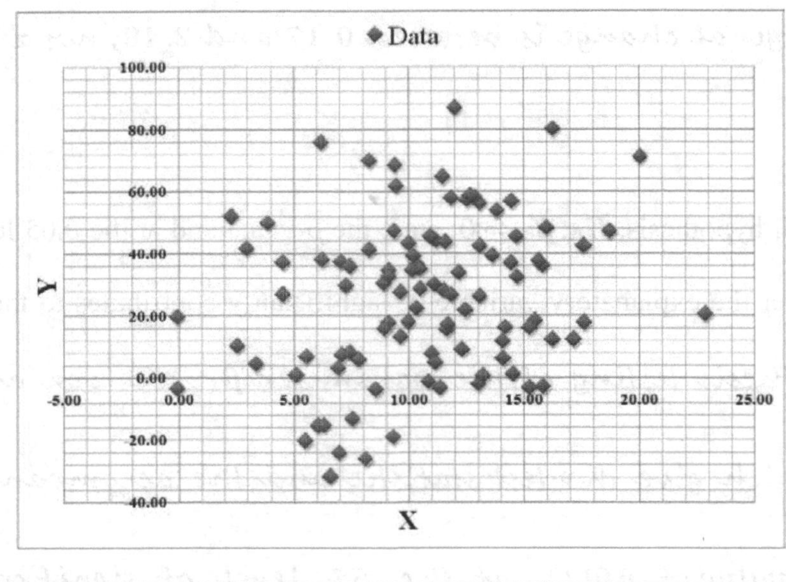

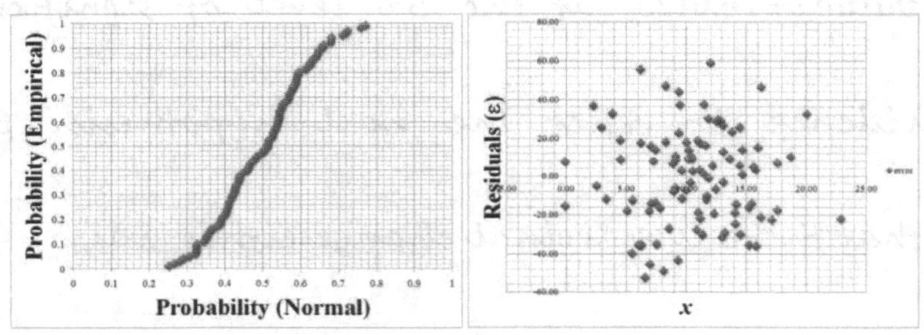

From the above graphics, we see that the data is rather spread out, there is a slight upward trend; however, as illustrated in the **PP plot**, there **residual errors** are **normally distributed** and as illustrated in the **residual plot** the **residuals** are **randomly** placed about zero. Here the only assumption not satisfied is **small variance** in the residual and indicated by the spread of values in the residual plot.

For **interpolation** and **extrapolation**, this will depend on the value place in cell **C31**. In the example above, when $x = 50$, this is **extrapolation** and the estimated response is give to be $\hat{y} = 12.0140 + 1.327(50) = 78.38$. Compared to the exact value $y = 5 + 2(50) = 105$. Note this value is not accurate. In fact, according to the printout, **we are at least 95% confident that the true response is between 59.96 and 96.80.** This is due to the fact that the value is outside of the data's domain.

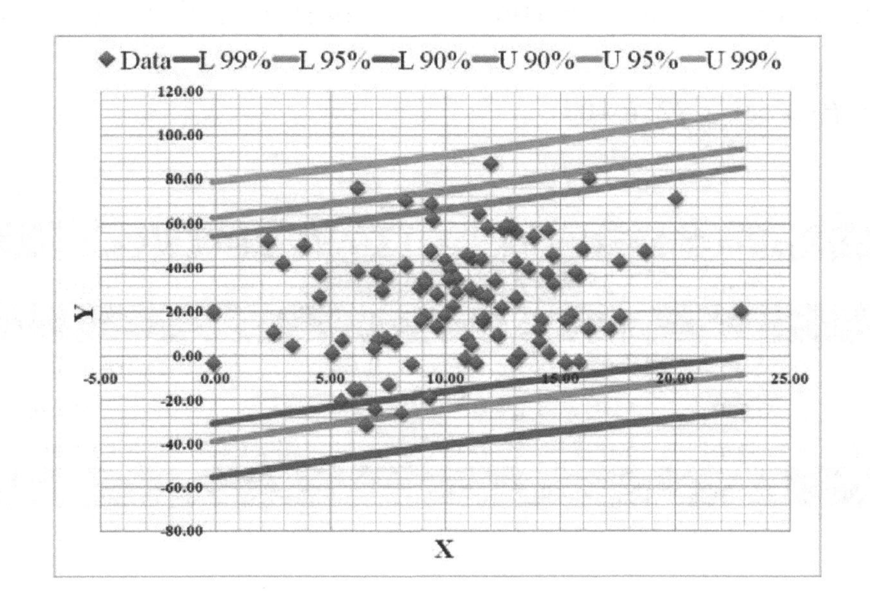

Question 2: Using the worksheet "**Analyzer 2P Matched Pairs**" to quickly analyze the information given in the following table. Discuss the correlation at that 95%

X	*Y*	*X*	*Y*
3	12	9	49
7	36	3	3
4	15	6	31
4	32	4	26
0	2	6	26
8	30	4	18
9	42	1	14
7	38	4	17
1	9	4	19
7	31	4	33

To compute the summary statistics for the given data, simply put the variables x *and* y *into the respective columns;* **J** *and* **K**, *respectively. Remember, anything highlighted in yellow can be changed. This worksheet can handle up to* **100** *matched pairs; that is, you can place any data in the cells* $J2{:}K101$.

	A	B	C	D	E	F	G	H
1		CONTROL PANEL: ANYTHING IN YELLOW CAN BE CHANGED						
2		Count	25			Degree of Confidence	95%	
3			X	Y	ε			
4		Sum	112.00	602.00	658.64	Correlation	0.9551	
5		Mean	4.48	24.08	28.64	Slope	5.55	
6		Standard Deviation	3.04	17.68		Intercept	-0.78	
7								

In the example above, the estimated **correlation coefficient** is 0.9551 (highly correlated), with an estimated **marginal change (slope)** of 5.55 and an **intercept** of -0.78. Hence, the **estimated model** is given by $\hat{y} = -0.78 + 5.55x$. This relationship is illustrated in the scatter plots below; the first with the trend line only and the second with 95% confidence bounds given in worksheets "**A Scatter Plot**" and "**A Confidence Envelope**", respectively.

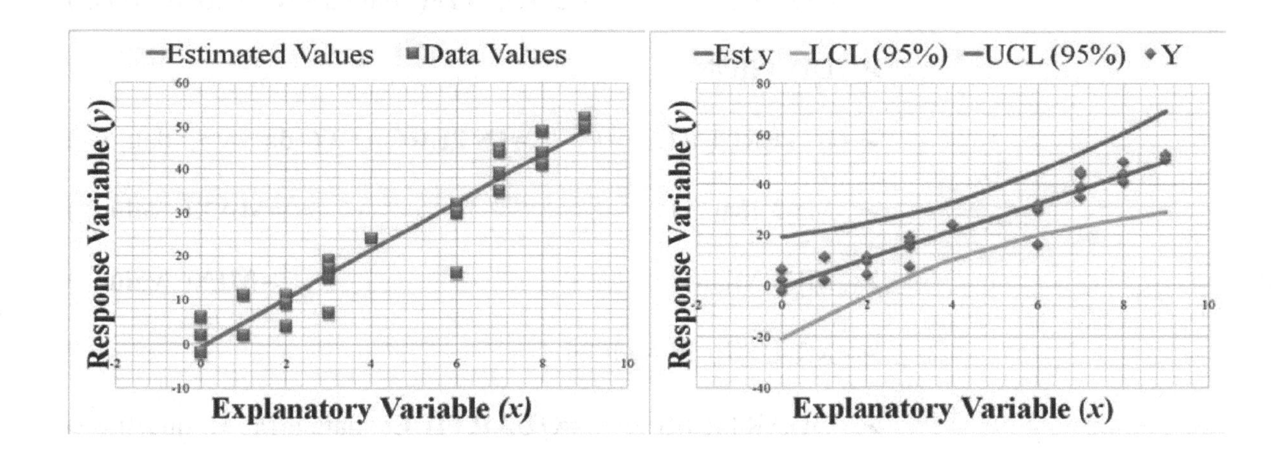

Note: in order to have the second graphic, the **confidence envelope**, drawn correctly, the values of must be sorted in ascending order in terms of the variable x.

EXCEL — BASIC COMMANDS USED IN THIS SECTION

❖ Note: these are just a few of the codes used in this section.

- ABSOLUTE VALUE **=ABS(**<value>)
- ADDITION +
- AVERAGE **=AVERAGE(**<data array>)
- CONDITIONAL STATEMENT **=IF(**<condition>,<action>,<alternative action>)
- CORRELATION **=CORREL(**<data array>,<data array>)
- COUNT **=COUNTIF(**<data array>,<conditions>)
- DIVISION /
- INTERCEPT **=INTERCEPT(**<data y>,<data x>)
- MAXIMUM **=MAX(**<value>)
- MINIMUM **=MIN(**<value>)
- MULTIPLICATION *
- QUARTILES **=QUARTILE(**<data array>,<quartile>)
- ROUND **=ROUND(**<value>,<sig. fig.>)
- SLOPE **=SLOPE(**<data y>,<data x>)
- SQUARE ROOT **=SQRT(**<value>)
- STANDARD DEVIATION **=STDEV(**<data array>)
- SUMMATION **=SUM(**<data array>)
- t-DISTRIBUTION **=TDIST(**<value>, <v>)

Additional Data Analysis

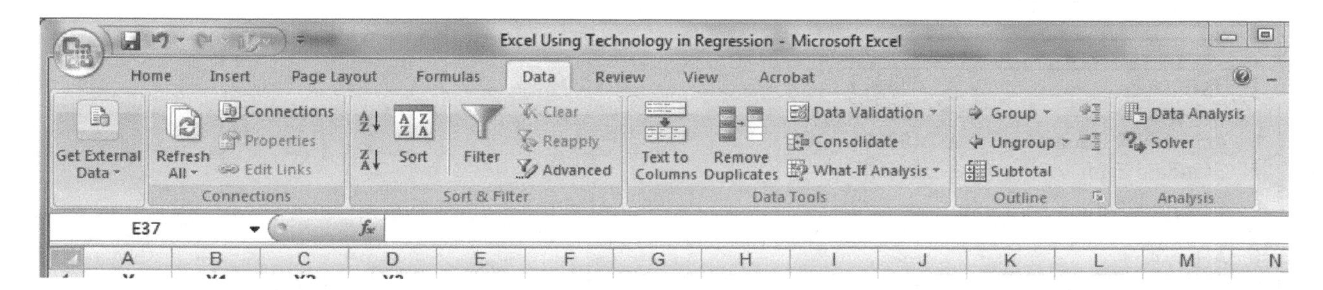

Under Data Analysis, select **Regression** and in the **Input Y Range** and **Input X Range**, place the data cells where the information is located and selected Labels if the first row is the variable labels.

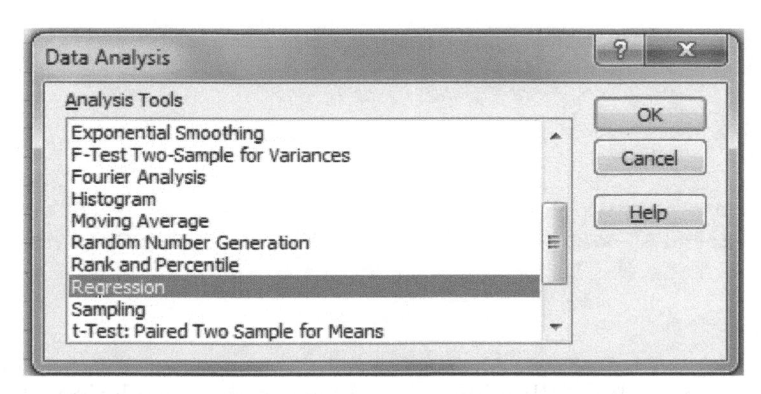

Then, once you enter OK, the summary information will be calculated and placed in a new worksheet.

The information included in this **SUMMARY OUTPUT** includes the **correlation coefficient** (**Multiple R**), the **coefficient of determination** (**R Square**), along with many other summary statistics, included the ***p*-values**.

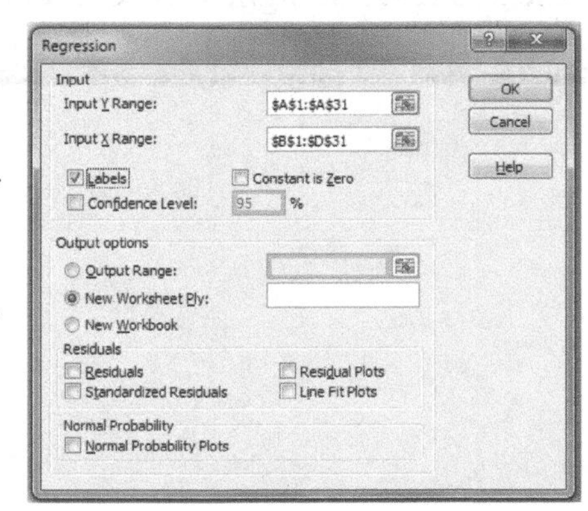

	A	B	C	D	E	F	G
1	SUMMARY OUTPUT						
2							
3	*Regression Statistics*						
4	Multiple R	0.992080343					
5	R Square	0.984223407					
6	Adjusted R Square	0.982403031					
7	Standard Error	5.576296017					
8	Observations	30					
9							
10	ANOVA						
11		*df*	*SS*	*MS*	*F*	*Significance F*	
12	Regression	3	50436.56134	16812.18711	540.6703758	1.55815E-23	
13	Residual	26	808.4720089	31.09507727			
14	Total	29	51245.03335				
15							
16		*Coefficients*	*Standard Error*	*t Stat*	*P-value*	*Lower 95%*	*Upper 95%*
17	Intercept	127.1557479	14.78952439	8.597690132	4.46246E-09	96.75544542	157.5560503
18	X1	-5.158608625	0.197468055	-26.12376273	3.45489E-20	-5.564510022	-4.752707228
19	X2	1.891285986	0.066408213	28.47970002	3.93756E-21	1.75478195	2.027790021
20	X3	-0.097481373	0.100404734	-0.970884227	0.340552037	-0.303866258	0.108903512

Regression using TI-83

Question 3: Analyze the information given in the following table. Discuss the correlation at the 5% level of significance, include a scatter plot.

X	*Y*
3	2
7	6
3	5
1	9
4	2

Using the TI-83, using the techniques outlined in Chapter 3 Using Technology in Graphical Representations of Data, put the data values and the frequencies in two distinct lists, say $L1$, and $L2$. Then press **2nd STAT PLOT**. This screen will allow you to turn on various statistical plots, select the first plot, the **scatter plot**. Make sure ***Plot*** **1** is on.

Then set the window; that is, set the minimum and maximum values of the two variables x and y; as our minimum value of x is 5 and our maximum observed value is 13, we will set the $\boldsymbol{Xmin} = 0$ and the $\boldsymbol{Xmax} = 15$. The minimum value of y is 2 and our maximum observed value is 7, we will set the $\boldsymbol{Ymin} = 0$ and the $\boldsymbol{Ymax} = 10$. We shall also set the scales equal to 1; that is, $\boldsymbol{Xscl} = 1$, $\boldsymbol{Yscl} = 1$ and $\boldsymbol{Xres} = 1$. Then press the ***GRAPH*** button.

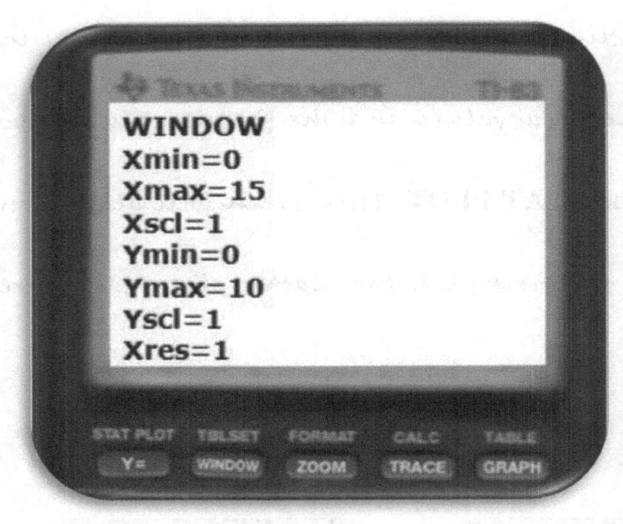
WINDOW
Xmin=0
Xmax=15
Xscl=1
Ymin=0
Ymax=10
Yscl=1
Xres=1
STAT PLOT
TBLSET
FORMAT
CALC
TABLE
Y=
WINDOW
ZOOM
TRACE
GRAPH

STAT PLOT
TBLSET
FORMAT
CALC
TABLE
Y=
WINDOW
ZOOM
TRACE
GRAPH

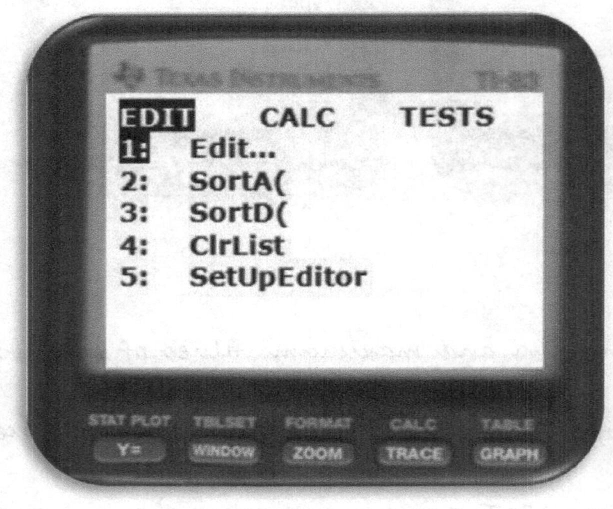
EDIT CALC TESTS
1: Edit...
2: SortA(
3: SortD(
4: ClrList
5: SetUpEditor
STAT PLOT
TBLSET
FORMAT
CALC
TABLE
Y=
WINDOW
ZOOM
TRACE
GRAPH

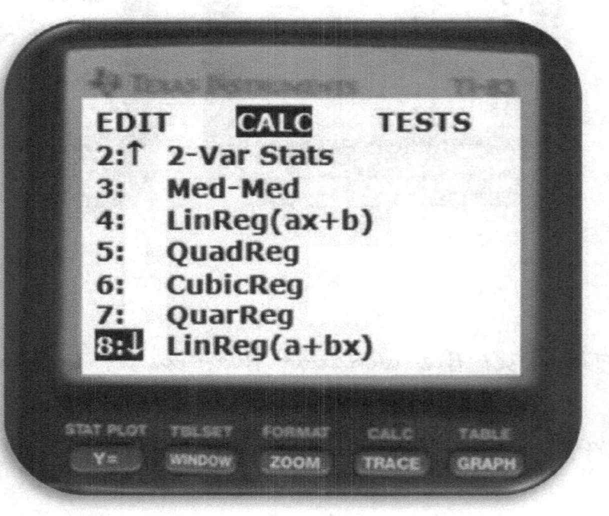
EDIT CALC TESTS
2:↑ 2-Var Stats
3: Med-Med
4: LinReg(ax+b)
5: QuadReg
6: CubicReg
7: QuarReg
8:↓ LinReg(a+bx)
STAT PLOT
TBLSET
FORMAT
CALC
TABLE
Y=
WINDOW
ZOOM
TRACE
GRAPH

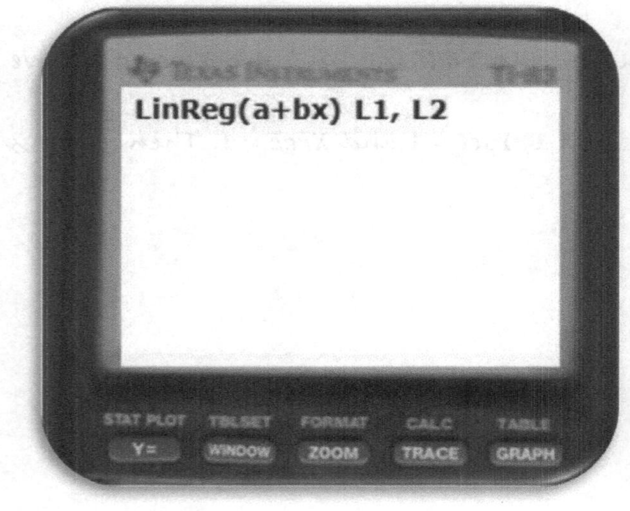
LinReg(a+bx) L1, L2
STAT PLOT
TBLSET
FORMAT
CALC
TABLE
Y=
WINDOW
ZOOM
TRACE
GRAPH

LinReg
y=a+bx
a=4.619047619
b=.0892857143
STAT PLOT
TBLSET
FORMAT
CALC
TABLE
Y=
WINDOW
ZOOM
TRACE
GRAPH

Note: TI83 does not automatically give the correlation coefficient, to turn this option on, under **CATALOG** (press **2nf 0**), jump down to the **Ds** by pressing x^{-1}, as alpha lock is set on when you select the catalog. Continue to scroll down to **DiagnosticOn**, then re-run the analysis above..

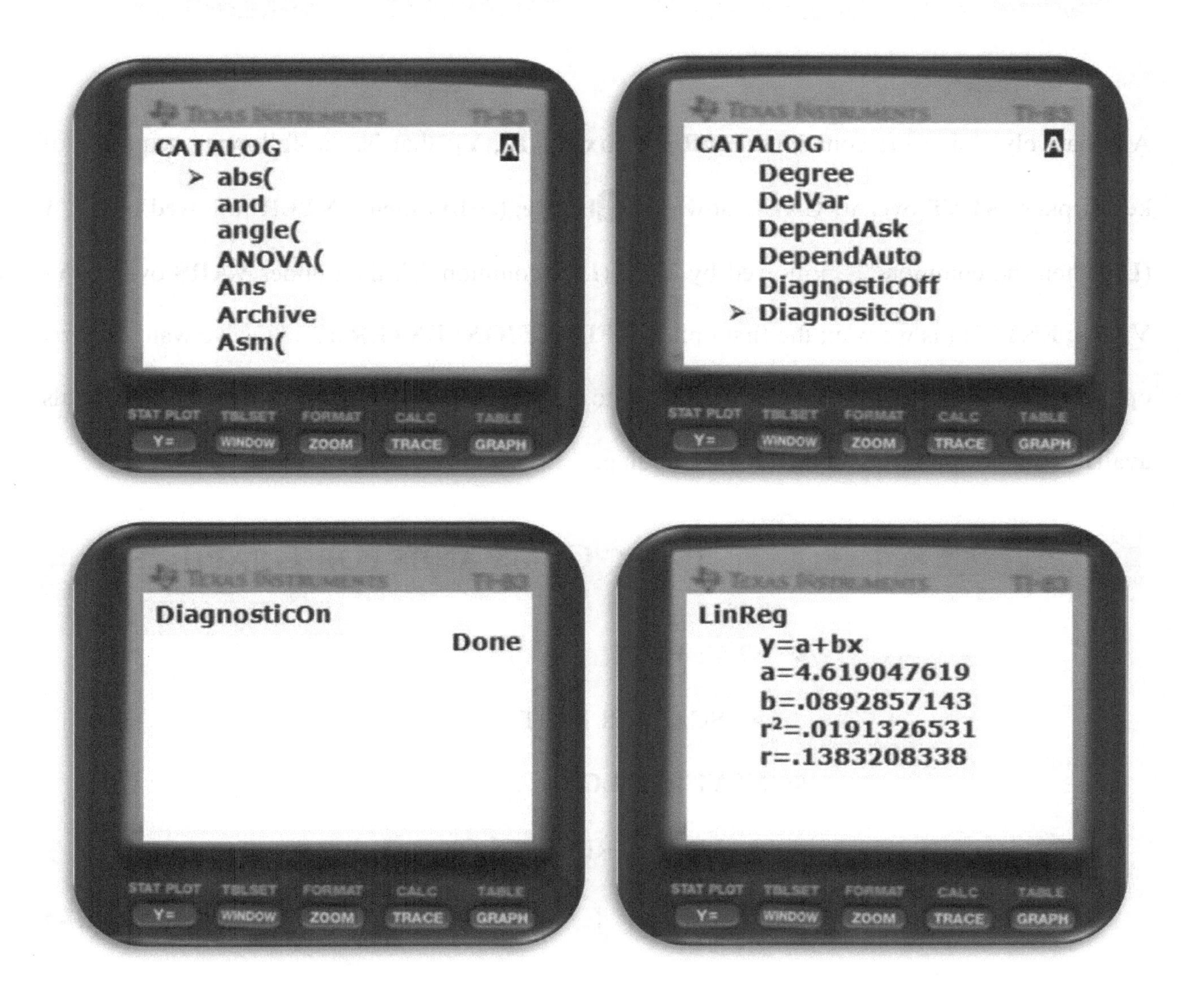

To add the trend line, under $Y =$ put the regression line and then press $\boldsymbol{GRAPH}$ again.

Alternatively, using the command **LinReg(a+bx)** $\mathbf{L_1,L_2, Y_1}$; that is, the following sequence of key strokes: **STAT** over to **CALC** down to **8↓LinReg(a+bx)** then **ENTER** followed by **2nd 1** ($\mathbf{L_1}$), then the common ",", followed by **2nd 2** (**L2**), common ",", then under **VARS** over to **Y-VARS**, **ENTER** (as we want the first option **1:FUNCTION**) **ENTER** again (as we want the first option **1:**$\mathbf{Y_1}$, followed by one more **ENTER** to run the code. Note: this will use all decimals available in the approximation with no rounding.

TI 83 — BASIC COMMANDS FOR GRAPHICS

- **STAT PLOT**
  - SCATTER PLOT
- **STAT > CALC**
  - LINEAR REGRESSION

LinReg L_1,L_2

Projects

Note: All files necessary for these projects are located on the accompanying disk under **Projects**. These files include the Word Bank for project 1 in a PDF file, the Excel files for each project by part the list of projects in Word form.

Project 1 **Dictionary**
This assignment is to illustrate the tedious take of gathering and organizing information - you will have to extract the terms from the PDF or re-type/handwrite the included terms - you will need to present this information clearly including a cover sheet and pagination - you will need to enumerate and alphabetize the 100 words selected.

Project 2 **Graphics & Descriptive Statistics**
This assignment is designed demonstrate the difficulty in locating Real World Data that appeals to your interest and describe it statistically (graphical representations and descriptive statistics) - given in the Excel file for Project 2 Part 1 find an example of data gleaned offline - note: you need to find your own data set (if possible).

Project 3 **Basic Probabilities**
This assignment is to illustrate the computation capability of Excel. In the worksheet "**Die Simulator**" simply by changing the count (Number of Rolls) to a number between 1 and 1000, the computer simulates a fair six sided die and for those who are interested, all coding is visible in the various cells. In the worksheet "**Three Coin Simulator**" by adjusting the probabilities of heads on a given coin, the computer simulates and counts the frequency of occurrence. This also ensures that no two students have the same question. Remaining worksheets work similarly.

Project 4 **Normal Probabilities**
This assignment is to illustrate the computation capability of Excel when working with normal probability distributions. For example, in the worksheet "**Normal Calculator and Graphics**" by changing the four values highlighted in yellow, the computer determines the relative z-scores, the probability in the defined regions and provides a graphical representation which can be copied into Paint and edited further - or further modifications can be made using Excel. In worksheet "Binomial to Normal" by changing the probability of success and the number of trials (Sample size, n), the computer determines if the assumptions are satisfied, gives the parameter estimates and graphically illustrates both the normal approximation and the underlying binomial distribution.

Project 5 **CI & HT**
This assignment is designed to use what you have learned up to this point to quickly determine point estimates, margins of errors, lower and upper confidence limits, test statistics, critical statistics and p-value in order to construct confidence statements and draw conclusions at various levels of significance.

Project 6 **Additional CI & HT and Regression**
This assignment is to be a continuation of the previous assignment.

Project 1: Dictionary

On the **Terminology List** are 210 words the many of which will be on the first tests as well as commonly used throughout the semester; 80 words of which that are flagged (⚐) and must be included. A minimum of **100 words** must be included in the first graded assignment, a dictionary.

I encourage you to incorporate as much technology as possible. The nicer presentations will include more detailed **formatting**; however, at least **paginate** all papers, **front only**.

Alphabetized and **enumerated** each word; entries must include the **term** (word) being defined and a **definition**.

The 210 terms were randomized using **EXCEL** and therefore are not presently in any specific order.

Since you will be able to download this page off blackboard, you can use **EXCEL** to sort these terms alphabetically – otherwise, you will have to organize this information manually.

You can then simply start alphabetically and use the index of the book or search online, or, my suggestion is first going by chapter, including all words found in the first few chapters. When using a word processor such as **WORD**, moving between entries can be easily done. Without the use of a computer, I suggest using index cards for the first draft, then alphabetize the index cards and create a final draft. Most words requiring definition can found in the text and others defined in class; all can be researching in the library or online, discussed with the TAs or me.

Project 2: Graphics & Descriptive Statistics

You must first gather information on a topic of interest to you. This data must include at least one **qualitative variable** and two **quantitative variables** (a **response variable** and an **explanatory variable.**) All questions must be addressed; information may need to be reorganized and/or summarized to produce some of the graphic representations, etc.

FORMAT: Bold key words to be **emphasized, label figures** and **tables,** and **paginate.**

1. **Data** source and description: website where data was gleaned, the variables of interest and sampling methods, etc.
2. Identify the **variables**

    a. Identify the type of **variables**

        i. **Qualitative** or **Quantitative**
        ii. **Discrete** or **Continues**
        iii. **Response** or **Explanatory**

    b. Identify the **level of measures** for each variable
    c. Give **descriptive statistics** for each of the variables (if the statistic exists); that is, the **mean, median, mode, minimum, maximum, quartiles, range, variance** and **standard deviation**. For example, for qualitative data the mode may exist, but no the mean. Include the **coefficient of variance** and the **10% trimmed mean.**
    d. Discuss any possible **lurking variables.**

3. **Graphics**

    a. Draw a **bar chart** for the qualitative variable. Comment, is this a **balanced** design? If so, then re-analysis the information so that there are varying count.
    b. Draw **histograms** for the quantitative variables Comment, on the **symmetry** or **skewness** of the data
    c. Discuss **outlines** and **gaps.**
    d. Draw **box plots** for the quantitative variables by category (that is, the qualitative variable) and include at least the **five-number summary**.
    e. If this is a **time series**, include line graph for at least the outlined response variable. By category if possible. Is there a **trend** or **seasonal effect**?

Project 3: Basic Probabilities

You will need to use the accompanying **EXCEL** file "Excel Part 2" to generate the information need for many of the following questions.

FORMAT: Bold key words to be **emphasized**, **label figures** and **tables**, and **paginate**.

1. **Simulate** or toss a single fair (new) coin with a sample size of 10, 50 and 100 and give frequency tables.

    a. **(5pt)** Include step by step outline of **simulating** or **experimental** procedure.
    b. **(5pt)** What is the **probability** of a head in your **simulation** or **experiment**?
    c. **(5pt)** Comment on the percent heads and how the **law of large number** applies.

2. Using the simulator given in the worksheet "Three Coin Simulator" which simulates tossing three "unfair" coins (a quarter, a dime and a nickel) with a sample size of 30, set the probabilities of heads to make the coins unfair – at present they are all set at 50%, that is, "fair" coins. In the **EXCEL** worksheet, QN represents the intersection of Q and N, or $Q \cap N$. Use the simulated information to draw the associated Venn diagram, included the number of tosses with no heads, that is, Q'D'N' or $Q' \cap D' \cap N'$. Answer the following questions: **(5pt) Venn Diagram**

    a. $n(Q' \cap D' \cap N')$
    b. $P(Q)$
    c. $P(D)$
    d. $P(N)$
    e. $P(D \cap N)$
    f. $P(D \text{ only})$
    g. $P(Q \cup D)$
    h. $\text{Odds}(Q)$

3. Given that the probability of an event **E** is 0.12 and the probability of event **F** is 0.24, if the probability these two events are **independent**, what is the probability that both events occur.

4. Using the generator in the worksheet "Tree diagram Values", change the number in the cell highlighted **yellow** and hit **ENTER**; then using the random values given, compute the following probabilities. Be sure to include a tree diagram illustrating the values given in the chart. Highlighted in **blue** are the numbers used in the example problems.

    a. $P(D)$
    b. $P(A|D)$
    c. $P(D')$
    d. $P(D|B')$
    e. $P(D|C)$

5. Compute the number of **permutations** and **combinations** for selecting three out of four objects; that is, given $S = \{1,2,3,4\}$, how many way can we permute three out of four and how many ways can we combine three out of four. Illustrate all **permutations** and **combinations.** Illustrate all **permutations** and **combinations** using $S = \{\Delta, \mathrm{O}, \Sigma, \Pi\}$.

6. Using the generator in the worksheet "Raffle", change the number in the cell highlighted **yellow** and hit **ENTER**; then using the random values given, determine the following information. Be sure to include the chart with you simulated data.

    a. How many winning tickets are in this raffle?
    b. Assuming there are 500 tickets sold, what is the expected winnings?

7. Using the generator in the worksheet "Linear Relation", change the number in the cell highlighted **yellow** and hit **ENTER**; then using the random values given, compute the mean and the variance of the data values *x* and the associated data *y* values, explain how this could have been figured using the slope and *y*-intercept.

8. Using the generator in the worksheet "Distributions," determine the expected value, the variance and the standard deviation for each of the three distributions. Show calculations and interpret results.

Project 4: Normal Probabilities

You will need to use the accompanying **EXCEL** file "Excel Part 3" to generate the information need for many of the following questions.

FORMAT: Bold key words to be **emphasized, label figures** and **tables**, and **paginate**.

1. Using the worksheet "Random Generator Normal", generate 100 simulated data values by setting the mean and standard deviation to 125 and 20, respectively. Compute the sample **mean** and the **sample standard deviation**, establish the three confidence intervals $(\mu - k\sigma, \mu + k\sigma)$ for $k = 1,2,3$ and then determine the **count** and thus the **relative frequency** of each of these intervals. Compare the parameters to the statistics as well as compare the **relative frequencies** obtained to the **empirical rule**.
2. Determine the following **probabilities** and illustrate **normal chart** – you many need to use **PAINT** or edit format in **EXCEL**. Include associated z-scores. Note: you may use the "Normal Calculator and Graphics" in **EXCEL** file "Excel Part 3."
   a. $P(87 \le x \le 102 \mid \mu = 100, \sigma = 12)$
   b. $P(92 \le x \le 112 \mid \mu = 125, \sigma = 36)$
   c. $P(x \le 52 \mid \mu = 45, \sigma = 7)$
   d. $P(x \ge 67 \mid \mu = 51, \sigma = 11)$
3. Compare the **binomial distribution** with $P(S) = 0.80$ and sample sizes 5, 10, 50 and 100 to there associated normal distribution. You may use the worksheet "Binomial to Normal" in the **EXCEL** file "Excel Part 3". Discuss the apparent **skewness** and how it changes as the **sample size** increase. State whether the assumptions are satisfied for each comparison. Under what condition would the **binomial distribution** be **symmetric**?

Note: the large the simulations, the more time it takes **EXCEL** to regenerate; please be sure that all calculation are renewed before you **COPY** and **PASTE SPECIAL** into another worksheet to finish remaining analysis. The % calculated is given at the bottom of the **EXCEL** window. Warning: if you are impatient, then you may copy and paste incorrect information, often zero occur in cells while the computer is recalculating the cell entries.

4. Using the worksheet "Sampling Distribution", set the **mean** equal to your age and the **standard deviation** to the number of siblings in your family (that is, if you are an only child, set the standard deviation to 1; otherwise, the number of brothers and sisters plus one, namely you.) Then set the **number of trials** (number of times the experiment is run) and the **sample size** (the number of data points in a single experiment) equal to the following values: 10, 50 and 100; hence, there will be nine comparisons. Compare the ratios of $V(\bar{x})$ to the given $V(x) = \sigma^2$. Discuss what these ratios should be and the accuracy of these ratios in terms of the **sample size** or the **number of trials**. Discuss how the **central limit theorem** applies.
5. Using the worksheet "Control Charts", generate three random control charts with the following parameters and determine if the process is out of control.
   a. $N(\mu = 32, \sigma^2 = 256)$
   b. $N(\mu = 16, \sigma^2 = 81)$
   c. $N(\mu = 100, \sigma^2 = 225)$

Project 5: CI & HT

You will need to use the accompanying **EXCEL** file "Excel Part 4" to generate the information need for many of the following questions.

FORMAT: Bold key words to be **emphasized, label figures** and **tables**, and **paginate**.

1. You may use the worksheet "HT Means" for verification in calculations and graphics; however, your write up must clearly discuss the following and include clear formulations and explanation.

A student receives an average of $\mu = 21.2$ credit card offers per month. The majority of these are unsolicited. Because of the large number of complaints, the government find themselves questioning the way such businesses are run. In an effort to the number of unsolicited credit card offers, a research team established minimum qualifications and maximum mailing restrictions. One year after the new requirements was put in place, a random sample of 85 students showed that an average of $\bar{x} = 18.2$ offers per month. The tracking of all such mailings showed that $\sigma = 16.1$. Has the restriction had any effect? Use a 5% level of significance to test the claim that there has been a reduction in the average number of credit card offers sent per month per student.

2. You may use the worksheet "HT Means" for verification in calculations and graphics as well as "Sample n<=30" to compute the sample statistics; however, your write up must clearly discuss all the points outlined in Question 1.

Based on the annual report of a research company, the research and development department wished to estimate how much time the average customer waits in line. A random sample of 12 where observed as the stood in line. The times recorded in minutes were 56, 59, 60, 61, 64, 67, 68, 104, 110, 117, 122, and 128. Using a 10% level of significance, test the claim that the mean wait time is less than 95 minutes.

3. You may use the worksheet "HT Proportions" for verification in calculations and graphics; however, your write up must clearly discuss all the points (a thru l) outlined in Question 1.

Before 1940, the proportion of female rats in the general population was about 60%; however, after 1970, a widespread effort to destroy rats. In a recent sample of 48 rats, there were only 23 females. At the 0.01 level of significance, do these data indicate that the population proportion of female rats is now less than 60% in the region?

4. Using the worksheet "Linear Combination", set $\mu_1 = 20$, $\sigma_1 = 4$, $\mu_2 = 30$, and $\sigma_1 = 7$. Then, for the following values of a and b, show using the estimated statistics how the randomly generated data satisfy the equations $E(y) = a\mu_1 + b\mu_2$ and $V(y) = a^2\sigma_1^2 + b^2\sigma_2^2$

, where $E(x_1)=\mu_1$, $E(x_2)=\mu_2$, $V(x_1)=\sigma_1^2$, $V(x_2)=\sigma_2^2$ and $y=ax_1+bx_2$. If these equations are not satisfied, discuss what assumptions are violated.

a. $a=1, b=-1$

b. $a=2, b=0.3$

5. You may use the worksheet "HT Difference of Means" for verification in calculations and graphics; however, your write up must clearly discuss all the points outlined in Question 1.

In the experiment, subjects were randomly divided into two groups to test a new drug create to reduce blood pressure: the experimental group received a new drug and the control group received a placebo. There were $n_1 = n_2 = 50$ subjects in each group. For the experimental group, the mean drop in blood pressure was $\bar{x}_1 = 27.9$ with sample standard deviation $s_1 = 4.8$. For the control group, the mean drop in blood pressure was $\bar{x}_2 = 25.9$ with sample standard deviation $s_2 = 5.2$. Use a 5% level of significance to test the hypothesis that there was no difference (either way) in scores between the two groups.

6. **(20pt)** You may use the worksheet "Mean Difference" to find summary statistics and "HT Means" for verification in calculations and graphics; however, your write up must clearly discuss all the points outlined in Question 1 and determine if the **mean difference** is 0. You select the level of significance.

Sample	RV 1	RV 2
1	91	127
2	107	109
3	73	91
4	49	110
5	68	96
6	102	119
7	142	139
8	105	103
9	115	53
10	132	88
11	112	88
12	89	59
13	39	46
14	123	70
15	99	121
16	161	65
17	99	116
18	83	65
19	89	163
20	93	101

Project 6: Additional CI & HT, and Regression

You will need to use the accompanying **EXCEL** file "Excel Part 5" to generate the information need for many of the following questions. Note: to regenerate, either change the number in the **yellow** highlighted cell, or double click between two column headings.

FORMAT: Bold key words to be **emphasized, label figures** and **tables**, and **paginate**.

1. Use $\chi^2 = \sum \frac{(O-E)^2}{E}$ with degrees of freedom, $df = (r-1)(c-1)$ to determine if in the clinical trails a success recovery is **independent** of the drug prescribed; that is, the null hypothesis is the events are independent. You may use the worksheet "HT Independence" to check your answer; however, you must show at least one calculation per chart. Include the following:
    a. Is the assumption for using a chi-squared statistic justified? Explain
    b. State the null hypothesis in context.
    c. Compute the expected count for each category (show **in a chart**).
    d. Compute the terms in the chi-squared statistics (show **in a chart**).
    e. State the chi-squared statistics, including the degree of freedom, clearly label.
    f. From the chart, determine at the $\alpha = 0.01$ significance level the comparative chi-squared value.
    g. Clearly, illustrate and state your decision in the form of a significance statement.

***O*-Observation**	**X**	**Y**	**Z**
A	69	63	67
B	32	42	48
C	65	65	72

2. The **M&M/Mars Company** claims that the proportions of **M&Ms** in bags of mini-packs are as follows in the table below; that is, the null hypothesis is that the desired distribution "fits" the data. You will need to purchase a King Size bag (or larger) bag of Plain M&Ms and test the goodness-of-fit of the distribution at the 0.05 level of significance. Note: the degrees of freedom, $df = n - 1$ where n is the number of categories. You may use the worksheet "HT Goodness-of-fit" to check your answer; however, you must show at least one calculation per column and include all parts outline in question 2 in addition to a bar chart illustrating the candy color distribution observed.

Color	**Expected Percent**	**Expected Frequency** E	**Observed Frequency** O	**Observed Relative Frequency**	$\frac{(O-E)^2}{E}$
Brown	13%				
Red	13%				
Yellow	14%				
Green	16%				
Orange	20%				
Blue	24%				
TOTAL	100%			100%	____

3. The electronic connection in a commuter must be re-soldered when wear on these parts indicates too much variability in the current as it passes through the circuits. A large commuter contains thousands of electronic connections, and safety regulation requires that variability measurements on the population of all electronic connections not exceed 0.12 ampere. An inspector took a random sample of 31 electronic connections with a sample variance 0.18 ampere. Using a 0.01 level of significance, is the inspector justified in claiming that all the electronic connection should be re-soldered?

4. Using the worksheet "Bivariate Random Generator" to generate at least two graphs that illustrate **positive** and **negative** correlation as well as **weak** and **strong** correlation; your write up must clearly discuss the following. To adjust variability set Std Y and Std X to varying positive values.

   a. State the estimated **correlation coefficient** r.

   b. Does the correlation coefficient indicate a low (weak), moderate, high (strong) correlation? Is this correlation positive or negative?

   c. Test for dependence/independence between the variables by creating a new variable that is a linear combination of the two main variables; namely, $w = ax + by$, for two sets of weights and compare expected values and variances:

      i. $a = 1, b = -1$

      ii. $a = 2, b = 5$

   d. State the regression model $\hat{y} = b_0 + b_1 x$.

   e. Use the above model to estimate the response that is an **interpolation.**

   f. Use the above model to estimate the response that is an **extrapolation**.

   g. Give the 90% confidence interval for β_1 and interpret.

   h. In testing the null hypothesis, $H_0 : \beta_1 = 0$; state the p-value and at the 0.10 level of significance determine whether the explanatory variable x significantly contributes to the response variable y.

   i. In the statistical model, $y = \beta_0 + \beta_1 x + \varepsilon$, where $\beta's$ are the weights that drive the estimates of the response variable and ε is the random error. State the assumption with respect to ε and how the accompanying figures (residual plot and PP plot) illustrate this point. Explain. W

   j. rite a complete sentence that describes the **coefficient of determination** in terms of the percent of the variation in the response variable, y, is explained by the least-squares regression model and the explanatory variables?

⚐	Term	⚐	Term
	Dependent		Conjunction
	Stem and Leaf Plot	⚐	Relative Frequency
	Statistical Inference	⚐	Pareto Chart
⚐	Placebo Effect		Poisson: Expected Value
	Sample Point		Expected Value
	Covariance	⚐	Parameter
	Disjunction	⚐	Census
	Location	⚐	Maximum
⚐	Likert Scale	⚐	Control (Control Group)
	Correlation Coefficient	⚐	Ordinal Measure
	Critical Statistic		Normal Probability Distribution
⚐	Simulation		Descriptive Statistics
	Seasonal Effect		Time Series Data
	Standardize plot	⚐	Systematic Sampling
	Continuous Uniform		Hidden Bias
	Point Estimate		Dot Plot
	Uniform Distribution		Variance
	Ranking	⚐	Outliers
⚐	Discrete Random Variable		Probability Distribution
⚐	Venn diagram	⚐	Degree of Freedom
	Confidential	⚐	Stratified Sample
	Randomization		Non Adherers
	Sampling Distribution	⚐	Margin of Error
⚐	Extrapolation	⚐	Continuous Measure
⚐	Quantitative Variable		Random Variable
	Correction for Continuity	⚐	Central Tendency
⚐	Treatment	⚐	Interpolation
⚐	Mode	⚐	Informed Consent
	Percentage plot		Discrete Measure
	Discrete Distribution	⚐	Central Limit Theorem
	Confounded Variables		Categorical Variable
⚐	Skewed	⚐	Valid Measure (Validity)
	Double Blind	⚐	Contingency Table
	Independent Random Sample		Relative-frequency
⚐	Median		Block Design
	Trimmed Mean	⚐	Measure
	Statistical Adjustment		Event
	Sample Variance		Class Limits
⚐	Replication		Gaussian Probability Distribution
⚐	Binomial		Class Width

⚐	Term	⚐	Term
	Random Sampling Error		Population Size
⚐	Count		Experimental Study
	Time Series Graph	⚐	Convenience Sampling
	Population		Skewed Right
	Sample Space		Cumulative Frequency
⚐	Inferential Statistics		Variable
⚐	Rate		Binominal Distribution
	Explanatory Variable		Sample Mean
	Counting rules		Regression
	Placebo		Degree of Confidence
⚐	Bias	⚐	Alternative Hypothesis
⚐	Cluster Sampling		Continuous Distribution
⚐	Voluntary Sampling		Ogive
⚐	Lurking Variable		Skewed Left
⚐	Continuous Random Variable		Voluntary Response
	Coefficient of Variation		Degree of Confidence
	Standard Score		Random Sample
	QQ plot		Expected Count (Independent Events)
	Tree Diagram	⚐	Minimum
	Incorrect arithmetic	⚐	Scatter Plot
⚐	Probability	⚐	Range
⚐	Qualitative Variable	⚐	Trend
⚐	Sample Size		Observational Study
	Institutional review board		Hypothesis Testing
	Experimental Design		Goodness-of-fit
⚐	Quartiles	⚐	Instrument
⚐	Deviations	⚐	Residuals
	Nominal Measure		Moments
	Percentiles	⚐	Shape
	Circle Graph (Pie Chart)	⚐	Experiment
	Single Blind		Inter-quartile Range
⚐	Spread		Independent
⚐	Type II Error	⚐	Odds
⚐	Response Variable		Conditional probability
⚐	Line Graph	⚐	Mean
⚐	Distribution	⚐	Ratio Measure
	Anonymous (Anonymity)		Frequency Polygon
	Dependent Random Sample		Sample Survey
⚐	Statistic	⚐	Null Hypothesis

⚐	Term	⚐	Term
	PP plot		Survey Error
	Sample Data (Sample)		Correlation
	Frequency Distribution		Population Standard Deviation
	Standard Deviation	⚐	Statistics
	Sample Standard Deviation		Reliability (Reliable Measure)
⚐	Type I Error	⚐	Causation
	Weighted Mean (Weighted Average)		Robust
⚐	Interval Measure	⚐	Box Plot (Box-and-Whiskers)
	Class Mark (Midpoint)	⚐	Individual
⚐	Variability	⚐	Symmetric
	Class Boundaries	⚐	Bar Chart
⚐	Simple Linear Regression		Discrete Uniform
	Statistically Significant	⚐	Marginal Change
	Mutually exclusive events	⚐	Histogram
⚐	Simple Random Sample		Compound event
	Standard Average		
⚐	p-value		